Project Wood

MATERIALS TECHNOLOGY WOOD

Dermot Gannon

Gill & Macmillan

Gill & Macmillan Ltd
Hume Avenue
Park West
Dublin 12
with associated companies throughout the world
www.gillmacmillan.ie

© Dermot Gannon 2011
978 0 7171 4714 4

Artwork by Peter Bull Art Studio.
Design and print origination by Design Image, Dublin.

The paper used in this book is made from the wood pulp of managed forests.
For every tree felled, at least one tree is planted, thereby renewing natural resources.

Any links to external websites should not be construed as an endorsement by
Gill & Macmillan of the content or view of the linked material.

For permission to reproduce photographs, the author and publisher gratefully acknowledge the following:

© Alamy: 21, 26TR, 26BL, 32, 35, 42TL, 44R, 63BR, 64TR, 64TL, 70T, 72, 84T, 87TR, 101R, 108TR, 110, 113TR, 121C, 121T, 123TL, 124B, 125B, 125T, 135TR, 236CR, 255B, 257, 264L, 281, 285TL, 285BL, 286CL, 287T, 302, 310, 311, 340, 352, 353L, 353R, 354TL, 354BL, 354CR, 355B, 355T, 356T, 367CL, 367CR, 381; © Artisan Specialities: 223BL; © Bambi Air Compressors Limited: 69BL; © Bernadette Livingston Furniture LLC: 253; © Blackfriar: 313R, 314T; © Blingmaster: 89; © BOSCH: 176, 177R, 178L, 178R, 179L, 181R, 182BR; © Brad Reeves: 267; © Bridgeman: 14TL; © British Standards Institution: 356B; © C. R. Clarke & Co.: 96R, 97, 185BR; © Coillte Panel Products: 78T; © Consmos: 74, 75, 76TR, 78BL; © Corbis: 13TL, 102, 139BR, 139TR, 299L; © DeWalt: 174, 177L, 179R, 182TL; © Di Legno Woodshop Supply: 277; © Dremel/BOSCH: 181L, 244BR, 286BR; © Enrico König © Goran Basaric: 13B; © Ford Ireland: 357; © Forestry Images: 62R, 63T, 63BL; © Garden Picture Library: 26TL; © Geocel Ltd: 314BL; © Gerard Romeo, Exotic Woods USA: 14TR; © Gerd Eichmann: 223T; 236BL; © Getty: 2B, 20T, 20B, 22, 34, 36, 70B, 71, 78BR, 84B, 101L, 106TR, 113BL, 114T, 114B, 135L, 135BR, 136L, 137T, 244TL, 266, 276, 285BR, 313L, 314BR; © Grizzly Industrial, Inc.: 182BL, 183L, 183R, 184T, 185T, 185BL, 186R, 187; © Hartville: 85BL; © Highland Import & Export: 94R; © Hugo Fergusson: 268L; © Imagefile: 14B, 39BR, 43, 69BR, 95L, 122TR, 293B; © J.Phillips/www.spiralpixel.com: 271L; © Jerry Hartzell: 244TR; © Lee Valley: 182TR, 226, 242T, 242B, 243TL, 243CL, 243BL, 243TR, 243CR, 244BL, 256, 268R, 271R, 279TR, 286, 287C, 287B, 288T, 288C, 288B; © Liam Bourke: 62TL; © Lignotec: 232; © Linxia Huaan Biological Products Limited Company: 284L; © The Lisnavagh Timber Project: 11T, 59R, 254; © Makita: 184BR; © Morgan Motor Company: 113BR; © www.MUTR.co.uk: 123BL; © Nickell Moulding: 79; © Original Marquetry: 255TR; © Photolibrary: 13TR, 87L, 122TL, 139BL, 272B; © Record Power: 231TR; © Regent Woods: 231BR; © Richard B. Smart: 62BL; © www.rockler.com: 78BR; © Rockwell: 184BL; © Ronseal: 69TR; © Saikyo International OU: 76TL; © Saint Gobain Abrasives: 279TL, 279CL, 279BL; © Science Photo Library: 124T; © Sinometer Instruments CO., LTD: 49R; © Sykes Timber: 5T, 5B, 6T, 6B, 7B, 8B, 9, 44L; © Teagasc's Forestry Development Unit: 59L; © Techno Inc.: 186L, 224TR; © Terry Smart/www.chestnutproducts.co.uk: 233; © Turners Retreat: 227; © Valkyrie Craft: 95R; © Wikimedia: 2T, 38L, 38R, 39L, 39TR, 42BL, 42BR, 51, 60, 78BL, 85TL, 86TR, 86BL, 90, 93, 94L, 103, 105L, 105R, 106TL, 106BL, 107L, 107TR, 107CR, 107BR, 108TL, 108BL, 108BR, 112, 119, 121B, 122BL, 123TR, 123BR, 129, 223BR, 231TL, 236LC, 236TR, 241L, 241R, 243BR, 264R, 272T, 279BR, 284R, 286BL, 293T, 296, 299R, 303, 333L, 333TC, 333BCR, 333R, 333BCL, 342; © Windsor: 49L; © Windsor: 52, 53; © The Wood Marketing Federation: 7T, 8T, 10, 11B, 12T, 12B; © Wood Panel Industries Federation: 76B, 77; © The Woodworks Company: 236TL.

The authors and publisher have made every effort to trace all copyright holders, but if any has been inadvertently overlooked we would be pleased to make the necessary arrangement at the first opportunity.

Contents

UNIT 1: THE THEORY OF WOOD

Gearr Ceisteanna 1-7

UNIT 2: PRACTICAL WOODWORK

UNIT 3: DESIGN

Preface

TO THE STUDENT

Project Wood has been designed and written directly with you in mind. Its overall aim is to allow you to study the Junior Certificate MTW course by yourself. The pure theory sections of your MTW course have been laid out in fifteen easy-to-read chapters – with the rest of the course set out so it can be explored and understood by hands-on learning.

All the chapters cover what you need to achieve the highest grades in the subject. If you wish to explore any chapter further follow the Internet Links at the end of each chapter. Trying out the various tasks in each chapter will make your learning experience more enjoyable and make it easier for you to retain the knowledge for your exams.

Step by Step guides to making joints, fitting clocks and locks, finishing techniques and many everyday woodwork tasks are included so that you can be independent in your learning process and require minimal help from those around you.

Designing projects and preparing a Folio for your JC project can be daunting, but by following the sample folio in the book you can get through your project in a simple and logical manner, which allows you to show off your design talent.

Please take note of all the Carbon Footprint issues throughout the book which will help you to be an environmentally friendly woodworker and designer.

Finally, I wish you the very best when completing your course and becoming a competent woodworker and designer by the end of the Third Year.

SPECIAL SECTIONS IN THIS BOOK

There are three special sections throughout this book:

    ❋   possible hands-on task for students

    ❋   carbon footprint information

    ❋   information for the student

IMPORTANT ABBREVIATION IN THIS BOOK

MTW = Materials Technology Wood

ACKNOWLEDGEMENTS

I would like to thank the following for their excellent efforts making Project Wood everything I wished it would be. The staff of Gill & Macmillan: Anthony Murray, Hubert Mahony, Emma Farrell and in particular Aoileann O'Donnell, Neil Ryan and Jennifer Patton who all worked tirelessly day after day with me to perfect Project Wood. Thanks also to Chris Thomas and the staff of Peter Bull Art Studios.

My colleagues in the MTW Department and the students of Árdscoil na Tríonóide, Athy, for constantly trying to become better woodworkers and designers – and especially for their concern for Green Schools and reducing their Carbon Footprint in the classroom and in their designs.

For inspiring me as a student to enjoy Drawing/Woodwork and become a MTW teacher Eugene Wall and Padraig Cawley, Coláiste Lorcáin, Castledermot. For instilling the love of teaching in me during my time at the University of Limerick, Michael D'Arcy.

To my wife Belinda (Amazing Woman), thanks for your patience and input during the writing of Project Wood. You are a credit to MTW teachers throughout the country.

DEDICATION

To Belinda and my beautiful daughter Aoife.

GLOSSARY

English	Irish	English	Irish
Analysis	Anailís	Metal	Miotal
Ash	Fuinseog	Mitre joint	Mítéaralt
Beech	Feá	Mortise gauge	Tomhsaire/rianaire moirtíse
Bench hook	Clárchrúca	Mortise and tenon joint	Alt moirtíse agus tionúir
Bevel	Beibheal		
Birch	Beith	Mortise machine	Meaisín moirtíse
Biscuit joint	Alt briosca	Oak	Dair
Bracket	Brac	Paint	Péint
Carving	Snoíodóireacht	Paintbrush	Scuab peint
Cherry	Silín	Photosynthesis	Fótasintéis
Chisel	Siséal	Pine	Crann péine
Circular saw	Sábh ciorclach	Pineboard	Clár péine
Clamp	Clampa	Plane	Plána
Cordless drill	Druilire gan sreang	Plastic	Plaisteach
Design brief	Dearadh coimre	Plug	Plocóid
Dovetail joint	Déadalt	Plywood	Sraithadhmad
Dowel joint	Dualalt	Preservative	Leasaitheach
Drill	Druilire	Project	Tionscadal
Drill bit	Béalmhír	Recycle	Athchúrsáil
Elm	Leamhán	Research	Taighde
Evaluation	Luacháil	Router	Cuasphlána
Fabric	Fabraic	Rule	Rialóir
File	Líomhán	Sander	Greanóir
Fir	Giúis/crann giúise	Sandpaper	Greanpháipéar
Forest	Foraois	Saw	Sábh
Fungus	Fungas	Sawdust	Min sáib
Germination	Péacadh	Sawmill	Muileann sábhadóireachta
Glue	Gliú	Screwdriver	Scriúire
Hacksaw	Sábh miotail	Seasoning	Stálú
Halving joint	Leathalt	Sliding	Sleamhnáin
Hammer	Casúr	Softwood	Bogadhmad
Handle	Hanla/lámh	Solder	Sádar
Hardwood	Crua-adhmad	Stain	Smál
Hinge	Inse	Steel	Cruach
Horse Chestnut	Cnó Capaill	Steel tape measure	Miosúr téip chruach
Ideas	Smaointe líníochtaí	Sycamore	Seiceamóir
Insect	Feithid	Teak	Téac
Iron	Iarann	Tools	Uirlisí
Jigsaw	Preabshábh	Tree bark	Coirt chrainn
Joint	Alt	Tree trunk	Stoc crainn
Kiln	Tornóg	Tropical forest	Foraois thrópaiceach
Lamp	Lampa	Try-square	Dronbhacart
Lathe	Deil	Varnish	Vearnais
Lock	Glas	Veneer	Veinír
Mahogany	Mahagaine	Vice	Bís
Mallet	Máilléad	Walnut	Gallchnó
Manufacture	Déantús	Warping	Freangadh
Maple	Mailp	Wood grain	Snáithe adhmaid
Marking gauge	Tomhsaire/rianaire marcála	Woodturning	Deileadh adhmaid
Marquetry	Obair inleagtha	Woodworm	Réadán

eTest.ie – what is it?

A revolutionary new website-based testing platform that facilitates a social learning environment for Irish schools. Both students and teachers can use it, either independently or together, to make the whole area of testing easier, more engaging and more productive for all.

Students – do you want to know how well you are doing? Then take an eTest!

At eTest.ie, you can access tests put together by the author of this textbook. You get instant results, so they're a brilliant way to quickly check just how your study or revision is going.

Since each eTest is based on your textbook, if you don't know an answer, you'll find it in your book.

Register now and you can save all of your eTest results to use as a handy revision aid or to simply compare with your friends' results!

Teachers – eTest.ie will engage your students and help them with their revision, while making the jobs of reviewing their progress and homework easier and more convenient for all of you.

Register now to avail of these exciting features:

- Create tests easily using our pre-set questions OR you can create your own questions

- Develop your own online learning centre for each class that you teach

- Keep track of your students' performances

eTest.ie has a wide choice of question types for you to choose from, most of which can be graded automatically, like multiple-choice, jumbled-sentence, matching, ordering and gap-fill exercises. This free resource allows you to create class groups, delivering all the functionality of a VLE (Virtual Learning Environment) with the ease of communication that is brought by social networking.

UNIT 1: THE THEORY OF WOOD

✹ Beautiful tree in rainforest

Introduction to Trees of Ireland and the World

There are many species of trees around the world in various regions. Many are suited to the area in which they grow and many adapt to the conditions of the soil and weather of harsh areas.

In general, hardwoods and softwoods grow in distinct belts of the globe as can be seen in the diagram opposite. Trees suited to the different belts grow in such abundance that they have become part of the character and economy of the countries in that belt.

Many of the trees we have in Ireland have been growing here for many thousands of years and are well suited to the climate of Ireland. Many of the trees introduced from other regions such as the Scandinavian countries do well on the poorer soils of our mountains.

Knowledge of the origin and characteristics of different trees is essential for the woodworker as s/he may wish to advertise that the woods are native or tropical, to help people to reduce their impact on the environment.

It is even more important to understand where wood can be used, and understand the properties of the wood, so that it performs well in use. Knowing how to identify the wood is essential and different features such as the shape of the tree, appearance of the leaf and seed, and wood colour make identification easier.

Key Elements to Understand for Junior Certificate Course

* macroscopic identification of native tree species
  * weight, colour, grain, leaf, seed and silhouette
  * uses
* properties of various woods
* world distribution of trees
* overview of other timber species

✹ Unusual Irish trees

The World
Chart of Timber Distribution

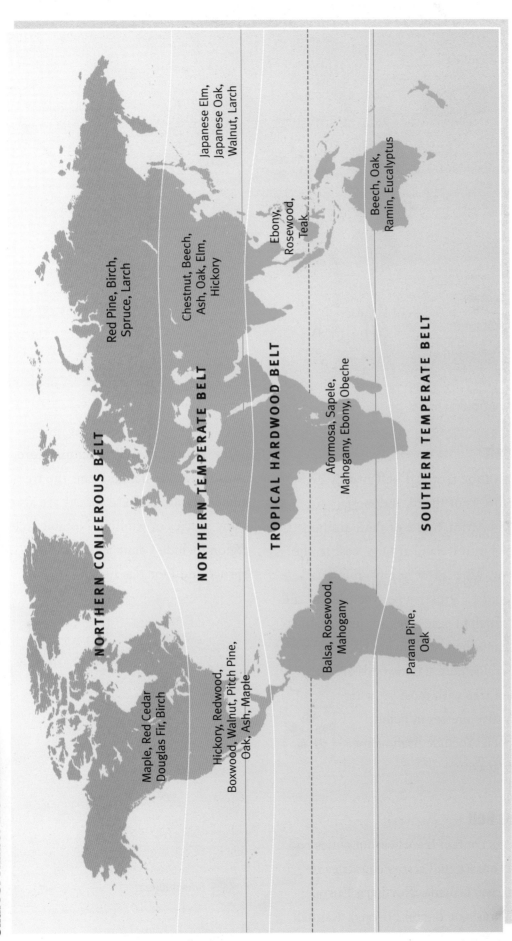

NORTHERN CONIFEROUS BELT

Red Pine, Birch, Spruce, Larch

Maple, Red Cedar Douglas Fir, Birch

NORTHERN TEMPERATE BELT

Chestnut, Beech, Ash, Oak, Elm, Hickory

Japanese Elm, Japanese Oak, Walnut, Larch

Hickory, Redwood, Boxwood, Walnut, Pitch Pine, Oak, Ash, Maple

TROPICAL HARDWOOD BELT

Ebony, Rosewood, Teak

Aformosa, Sapele, Mahogany, Ebony, Obeche

Balsa, Rosewood, Mahogany

SOUTHERN TEMPERATE BELT

Beech, Oak, Ramin, Eucalyptus

Parana Pine, Oak

 World distribution of timbers

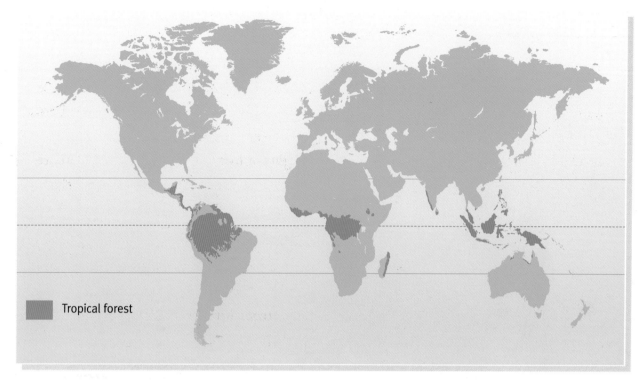

● Location of tropical forest

Tropical Belt

The woods of the **tropical belt** mainly grow in the rainforests of Brazil, Indonesia, Australia and Africa. Some of these timbers are imported into Ireland at huge cost to the environment. Trees grow at a phenomenal rate of around 1.75 metres per year due to the heat and rainfall. These trees are important to wildlife because half of all living species on the planet reside here. Hardwoods are the main type of tree with most growing over eighty-five metres in height. Notable species include Mahogany, Ebony and Teak.

Coniferous Belt

These forests contain trees bearing cones and needles and are located across countries in North America, Canada, Northern Europe and Asia (Eurasia or Boreal Forests). Rainfall

in this region, as well as temperature, is normally moderate and thus the trees grow at moderate rates. These forests are also home to many species of wildlife. Notable trees in this region include Giant Sequoia, Sitka Spruce and Douglas Fir.

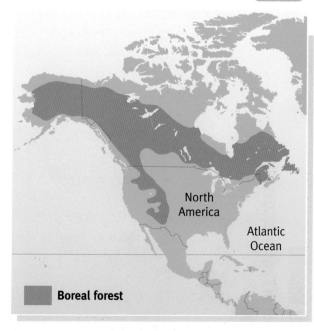

● Location of boreal forest

Ireland
Hardwoods

1. Oak

(dair)

* Silhouette of Oak tree

* Leaf of Oak tree

* Seed of Oak tree

* Timber of Oak tree

There are two main Oak tree species native to Ireland – Common Oak and Sessile Oak. Oak trees are slow growing but will reach heights of forty metres and a circumference of three to five metres. Oak will only grow strong on well-drained soils.

Oaks are easily identifiable by the large round crown, lobbed leaf edge and the acorn seed. The wood is very attractive in appearance with a very straight grain pattern.

It is a very durable timber yet flexible enough to use in Steam Bending. Oak is used in timber flooring, furniture-making, shipbuilding and woodturning.

2. Beech

* Silhouette of Beech tree

(fheó)

* Leaf of Beech tree

* Seed of Beech tree

* Timber of Beech tree

Beech is one of the most common trees in Ireland and can grow to heights in excess of thirty metres. Beech will grow in a variety of soils as long as the soil is well drained.

Beech can be identified by the large crown with a smooth grey bark. The leaves are dark green and very smooth to the touch. The seeds (masts) have the appearance of a three-angled nut contained in a husk.

Beech wood is straight-grained with a high shock resistance with reddish brown heartwood.

Beech is used for furniture-making, firewood, tool handles, wooden food containers and picture frames.

3. Ash

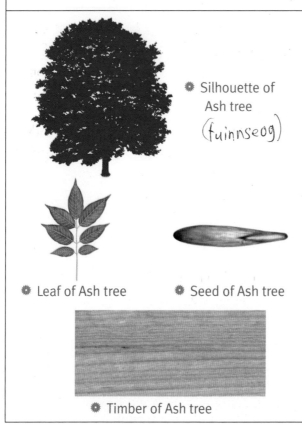

● Silhouette of Ash tree (fuinnseog)

● Leaf of Ash tree

● Seed of Ash tree

● Timber of Ash tree

Ash is widely grown in Ireland and grows to heights in excess of forty metres. Ash will grow on many soil types.

Ash is identified by the very irregular shape of the branches. The leaves grow in a distinct pattern – growing in pairs opposite each other (as shown above). The bark is smooth and grey in colour. The seeds are elliptical in shape, often looking like earrings.

The wood is light cream in colour with straight grain and coarse texture. The wood has a high shock resistance and excellent flexibility.

Ash is used for making quality furniture, hurleys and in flooring.

4. Sycamore

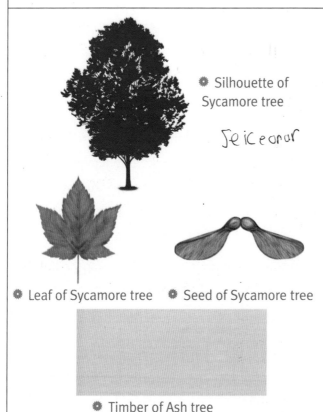

● Silhouette of Sycamore tree

Seiceanar

● Leaf of Sycamore tree

● Seed of Sycamore tree

● Timber of Ash tree

Sycamore trees can grow to a height of over thirty-five metres and still have the best ability to stand up to high winds.

Sycamore can be identified by the leaves (which are similar to the Maple) and the rough grey bark of the mature tree. The seeds grow in opposing pairs and are known commonly as **helicopter** seeds.

The wood has only moderate strength and flexibility but will bend well under steam bending processes.

The wood is used for flooring, butchers' blocks and crates.

5. Birch

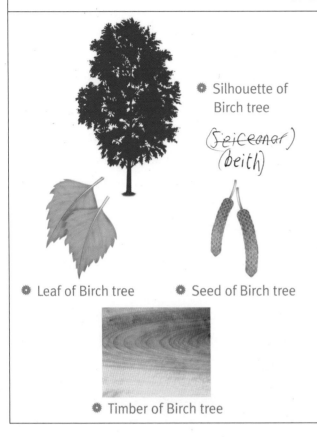

• Silhouette of Birch tree

(Seiceanar)
(beith)

• Leaf of Birch tree   • Seed of Birch tree

• Timber of Birch tree

Birch trees do not generally grow as tall as other hardwood trees and reach heights of around twenty-five metres. Silver Birch is one of the most common species found in Ireland.

Birch is easily identifiable by the thin trunk on which the bark appears to be peeling off. Bark is smooth and grey/silver in appearance. The leaf is heart-shaped with jagged edges. The seeds of the Birch form in clusters known as catkins.

The wood is white in appearance at the sapwood area with high flexibility and strength. The wood can be straight- or curly-grained.

Birch is used in flooring, cabinets, woodturning, plywood and toys.

6. Maple

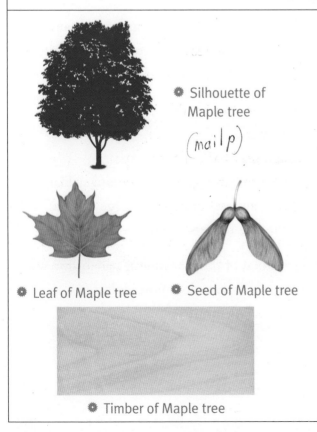

• Silhouette of Maple tree

(mailp)

• Leaf of Maple tree   • Seed of Maple tree

• Timber of Maple tree

Maple trees grow to forty-five metres in height and are mostly deciduous. Some Maple trees in the Mediterranean region are evergreen.

Maple trees are identifiable from the large fan-shaped leaf on the Canadian flag. The seeds are similar to the helicopter seeds of the Sycamore tree. The bark is rough and grey in colour.

The wood is straight-grained and reddish in colour at the heartwood and turning white toward the sapwood region.

Maple is used in flooring, cabinets, musical instruments and the sap is used to make Maple syrup.

7. Cherry

Silhouette of Cherry tree

silíní

Leaf of Cherry tree   Seed of Cherry tree

Timber of Cherry tree

Cherry is a member of the Rose tree family and grows to approximately thirty metres in height. Cherry trees can live for extremely long periods – up to many hundreds of years.

Cherry is identified by the beautiful pink blossoms in the spring and from the rose-like appearance of the mature tree. The leaf is elongated and has jagged edges. The seed is easily identifiable as the Cherry we buy in fruit shops.

The wood is only usable after kiln-drying as it has a tendency to shrink. The wood has moderate strength and very good bending characteristics.

8. Horse Chestnut

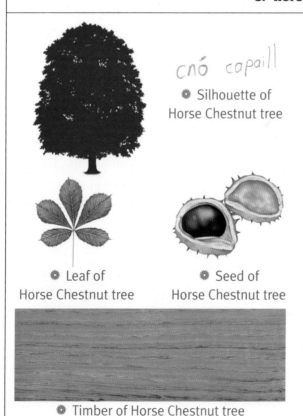

cnó capaill

Silhouette of Horse Chestnut tree

Leaf of Horse Chestnut tree   Seed of Horse Chestnut tree

Timber of Horse Chestnut tree

The Horse Chestnut tree grows in many areas of Ireland and is better known for its seed or **conkers** which are contained in the familiar spiky green shell. The tree can reach heights of thirty-five metres or more in this country.

The tree is identifiable by the finger-like leaves (digitate) that can be large and the candle-like flowers on the tree in spring.

The wood of the Chestnut is pale brown and very soft, making it almost useless as a structural or furniture timber. It is used in crates, cheap furniture and as firewood.

9. Elm

❋ Silhouette of Elm tree

E leamhán

❋ Leaf of Elm tree

❋ Seed of Elm tree

❋ Timber of Elm tree

Elm is one of the tallest native hardwoods in the country and grows to forty metres. It almost became extinct across Ireland and Europe when a disease called Dutch Elm Disease nearly wiped out the entire species.

The tree is identifiable by a flat oval leaf, which has many veins and is non-symmetrical. The seed is contained in a heart-shaped leaf structure.

The wood is very strong due to its interlocking grain and is used for furniture, wooden wheels and coffins.

Softwoods

10. Scots Pine

péinne albanach

● Silhouette of Scots Pine tree

● Leaf of
Scots Pine tree

● Seed of
Scots Pine tree

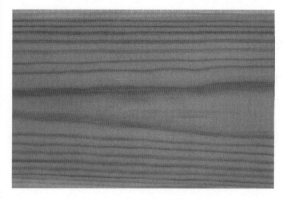

● Timber of Scots Pine tree

Scots Pine grows widely across Northern Europe. It is an evergreen growing up to forty-five metres tall when mature. There are some examples of Scots Pine which are even taller than this which can achieve an average age of 300 years.

The tree is identifiable by the crown which sits high above the ground (as shown above), and the needles which form in pairs. The bark is dark grey-brown at the bottom of the trunk and changes to a brown-orange at the top of the tree.

The wood of the Scots Pine is pale brown in colour. The timber is widely used in the construction industry especially for Pine doors. This is a common wood to find in the MTW room and is often called **Red Deal**.

síorghlas

Síorghlas
evergreen

11. Douglas Fir

❋ Silhouette of Douglas Fir tree

giúis dhúlgais

❋ Leaf of Douglas Fir tree

❋ Seed of Douglas Fir tree

❋ Timber of Douglas Fir tree

Douglas Fir was introduced to Europe by David Douglas from the tree's native home of North America. They normally only grow to around twenty metres making them ideal for their normal function as Christmas trees in town centres. These trees need well-drained deep soils to grow well.

The tree is identifiable by the flat needles, which grow randomly around the twig. The cones are oval in shape.

The wood is a red-brown colour and is very durable.

The timber is used for structural joinery (roofs), wooden aeroplanes and wooden chassis cars.

12. Norway Spruce

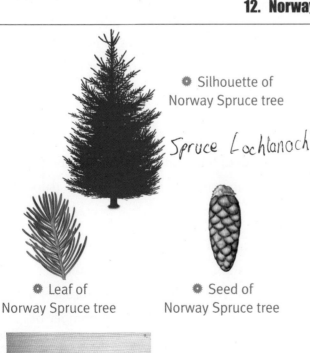

❋ Silhouette of Norway Spruce tree

Spruce Lochlanoch

❋ Leaf of Norway Spruce tree

❋ Seed of Norway Spruce tree

❋ Timber of Norway Spruce tree

Norway Spruce can grow to enormous heights of up to fifty-five metres. It flourishes right across Europe from Norway to Poland. It can live for long periods of time and was reputably the oldest tree in the world at over 8,500 years old.

The tree is identifiable from the thick crown of needles (as shown above) and the long thin cones.

The tree can be used as an indoor Christmas tree and the wood for papermaking, floorboards and skirting boards. It is commonly referred to as **White Deal**.

13. Sitka Spruce

☀ Silhouette of
Sitka Spruce tree

Sprús Siteach

☀ Leaf of
Sitka Spruce tree

☀ Seed of
Sitka Spruce tree

☀ Timber of
Sitka Spruce tree

This is a very tall tree growing up to seventy metres tall. Its name comes from an area in Alaska known as Sitka.

The tree is identifiable by the thin flaky bark and stiff sharp needles. The mature tree has no branches below ten metres from the ground. The cone is oval-shaped and pale brown in colour when ripe.

The wood is very strong and is used in roofing, chipboard and on the tips of military missiles.

14. Lodgepole Pine

☀ Silhouette of
Lodgepole Pine tree

Pinne Contórtach

☀ Leaf of
Lodgepole Pine tree

☀ Seed of
Lodgepole Pine tree

☀ Timber of
Lodgepole Pine tree

Lodgepole Pine originates in north-west America and can grow to thirty-five metres tall. The tree can grow in a variety of soil types. The crown of the tree does not form the traditional cone shape of other evergreens but is more oval in outline (as shown above). The needles grow in pairs in a spiral pattern.

The wood of the Lodgepole Pine is red-brown and is used to build log cabins, firewood and fence posts. It is not ideal for woodworking due to the high number of knots in the wood.

Other Timbers of the World
Teak

☀ Teak furniture

téac

Teak is actually a member of the Mint family and thus has a subtle mint smell when sawn. Normal Teak trees grow to only forty metres high but can be many metres wide. Most Teak originates in India, Burma and the Philippines. The wood is used in boat decks, furniture, windows and as a high-grade veneer. In fact, the natural oils contained in Teak make it excellent for outdoor usage. The wood is a very distinct shade of red-brown (as shown above).

Mahogany *Mahagaine*

Mahogany is the natural tree of the Dominican Republic but is widely grown in South America and Africa. Mahogany is a dark red-brown colour and is excellent in furniture-making due to its straight grain. It is used for high-quality furniture, veneers and also in guitars such as the famous Gibson Les Paul guitars.

☀ Mahogany bed

Ebony *Éabann*

Ebony is a very heavy black-coloured wood from the tropics. It is grown in large quantities in India and Sri Lanka. Its high density makes it ideal for carving sculptures, which can be polished to a high gloss. It is one of only a few timbers which sink in water. It is also widely used in piano keys and chess sets.

☀ Ebony table

Walnut *gall chnó*

Walnut is grown mainly in North America and Europe. The tree can grow to fifty metres in height and is famous for the nuts it produces in early autumn. The wood of Walnut has a tightly packed grain, making it ideal for furniture-making. Also, the wood has a chocolate colour with a corresponding

Lignum Vitae

🌸 Walnut chest of drawers

🌸 Lignum Vitae pestle and mortar

crann adhmaid beath

Lignum Vitae, the wood of life, is another timber which will not float in water and is renowned for its strength and hardness. It is a very slow-growing tree and therefore has become an endangered species. It is so tough that it is used to make cricket balls, police truncheons and parts in wooden clocks. The wood varies in colour from light brown to very dark brown-black.

chocolate smell when cut. Occasionally Walnut trees will develop a tumour (mass of small branches) on its external surface. When the tree is felled and converted, this tumour gives a beautiful and much sought after timber called Burred Walnut (as shown below).

Where possible you should select Irish timber in preference for your projects. Alternatively use hardwood veneers to cover cheaper wood or select wood with the FSC logo to show that a new tree has replaced the tree cut for your timber.

🌸 Burred Walnut piano

Hands-on Tasks

1 Gather five leaves and five seeds from the forest and try to identify them from the images above.

2 From the Internet, find five different types of wildlife that live in the rainforests of Brazil or Africa.

3 Use the Internet to find out which species of tree is the tallest, and which one is the oldest, in the world.

4 Make a bark rubbing of five different trees around your home or school.

5 Cut out four different types of timber into blocks measuring 4 cm × 4 cm × 4 cm. Weigh them and calculate which one is the densest.

INTERNET LINKS AND TASKS

Visit the following (or similar) websites for more facts in relation to trees from Ireland and the World.

Modern rainforests

> http://www.rainforesteducation.com/life/canopy1.htm

Action on trees in Ireland

> http://www.treecouncil.ie/

SEARCH

Homework Sheet on Trees of Ireland and the World

1 Why is it important to know the different properties of various tree species?

2 Name three different trees from the Northern Temperate Belt.

3 Name three different trees from the Tropical Forest Belt.

4 Why do Tropical Hardwood trees have small spacing between their annular rings?

5 Identify the trees below from their **silhouette**.

(a)    (b)    (c)

6 Identify the trees below from their **leaves**.

(a)    (b)    (c)

7 Identify the trees below from their **seeds**.

(a) 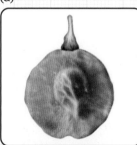   (b)    (c)

8 What are the Environmental implications of transporting Hardwood timber from Tropical regions of the planet to Ireland?

Sample Exam Questions on Trees of Ireland and the World

Ordinary Level 2010

State from which trees in the lists these **seeds** come.

A

B

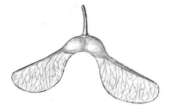

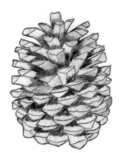

Pine
Oak
Sycamore
Ash
Holly

TREE A ____________________ **TREE B** ____________________

Ordinary Level 2010

Trees are divided into two groups, deciduous and coniferous.

(i) Describe, using notes and neat freehand sketches, **four** characteristics of deciduous trees.

(ii) Describe, using notes and neat freehand sketches, **four** characteristics of coniferous trees.

(iii) Choose a tree from the list below. Using notes and sketches, describe this tree under the following headings:

(a) Leaves and seeds

(b) Uses for the wood.

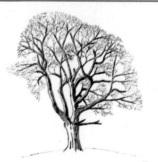

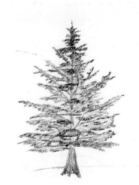

Ash
Oak
Beech

Ordinary Level 2009

State which trees in the list these **leaves** come from.

Sycamore
Oak
Beech
Ash
Horse Chestnut
Pine

A

B

TREE A _____

TREE B _____

Ordinary Level 2008

State from which trees in the list these **seeds** come.

Sycamore
Pine
Holly
Horse Chestnut
Beech
Ash

A

B

NAME A _____

NAME B _____

Higher Level 2010

The diagrams show the leaves of three common Irish trees.

In the spaces provided, name the trees.

_____   _____   _____

Higher Level | 2009

The diagram shows the leaves and fruit of three common Irish trees.

In the spaces provided, name the trees.

 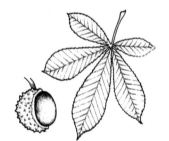 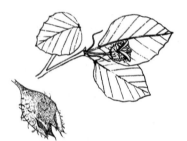

_____ _____ _____

Higher Level | 2007

The diagrams show the leaves of three common Irish trees.

Name the trees in the spaces provided.

_____ _____ _____

Higher Level | 2006

The diagrams show the silhouette and seeds of three common Irish trees.

Name the trees in the spaces provided.

_____ _____ _____

CHAPTER 2

Hardwoods and Softwoods

Introduction to Hardwoods and Softwoods

❋ Hardwood tree

❋ Softwood tree

There are two main grouping of trees in the world – Hardwoods and Softwoods. An understanding of these two groups allows the woodworker to select the correct timber for a specific job. This is very important in the modern world because using timbers that have taken hundreds of years to grow and have travelled thousands of miles is not environmentally sound practice.

Identifying hardwoods and softwoods is not primarily a matter of deciding which one is harder – it is on a microscopic level that the differences reveal themselves. There are also some features of the external structure which can help identify the type of tree.

Overall, the goal is to identify which tree is a hardwood and which is a softwood, which allows us to work out what seasoning procedure to follow, what type of preservatives to use and whether to use the more expensive hardwoods for our application.

Key Elements to Understand for Junior Certificate Course

* classification of trees
* microscopic identification – cell structure of hardwoods and softwoods
* uses of hardwoods and softwoods
* macroscopic identification

Tree Classification

Trees are split into two main groupings, Deciduous and Coniferous.

Deciduous

* broad leaves
* seed housed in a fruit
* shed their leaves
* irregular shaped trunk and crown
* grow slowly (sometimes over 100 years)
* give us mostly hardwood trees

Coniferous

* needles
* seed housed in cones
* evergreen
* symmetrical shape
* long straight trunk
* grow quickly (about 40 years)
* gives us mostly softwood trees

Softwoods

* Softwood timber in floor

Macroscopic Features

* mostly as for conifers above
* wood light in colour
* visible large cells when looking at end grain
* easily dented by a hardwood timber

Softwood Cells

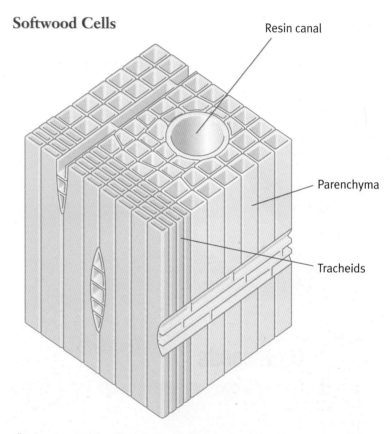

Resin canal

Parenchyma

Tracheids

* Structure of softwood

Softwoods contain different types of cells including xylem and phloem as discussed in Chapter 3.

Tracheids – interlocking cells giving strength to the tree. Water and minerals are also carried in these cells. They make up most of the tree.

Parenchyma – cells that store food enabling growth of the tree.

21

Cell Structure of Softwood

The cells of softwood are like a bunch of thick straws from a fast food outlet. Not many will fit in your fist and the ones that do are easy to squeeze and deform.

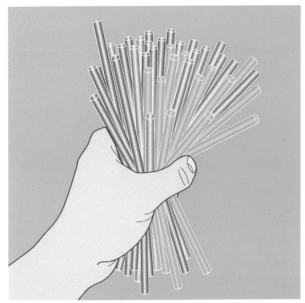

❋ Larger softwood cells crush easily

Hardwoods

❋ Hardwood timber in floor

Macroscopic Features

❋ mostly as deciduous trees above
❋ wood usually dark in colour
❋ not easy to see cells at the end grain
❋ will not be dented easily by softwoods

Hardwood Cells

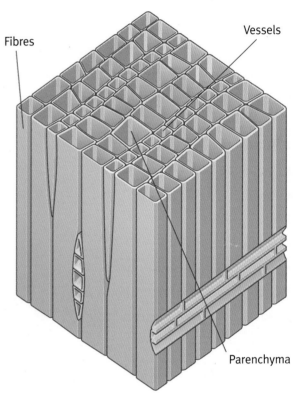

❋ Structure of a hardwood

Hardwoods contain different types of cells including xylem and phloem as discussed in Chapter 3.

Vessels – carry water up the tree from cylindrical cell to cylindrical cell.

Parenchyma – the food storage cells of hardwoods.

Fibres – These cells give the tree its strength due to the thick cell walls.

Cell Structure of Hardwood

The cells of hardwood are like a bunch of thin straws from a fast-food outlet. Many will fit in your fist and are not easy to squeeze and deform.

❈ Smaller hardwood cells do not crush easily

Hands-on Tasks

1 Draw a chart to compare and contrast the properties of a hardwood and a softwood.

2 Search the Internet to find microscopic images of the cells of hardwood trees.

3 Search the Internet to find microscopic images of the cells of softwood trees.

Homework Sheet on Hardwoods and Softwoods

1 Why is it important to know the difference between hardwood and softwood?

2 List five characteristics of a hardwood timber.

3 List five characteristics of a softwood timber.

4 Make a sketch to show the difference between the microstructure of hardwood and softwood.

INTERNET LINKS AND TASKS

Visit the following (or similar) websites for more facts in relation to the hardwoods and softwoods.

Properties of different hardwoods and softwoods

> http://www.dtwoodturning.co.uk/timber.htm

Different tree species

> http://www.woodforgood.com/tree_species.html/

The anatomy of wood

> http://waynesword.palomar.edu/trjuly99.htm

SEARCH

Sample Exam Questions on Hardwoods and Softwoods

Ordinary Level	2009

Trees can be divided into two main categories, coniferous and deciduous. Show by means of a tick (✓) the correct category for each tree listed below.

TREE
Beech
Ash
Lime
Pine
Sitka Spruce

Coniferous	Deciduous
Sitka Spruce	Fheá
Péinne albánach	Fhuinnseog

Ordinary Level	2008

An unfinished diagram of a block of wood is shown.

Draw in the end grain.

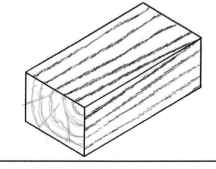

The diagram shows a piece of wood with a face side mark. Show the **face edge** mark in its proper place on the sketch.

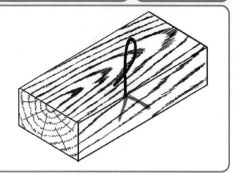

When sawing logs into planks the bark can sometimes be left on. When dry this bark often falls off. What is this defect called?

_____

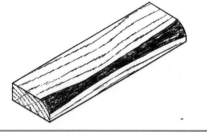

Using a tick (✓), indicate whether the following trees are Hardwoods or Softwoods.

Trees	Hardwood	Softwood
Ash	✓	
Sitka Spruce		✓
Douglas Fir		✓
Birch	✓	
Holly	✓	

Introduction to How a Tree Grows

🌸 A tree seedling

🌸 A mature tree

Looking at trees from around Ireland and the rest of the world, a greater appreciation and understanding of them can be had by examining how they grow. This may eventually encourage you to grow your own trees and maybe someday use them to make beautiful things.

The old saying 'from a small acorn a mighty Oak grows' is very true and it's truly amazing to watch the tree you planted one day becoming a full adult tree.

All trees have the same means of growing and reproducing. A seed falls and, with the right conditions, begins to send out shoots – hopefully one day growing into a full tree.

🌸 A tree sapling

Having examined how the tree grows, it would be an interesting task for you to gather some tree seeds, then sow them where you can watch them grow over the years.

Key Elements to Understand for Junior Certificate Course

* how a tree grows
* structure and parts of a tree
* cell structure of a tree

Germination

The growth of a seed can be tracked at different stages over a period of months. This process involves what we refer to as **germination**.

Stage 1 – Dispersal

The seed falls from the tree and finds its way to a resting location due to animals, birds, wind and water etc.

Stage 2 – Condition

If the conditions are correct for a seed to germinate, it will do so. These conditions are heat, moisture and food.

Stage 3 – Radicle

A small shoot sent down to the soil to obtain water and minerals.

Stage 4 – Plumule

A shoot that grows up to obtain light to start the process of photosynthesis so that the tree can make its own food.

Stage 5 – Sapling

Leaves appear and the tree begins to grow rapidly.

Germination process

Photosynthesis

Photosynthesis is a process where the tree can make food using the sunlight and the nutrients it has sucked from the ground. This sucking action is known as **osmosis** and occurs because the tree releases water from its leaves in a process called **transpiration** and the water and minerals move in to replace this lost water. The process can be clearly seen in the diagram opposite.

Parts of a Tree

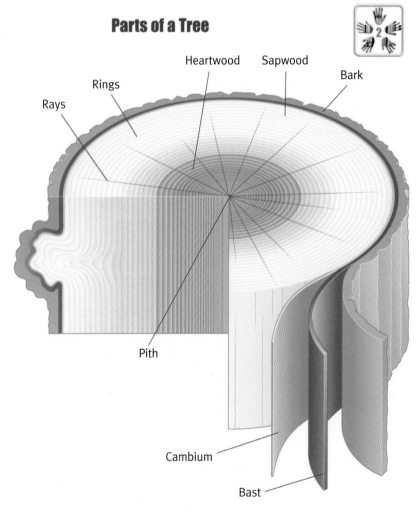

* Internal parts of a tree

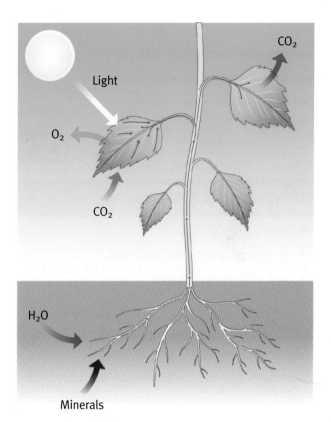

* Tree photosynthesis

Heartwood

The inner dark wood of the tree. This is where the best timber of the tree is to be found due to its lack of moisture and compression.

Sapwood

More recently formed timber. It is moister than the heartwood because it carries the water and minerals to the leaves from the roots. Sapwood requires careful seasoning to prevent warping.

Medullary Rays

Lines or ribbons which extend from the centre of the tree perpendicular to the rings. Their function is to allow sap to pass through the trunk and enter the inner tree. Rays are responsible for the beautiful silver-grain effect in Oak timber.

Pith

The original sapling, or young tree, which is dark in colour and eventually dies away.

Annual Rings

Annual rings are formed by the growth process. In the summer when more growth occurs, the rings are wider and less dense. The opposite happens for the winter. In the tropics, where there is growth all year round, it is often harder to tell the rings apart. Rings can tell the history of an area over the life of a tree. Using dendrochronology, the art of studying tree rings, a scientist can tell when great droughts and floods took place in the past.

Vascular Cambium

This is a layer of cells used to carry nutrient-rich food from the leaves down the tree so that the tree can grow. These food cells are known as **phloem** cells. Also in the cambium layer is a layer of cells called **xylem** cells, which will form the heartwood of the tree.

Bast

This is the layer just under the bark of the tree. It also contains phloem cells and is the moistest area of the tree.

Bark

The outer rough part of the tree, which has a number of functions.

* moisture retention
* animal, insect and fungal protection
* rainwater transfer to the roots

The bark of a tree also gives us products such as spices, latex and medicines.

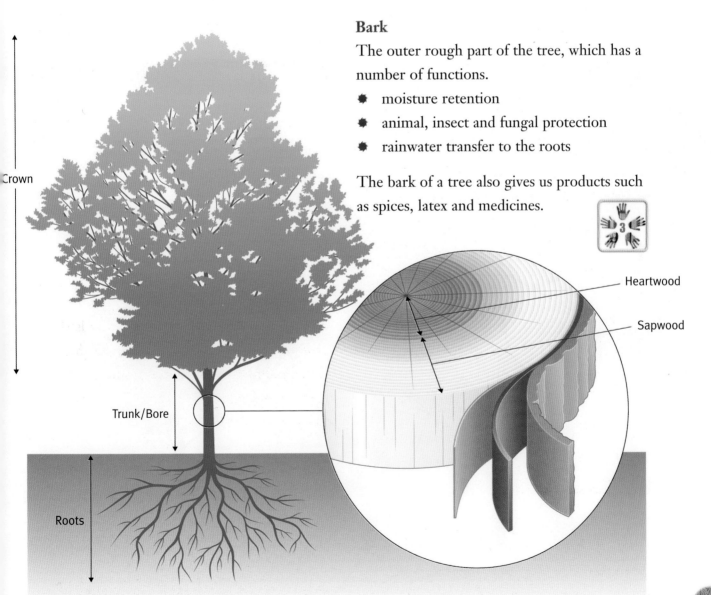

Crown

Trunk/Bore

Roots

Heartwood

Sapwood

❈ External parts of a tree

The External Tree

Roots
Used for anchoring the tree to the ground as well as absorbing water and minerals.

Trunk (Bore)
The trunk carries water and minerals upward and food downward. It also holds the leaves up to the sun.

Crown
This is the branches and leaves.

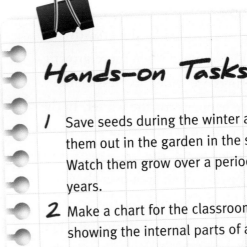

Hands-on Tasks

1 Save seeds during the winter and plant them out in the garden in the spring. Watch them grow over a period of years.

2 Make a chart for the classroom showing the internal parts of a tree.

3 Make some bark rubbings of trees in your school and make a collage to hang on the classroom wall.

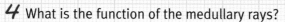

Homework Sheet on How a Tree Grows

1 Name three methods by which seeds can be dispersed from the mature tree.

2 What is the difference between the radicle and the plumule?

3 Name the process by which water and minerals are absorbed up into the tree.

4 What is the function of the medullary rays?

5 Label the parts of the diagrams below.

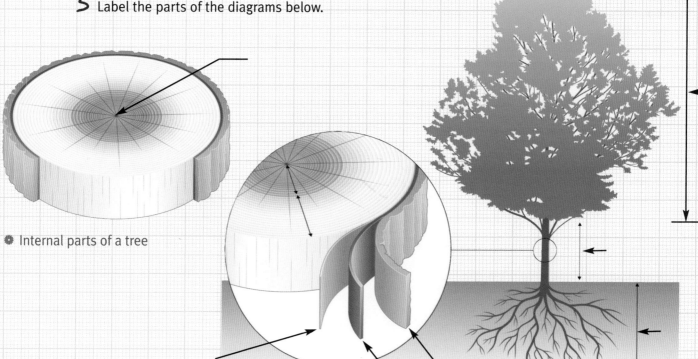

● Internal parts of a tree

● External parts of a tree

INTERNET LINKS AND TASKS

Visit the following (or similar) websites for more facts in relation to the how a tree grows.

What are the parts of a tree?

http://www.ecokids.ca/pub/eco_info/topics/forests/parts_of_a_tree.cfm

Inside a tree trunk

http://www.botany.uwc.ac.za/ecotree/trunk/woodanatomy.htm

Bark rubbing

http://www.dave-cushman.net/bee/barkrub.html

SEARCH

Sample Exam Questions on How a Tree Grows

Ordinary Level	2010

The diagram shows part of the cross section of a tree.

Show, using an arrow, where the pith is.

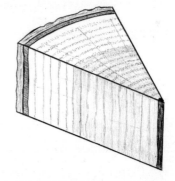

Ordinary Level	2009

The leaves of a tree use light, carbon dioxide and sap to make food for the tree.

What is this process called?

Answer: _____

Ordinary Level | 2009

The diagram shows part of the cross section of a tree.

Give the full name for the cells shown at **A**, which are directly underneath the bark.

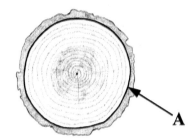

Name: _____

Ordinary Level | 2008

The diagram shows part of the cross-section of a tree.

Give the full name for the cells shown at **A**, radiating from the tree centre.

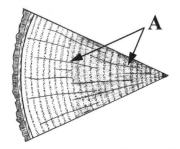

Name: _____

Ordinary Level | 2008

The photograph shows a section of managed forest in Ireland.

(i)   Describe the management of a forest under the following headings:
   (a)   Planting of young trees.
   (b)   Thinning.
   (c)   Harvesting.

(ii)   Give two common uses for thinnings.

(iii)   Give one reason why coniferous trees rather than deciduous trees are usually grown in these forests.

Ordinary Level — 2007

Name the grain feature shown at **A**.

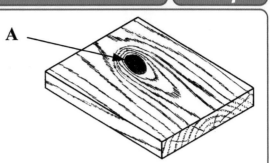

A

Name: _____

Higher Level — 2010

Name **THREE** of the raw materials necessary for photosynthesis to take place in a leaf.

1 _____

2 _____

3 _____

Higher Level — 2010

The diagram shows a cross-section of a tree.

Name the areas labelled **A** and **B**.

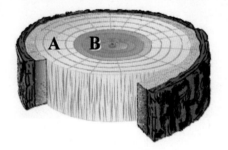

A B

Area **A** _____

Area **B** _____

Test Yourself eTest.ie

❋ Irish forest

Introduction to Forestry in Ireland

Forestry is not a new business in Ireland as, until recent centuries, the entire country was covered in trees. Many years ago, control of the forests and their produce would have been a random operation, however the start of the 1900s heralded the start of state intervention and control of the forests.

Forests are to be seen all around us today, most of them planted and controlled by the state with some private woodlands. These provide habitat for the flora and fauna of the country, a renewable resource and a leisure facility for us all to enjoy.

Forestry in Ireland, and all related industry, is largely controlled by the state body Coillte. Coillte was set up in 1989 to run the state forests for the good of all. Apart from running the forests, Coillte is also engaged in renewable energy solutions and panel products.

There are many industries in Ireland based around timber and its by-products. Finsa make manufactured boards in Co. Clare, Medite in Clonmel make MDF products and OSB is made in Waterford.

Many other industries such as furniture-making, garden products and timber for building applications contribute to the national economy.

Key Elements to Understand for Junior Certificate Course

* forestry in Ireland
* national distribution of timber species in Ireland
* field trips

Forestry in Ireland

* Tree-felling tractor at work

One per cent of Ireland was covered in forest at the turn of the 1900s (about 52,000 hectares). The first forest owned by the state was established in 1903 in a bid to increase this figure. Today seventy per cent of all forests in Ireland are owned by the state. By the late 1960s, forestry in Ireland had developed to a stage where it was an efficiently managed natural resource – it has continued that way ever since.

In the 1970s, forest parks were developed to allow the public to enjoy this natural resource with the establishment of forest trails and picnic areas.

Irish Forest Facts

Land Use Type	Gross Area (ha)
Broadleaf High Forest	11,563
Conifer High Forest	352,798
High Mixed Forest	13,658
Scrub	2,350
Undeveloped	5,499
Total Forested Area	385,868
Bare Plantable	11,819
Blown	1,607
Burned	1,150
Felled	11,251
Total Plantable Reserve	25,827
Bare Unplantable	22,394
Bare Marginal	5,944
Miscellaneous	261
Swamp	1,031
Water	1,530
Total Unplantable Reserve	**31,160**

Over seventy million trees are planted in Ireland each year.

Forestry in Ireland now employs around 16,000 people. A further 14,000 farmers have also planted an average of 10 hectares each in recent years.

Forestry is now a major Irish industry worth €700 million per annum, and is set to grow at ten per cent per annum. This should climb to over €1 billion by 2015, which will then make the industry as important as the beef or dairy industry is today.

National Distribution of Timber Species in Ireland

Species	Net Area (ha)
Sitka Spruce	231,395
Norway Spruce	17,886
Lodgepole Pine	51,015
Douglas Fir	8,220
Larches	13,306
Scots Pine	4,926
Other conifers	4,752
Broadleaves	18,852
Total	**350,352**

Source: Tree Distribution in Ireland, Coillte.

Field Trips

Field trips can be organised by your teacher to local forest parks. Simply obtain permission from Coillte and if possible get a guided tour of the forest.

Many tasks can be undertaken on the trip including bark rubbings, leaf pressings, tree identification from seeds, twigs as well as outlines and wildlife identification.

❋ Forest recreation

Hands-on Tasks

1 Make a list of three state-run forests in your locality or county.

2 List five different outdoor and school activities you could undertake in a local forest.

3 Visit the websites of the companies named in this chapter – make a poster of the manufactured boards they produce and the advantages of these products over solid timbers.

4 Make a poster bar chart for the figures for tree distribution in Ireland.

5 Get a teacher to organise a field trip to a local state forest – make leaf and bark rubbings of the most common trees.

Homework Sheet on Forestry in Ireland

1 What has been the increase in forestry coverage in Ireland since 1903?

2 In what decade did forest parks become established?

3 Name the state body in control of our forests.

4 Name one company involved in timber products from Ireland.

5 Name another industry in Ireland dependant on trees for raw materials.

INTERNET LINKS AND TASKS

Visit the following (or similar) websites for more facts in relation to forestry in Ireland.

Forestry in Ireland

http://www.coillte.ie/

Awareness of forestry in Ireland

http://www.treecouncil.ie/

Native Irish trees

http://www.gardenplansireland.com/forum/about69.html

SEARCH

Sample Exam Questions on Forestry in Ireland

No exam questions in recent years on forestry in Ireland.

CHAPTER 5

Timber and the Environment

The Theory of Wood

Introduction to Timber and the Environment

🌸 Destruction of the rainforests

We may take timber in the MTW room for granted. By now we are aware that the wood we use grows from a seed and then into a large tree, which is cut down (felled) to make the everyday items we see around us. Thankfully wood is a renewable material and, if managed properly, will be used by generations to come. Unfortunately, there are forests being cut down in the rainforests along the Equator, which are not being replanted. Where possible we should avoid timber from these areas and use timber stamped with proof that the trees are being replanted.

On a smaller scale, we all can help the environment by careful use of the wood resources we grow and use here in Ireland.

Key Elements to Understand for Junior Certificate Course
- climatic/environmental effects of/on trees
- human effects of/on trees and tree aesthetics (appearance)
- trees and wildlife

Climatic Effects of Trees

🌸 Living rainforest

Trees are crucial to our everyday existence. They take in vast quantities of CO_2 gas and release oxygen. Each mature tree in the world releases enough oxygen each year to support two human beings.

The shade provided by one tree planted near your home in the summer is estimated to save the equivalent of ten air conditioning units running twenty hours a day. This saves on air conditioning bills for many homes in the

world. Trees planted in cities absorb much of the heat from the sun, thus reducing the overall temperature of the urban area.

Both of the above factors help to reduce global temperature rises and slow the process of global warming.

Climatic/Environmental Effects on Trees

❀ Bush fire

Damage to the **ozone** layer is leading to drier spells of weather in many parts of the world during the summer season. When bush fires occur they take longer to extinguish and as a result more trees are lost. This, in turn, leads to greater damage to the ozone layer and bigger fires.

In other parts of the world, huge amounts of rain washes away the topsoil around the tree bases which causes the trees to die or fall down. This also leads to a reduction in the number of trees in the world.

Human Effect of Trees and Tree Aesthetics

Trees make us feel good about the planet we live on. A walk in the forest on a warm day leaves memories of beautiful trees and wildlife

❀ Bonsai tree

in our minds. Trees have a well-known effect of reducing stress and causing us to relax. The ancient Japanese art of Bonsai tree pruning is a case in point.

Trees provide shelter for us on rainy days and provide shelter from wind.

Human Effect on Trees

❀ Effects of deforestation

Where humans plant trees in large forests, beautiful walks can be created and used by everyone. When humans decide to cut down large sections of forest and not replant them, we get the problem of **deforestation**.

Deforestation largely occurs in the rainforests around the equator. Huge hardwood trees are felled and transported across the world.

We engage in this practice:
* to obtain high-quality wood for the developed world
* to clear land for agriculture
* to clear land for road building

In addition to the effect on global warming, deforestation also causes:
* soil erosion in heavy rains
* loss of habitat for birds and animals
* displacement of native tribes in the jungles

Fortunately, you can make a difference to deforestation in the MTW classroom.

> * Use veneered boards rather than solid hardwoods where possible.
> * Use timbers from home grown plantations to reduce your **carbon footprint**.
> * Cut down on waste wood by marking and cutting your wood properly.
> * Place waste wood in a recycling bin in the classroom for others to use.

Trees and Wildlife

Trees give shelter to many animals and birds as well as providing them with food such as leaves and insects.

Cutting down trees removes these habitats and therefore all trees felled should be replaced.

Large forests created by large forestry companies (such as Coillte in Ireland) provide new habitats in which our native species can survive and prosper.

Snags (dead trees) provide shelter as well as food for animals. Butterflies often lay their eggs on snags. Some animals and birds find it easier to dig out homes in dead trees rather than in live trees.

Hands-on Tasks

1 Research at your local timber yard to find native hardwoods – which could be used in your projects instead of imported hardwoods from rainforest areas.

2 Try to establish from Internet research the quantity of trees lost from **bush fires** each year in Australia or other country of your choice.

3 Make a collage (on A4 paper) of images from deforested areas of the world and put pictures of **unaffected** forest beside them. Place these posters on the walls for others in the class to see.

4 Set up a waste bin for scrap timbers, and a poster to go over it, so that other classes can become aware of saving trees and timber in the MTW room.

5 Take a digital camera to the forest and take some pictures of the wildlife you encounter near, or actually on, the trees. Print pictures to display in the classroom.

Homework Sheet on Timber and the Environment

1 What is meant by the term **renewable**?

2 Give another name for cutting down a tree.

3 Where in the world would one find most **rainforests**?

4 Which two gases do trees take in and release?

5 Name any two advantages that trees provide for humans?

6 What is meant by the term **deforestation**?

7 What effects can deforestation have on the environment around us?

8 List three ways you can help in the fight against deforestation.

INTERNET LINKS AND TASKS

Visit the following (or similar) websites for more facts in relation to trees and the environment.

Irish trees and the environment

http://www.coillte.ie/environment/

How trees benefit the environment

http://findarticles.com/p/articles/mi_moEPG/is_4_35/ai_71767533/

Tree planting in the community

http://www.newbridgetidytowns.com/wildlife-%7C-trees-page8764.html

Benefits of trees in urban areas

http://www.treecanada.ca/publications/trivia.htm

SEARCH

Sample Exam Questions on Timber and the Environment

No relevant whole questions in previous years.

Topics may show up as small parts of other questions relating to trees.

Introduction to Conversion of Timber

❋ Tree felling machine

The journey of the piece of timber in your MTW room is nothing short of amazing. From a little seed the tree grows to full maturity and is then felled and sawn into planks for use in your MTW room.

The tree is cut down (felled) in the forest by use of a tree cutter.

❋ Log transporter

This machine strips the branches off the tree before they are piled up and transported to the **sawmill**. Once at the sawmill they are cut (converted) into planks, sent for drying and then delivered for use in the MTW room.

Key Elements to Understand for Junior Certificate Course

* conversion methods
    * through and through sawing
    * radial sawing
    * tangential sawing

Methods of Conversion

❋ Sawmill operation

Through and Through

In this method of changing logs to planks, the tree is cut on a bandsaw in the same way one would slice a block of cheese. Parallel runs of the log are made as in the diagram below. This produces the widest boards possible from a conversion method.

This is a simple and fast way to cut up a tree and has both advantages and disadvantages. It produces some radial boards and some tangential boards as a result. Through and through timber is widely used in the construction industry in beams etc.

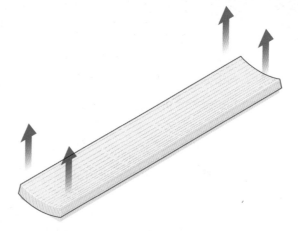

❋ Cupping from through and through sawing and poor seasoning

❋ Through and through sawing at the mill

❋ Through and through sawing

Advantages

❋ fast method of obtaining planks
❋ little waste in the process
❋ not labour intensive process
❋ low cost method of conversion

Disadvantages

❋ Boards have a huge tendency to cup.
❋ Some planks contain heartwood and sapwood.
❋ Grain pattern is not as attractive as other methods.

Radial Sawing

This is also known as **quarter sawing boards**. It produces the silver ribbon effect we often see in Oak planks. Growth rings form angles of greater than forty-five degrees and often up to ninety degrees if converted skilfully. Radial sawn timber is used for fascia boards, mouldings and bench tops. Little deformation

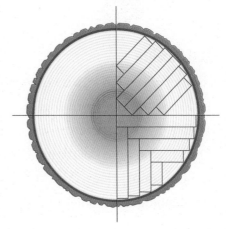

❋ Radial sawing

is found in the planks as the method carefully reduces the stress on the log throughout the process.

Advantages

* Cross-sectional strength of timber is improved.
* Beautiful grain pattern effects especially in Oak (silver grain effect).
* No great tendency to cup due to narrower boards.

Disadvantages

* Most expensive to produce due to increased labour.
* Smaller boards produced toward the edge of the log.
* It is difficult to stack.
* Twenty per cent of the tree is wasted in the process.

❁ Radial board grain pattern

Tangential Sawing

This is also known as **flat sawn conversion**. The annual growth rings form angles of less than forty-five degrees as seen on the end grain. In this method the boards are cut at tangents to the annual rings. The boards can suffer from cupping if not stacked properly. These boards are used as structural wooden

beams in construction. This method produces the strongest type of planks. The method produces the flame effect (flame figuring) one often sees on high-quality furniture.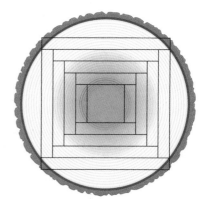

❁ Tangential sawing

❁ Flame figure from tangential sawing

Advantages

* A beautiful flame effect on the face of the board.
* Boards contain mostly sapwood or heartwood (thus deformities are reduced).
* Very strong boards are produced.

Disadvantages

* high labour and cost
* some waste produced in the process
* cups if not properly stacked

Hands-on Tasks

1 Using the Internet, locate pictures of timber harvesting machines in use and save them in your documents.

2 Create an A3 size coloured poster to show **through and through** sawing to your classroom.

3 Create an A3 size coloured poster to show **radial** sawing to your classroom.

4 Create an A3 size coloured poster to show **tangential** sawing to your classroom.

Homework Sheet on Conversion of Timber

1 Create a comparison poster for your own wall comparing the three types of conversion in a visual format.

2 Obtain 300 mm wide logs. Draw (with a marker) the planks which will be cut into the ends, as shown in the diagrams in this chapter.

3 List two key advantages and disadvantages with each type of conversion.

4 Try sketching wood patterns from furniture in the home or at school. Try to identify the type of conversion used to create the wood used.

INTERNET LINKS AND TASKS

Sustainable use of timber

http://www.trada.co.uk/techinfo/tsg/

How to radial saw

http://www.radialtimber.com/radial.html

SEARCH

Sample Exam Questions on Conversion of Timber

Ordinary Level | **2010**

Why is **through and through** sawing the most popular method, in Ireland, of converting logs into planks?

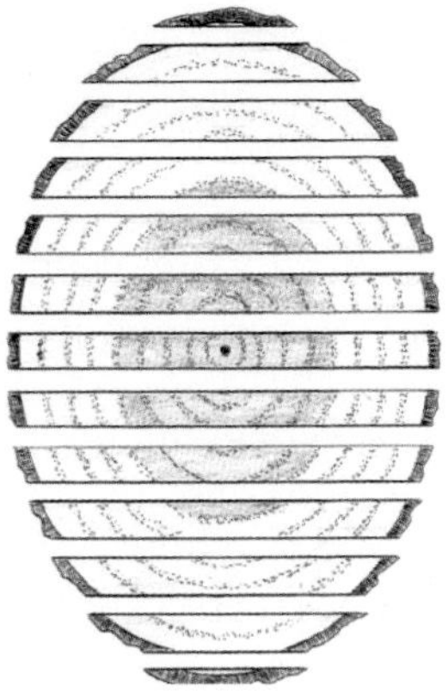

ANSWER ______________________________

____

Ordinary Level | **2009**

Name this method of converting a log into boards.

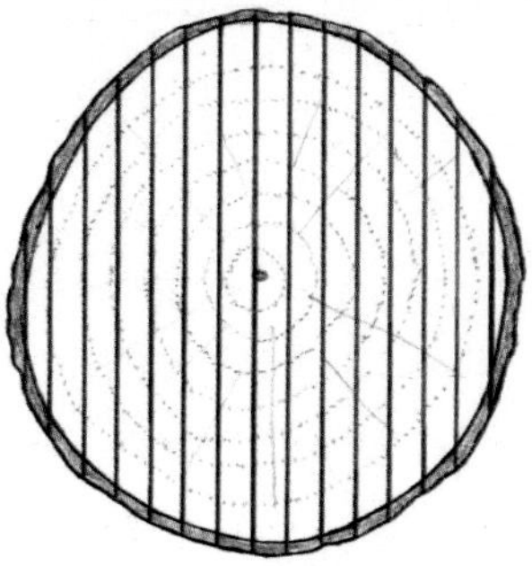

ANSWER ______________________________

Ordinary Level — 2008

Name this method of conversion.

ANSWER _____

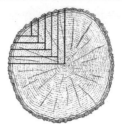

Higher Level — 2010

(i) Name the method of timber conversion shown in the diagram.

NAME _____

(ii) Name the grain pattern produced by sawing oak in this manner.

PATTERN _____

Higher Level — 2009

The diagrams show two methods of timber conversion

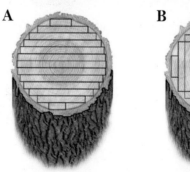

A   **B**

(i) Name the **TWO** methods of conversion.

(ii) State **TWO** advantages and **TWO** disadvantages of **each** conversion method.

(iii) The board shown on the right is prone to **cupping**. Using a *neat freehand sketch*, show the direction of the cupping and explain why this happens.

(iv) With increasing awareness of environmental issues, there is a greater focus on the protection of existing tropical rain forests and on the conservation of hardwoods.
(a) State **TWO** reasons why we should conserve our rainforests.
(b) Suggest **TWO** ways that we can reduce our use of hardwoods.

The diagram shows a method of converting logs.

(i)   Give the correct name for this method of conversion.

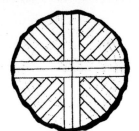

METHOD _____

(ii)   This method of conversion reveals a grain feature in Oak boards.
       What is the grain feature called?

FEATURE _____

7 Timber Seasoning

Introduction to Timber Seasoning

All timber, which has been felled, will require drying out due to the high level of moisture in the wood. Trees that have been felled and not dried out are known as **green timbers**. To allow the wood be used to make products, it must be dried to achieve a moisture content level appropriate to the end usage area. In general, wood will rot if the moisture content is above twenty per cent and therefore the goal is to dry (season) the timber to achieve this level of moisture.

❋ Wood drying kiln

Poor drying out will lead to other problems such as warping, with which many people are familiar. Seasoning can be as simple as allowing the timbers to dry naturally over a long period of time in a shed or relatively quickly in giant ovens called **kilns**.

Seasoned timber has many advantages over green timber such as:

❋ lighter to carry
❋ easier to work with
❋ stable in final environment
❋ stronger wood (due to dry or stiff cells in the planks)
❋ less artificial defects

Key Elements to Understand for Junior Certificate Course

❋ finding the moisture content of wood samples
❋ correct seasoning processes

Moisture Content

The first thing to know in relation to timber seasoning is how to find the exact moisture content of the timber. To do this, a moisture meter is used as shown below.

This meter passes a small current through the wood and reads how much current comes back. The more current returning through the pins, the more moisture there is in the sample.

❋ Moisture meter

It also has a gauge to show the limits of rot for the timber. Measurements should be taken along the whole length of the sample to get an average for the piece of wood being tested.

If such a device is not available you can find the moisture content through experimentation as described below.

Experiment to Find the Moisture Content of a Wood Sample

1. Weigh a small sample of green timber.
2. Place the timber in an oven (under supervision) and allow to dry for some hours. Do not allow to burn.
3. Weigh the sample and note the result.
4. Place the sample in the oven and repeat steps 2 and 3 until there is no change in weight.
5. Using the formula below calculate the percentage moisture content for the sample.

Formula

Moisture Content Percentage $= \dfrac{W1 - Wf}{Wf} \times 100$

Where W1 = the weight of the green (moist) wood

Wf = the final dry weight of the dry wood

The answer is expressed as a percentage.

Relative Humidity (RH)

As you may have discovered in science class, air contains moisture that we cannot see. This is the **relative humidity** of the air. If the wood is lower in moisture than the air, moisture will enter the wood and raise the moisture content thus causing the wood to swell and vice versa. This is why floorboards are left to acclimatise to the room in which they are to be laid – to prevent the floors rising when they are laid. This is also the cause of doors swelling in the winter and shrinking back in the spring. This may well happen in your home!

When the moisture content of the wood reaches the same moisture content as the air around it, this is known as the Equilibrium Moisture Content (EMC). The table below shows appropriate moisture content levels for different uses.

Moisture Content (%)		Use of the Wood
20		Limit of rot occurrence
16		Outdoor timber usage
12		Rooms heated intermittently
11		Long-term heated rooms
10		Always heated areas

There are a number of methods by which the timber can be dried and one of these is available to you.

Natural Seasoning

Natural seasoning means that the timber planks are stacked (as shown below) in a covered shed and allowed to air dry over the course of a year or so. When the desired moisture content is reached the timber can be used to make products.

❋ Natural seasoning

It is important that all the planks have air movement around them to dry evenly. This is achieved by the use of **stickers** (as shown below). Even so, some wood will remain green as rain can penetrate the outside layers. The end planks can be protected as shown in the diagrams on the right:

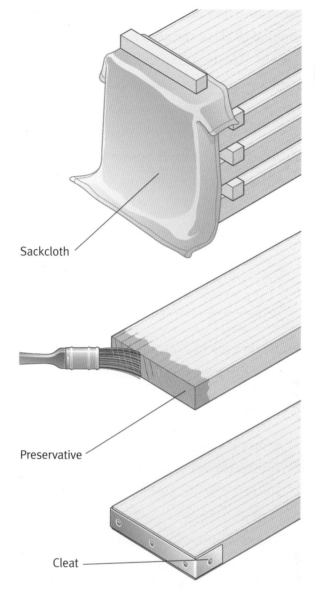

Sackcloth

Preservative

Cleat

❋ Protecting ends of boards from splitting or distorting

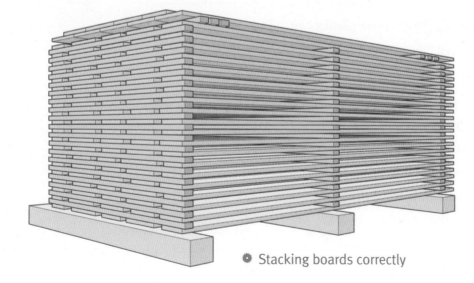

❋ Stacking boards correctly

The drying time will depend on the relative humidity (RH) of the area in which the wood is stored. The resulting timber will be most useful for outdoor artefacts because a low moisture content is not possible.

Advantages of Natural Seasoning

* No specialised equipment is required.
* Large sheds can be used for the material.
* It is a relatively cheap process.
* No artificial energy is required to complete.

Disadvantages of Natural Seasoning

* It takes a long time to complete (one year to 25 mm thickness of plank).
* The boards on the outside are not as dry as on the inside.
* The treatment of end grain is required.
* Sheds are in use for long periods of time.
* There is little control over defects in the drying process.

Kiln-drying

There is a faster way to season the timber than natural seasoning. The timber planks can be placed in large oven-like rooms and dried out.

Compartment Kiln

The wood is stacked in this kiln and the drying process is controlled by using lesser amounts of steam over time until the desired moisture content is achieved. This method reduces the chances of

defects as outlined in Chapter 8, Defects and Diseases in Timber.

◉ Compartment kiln

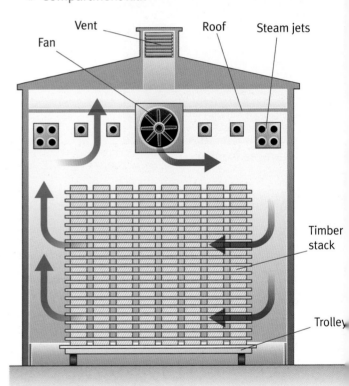

◉ Inside compartment kiln

Progressive Kiln

Here the stacked wood passes through a longer kiln on movable trolleys. It dries in the same manner utilising steam as the controlling force. Timber of different thickness and species are stacked together to further control the process.

Advantages of Kiln-drying

* More timber can be dried quickly.
* It prevents many defects such as case-hardening.
* The exact moisture content can be achieved for different species.

Disadvantages of Kiln-drying

* It requires highly trained individuals to operate it.
* A large initial cost to set up.
* An expensive process requiring a lot of energy.

❉ Progressive kiln

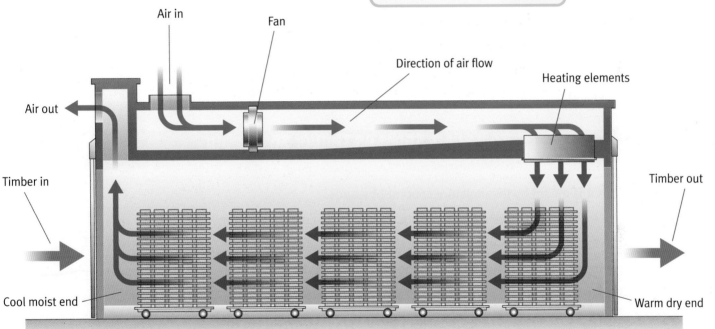

❉ Progressive kiln – how it works

Hands-on Tasks

1 Make a neat rendered 3-D sketch of a moisture meter and label parts.

2 Using a moisture meter, find the moisture content of three different varieties of wood in the MTW room.

3 Under supervision, use a green piece of wood and find the moisture content using the experimental method. Compare the result to the moisture content found using a moisture meter.

4 Use the Internet to list two items which would require a moisture content the same as each of the contents of our table, e.g. Table moisture content = 11%.

5 Can you suggest any way to speed up the natural drying process?

6 Make a neat freehand rendered sectional sketch of a Compartment kiln.

7 Make a neat freehand rendered sketch of a Progressive kiln.

Homework Sheet on Timber Seasoning

1 What is meant by the moisture content of wood?

2 How does a moisture meter measure the moisture content of a material?

3 Describe an experiment to measure the moisture content of a log.

4 Using diagrams and annotations, show how planks are to be stacked properly for seasoning.

5 What are the advantages of **kiln** seasoning over **natural** seasoning?

6 What would the preferred moisture content be for the following items:

* table and chairs
* garden furniture
* wooden fencing
* coffee table
* bed
* desk

7 Draw a cross-section through a **compartment** or a **progressive** kiln.

Sample Exam Questions on Timber Seasoning

Ordinary Level	2009

The diagram shows a stack of wood being air-seasoned.

(i) Describe **three** important steps to follow when building the stack.

(ii) List **three** advantages of seasoning wood.

(iii) The ends of the planks tend to split during seasoning.
Describe **one** method that can be used to prevent this from happening.

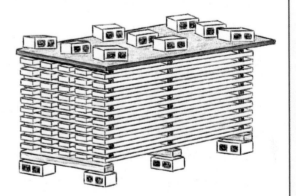

Ordinary Level	2007

Show by means of a tick (✓) which type of seasoning is most suitable for timber used in the following locations:

	Air Seasoning	Kiln	Seasoning
Fencing posts			
Floorboards			
Shelving			
Dog kennel			
Kitchen table			

Ordinary Level 2007

Why are the ends of planks painted before seasoning?

ANSWER

____

Ordinary Level 2006

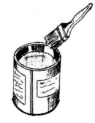

The diagram shows a stack of wood being kiln seasoned.

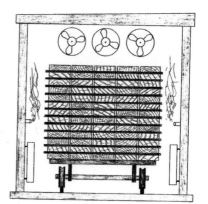

(i) Name the pieces of wood which are used to separate the planks. Explain why these pieces of wood are used.

____

____

____

(ii) Planks that are seasoned too quickly can develop several types of defect. Using notes and sketches describe any **two** of these defects.

____

____

(iii) The other method of seasoning is air or natural seasoning. Compare both methods of seasoning under the following headings:

(a) Moisture content.

(b) Time.

(c) Cost.

Higher Level — 2010

The diagram on the right shows one method of seasoning timber to reduce its moisture content.

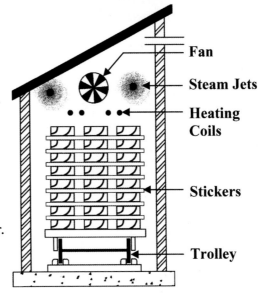

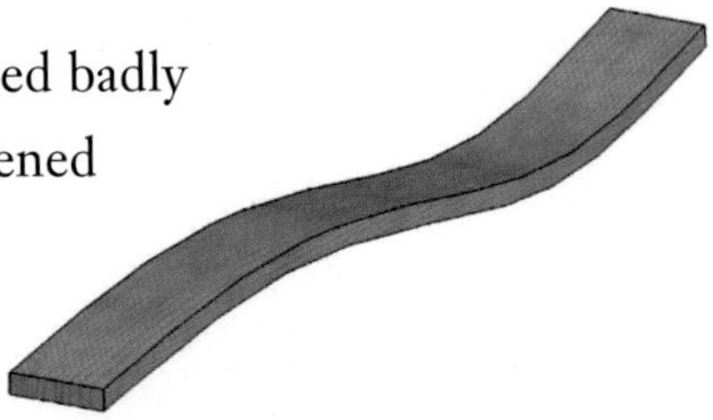

Fan
Steam Jets
Heating Coils
Stickers
Trolley

(i) What is the correct name for this method of seasoning?

(ii) Explain what happens during the seasoning process, making particular reference to the function of the parts labelled in the diagram.

(iii) Name **ONE** other method of seasoning timber. State **TWO** advantages and **TWO** disadvantages of this second method of seasoning.

(iv) The diagram on the right shows a board which warped badly during seasoning. Explain why this might have happened and, using notes and a ***neat freehand sketch***, show how the warping might have been prevented.

Higher Level — 2008

The diagram shows a method of seasoning timber.

(i) What is this method of seasoning called?

METHOD ______________________________

(ii) State **one** disadvantage of this method of seasoning.

DISADVANTAGE ______________________________

____

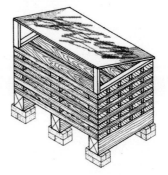

(i) Name the two methods of seasoning, **A** and **B**, shown in the diagrams and state **two** advantages and **two** disadvantages of each method of seasoning.

A 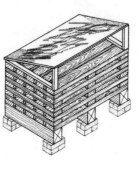   B

_____   _____

_____   _____

_____   _____

(ii) Explain what is meant by the term **equilibrium moisture content** (EMC).

_____

(iii) When wood is used in external situations it is normally treated with a **preservative**. State **two** reasons for the use of preservatives and name **two** classes of preservative. (See chapter 9.)

_____   _____

_____   _____

(iv) Name **three** methods of applying preservatives, and state **one** advantage and **one** disadvantage of each method. (See chapter 9.)

_____   _____   _____

_____

_____

The diagram shows a method of seasoning timber.

(i) What is the correct name for this method of seasoning?

ANSWER _____

(ii) What is the function of the steam in this method of seasoning?

ANSWER _____

Introduction to Defects and Diseases in Timber

Timber can be damaged whilst the tree is still growing, whilst it is being felled, or during transportation from the forest to the sawmill. Damage may also occur after the planks have left the sawmill and are stored in the workshop store room. A lot of the damage is caused by human error but also from natural sources such as insect and fungal attack. However, with the proper care the wood can be kept free from most defects.

The goal of everyone involved in the timber conversion and storage process is to limit damage as well as reducing wastage and cost.

Key Elements to Understand for Junior Certificate Course

* wood in its in-use environment
* wet and dry rot
* insect attack
* human cause of destruction
* climatic influence on wood

Defects

Natural

There is very little one can do to prevent defects which occur in the forest. These natural defects can be kept in the wood as a design feature or removed to prevent any loss of strength. The latter is particularly important for structural timbers.

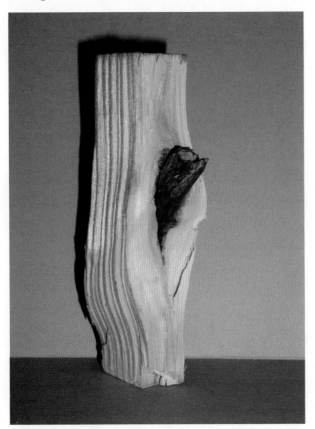

* Knot defect in wood

* Burring

🔆 Knots in wood

Live Knots

Live knots form where a branch was connected to the tree. They are light in colour and generally never fall out. They are often seen in **pine** timber used in the MTW room.

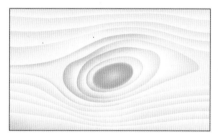

🔆 Live knot

Dead Knots

Also formed where a branch joined the tree, these are darker in colour and often break away from the wood during seasoning – often falling out. These can be in **red deal** in the MTW room and in **pine** furniture at home. Dead knots can have a detrimental effect on the strength of the timber.

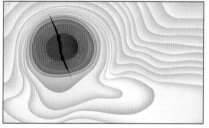

🔆 Dead knot

Resin Pockets

In the MTW room you may sometimes come across wood with sap or resin in a groove in the wood. These resin pockets can occur anywhere in the tree and weaken the strength of the wood. This sap can be difficult to remove from the wood as well as your hands and tools.

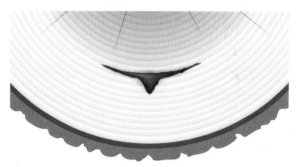

🔆 Resin pocket

Shakes — Fabht

Shakes are cracks in the end grain of wood and can be easily seen in the timber while it is still in log form. These cracks are caused by growth stress building up in the tree and releasing when the tree is felled. Furthermore, if the trees are transported or stacked poorly, further shake damage may occur.

Fabht croi

Heart Shake
~~Icar Fabht~~

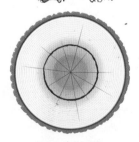

Ring Shake
Fobht Fáinne

Cup Shake
fabht cupán

Star Shake
Fabht realt

Frost Shake
Fabht sioc

60

Poor Stacking and Seasoning

This can also lead to defects on full-length planks. Many of them will be familiar to you in the course of your work with wood.

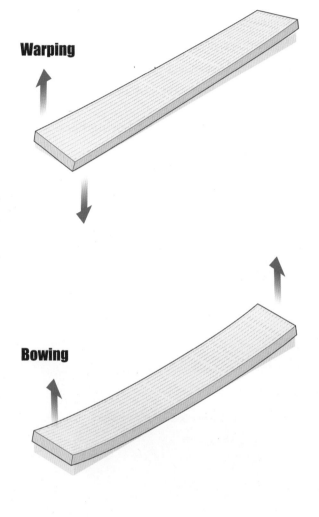

Warping

Bowing

Cupping

Springing

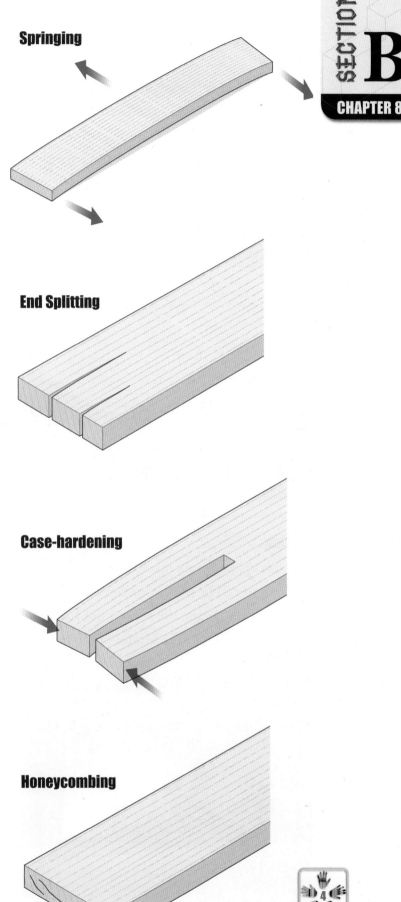

End Splitting

Case-hardening

Honeycombing

Other Defects
Spalting

This occurs when fungus attacks the wood causing black lines and patches to form after a number of months. Although this affects the strength of the wood, the effect can look impressive when the wood is waxed and used in furniture-making.

❊ Spalted Beech bowl

Burring

This occurs as disease takes hold of the growing tree. The most common is burred Elm and Oak. Again, the strength of the wood is compromised, but the beauty of the burring on the wood makes some interesting patterns which can be used in fine furniture-making.

❊ Burred Oak mirror

Insect Attack

Most timbers are susceptible to attack from insects. Woodworm is common in Ireland in places such as household furniture and the exit holes can be clearly seen in the wood. The woodworms are the larval stage of adult beetles and are not a separate species themselves. Most insect attack leads to the degradation of the wood and a loss in strength.

A number of different wood-boring beetles are often seen.

Deathwatch Beetle

Approximately 7 mm long, this beetle can be heard tapping on wood in attics and other quiet places at night. It lays its eggs in the wood and these emerge as larva at a later time.

❊ Deathwatch beetle

House Longhorn Beetle

Found all over the world, this beetle often gets into the wood at the sawmill stage and emerges in house rafters shortly after. This beetle prefers softwoods such as pine. The larvae mature in spring and the adults grow to 10 mm long. These beetles are black in colour.

● House longhorn beetle

Eggs

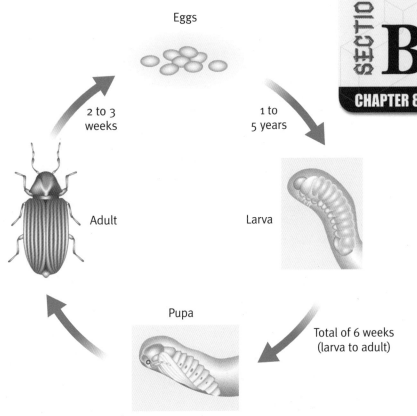

2 to 3 weeks

1 to 5 years

Adult

Larva

Pupa

Total of 6 weeks (larva to adult)

● Life cycle of insects

Powderpost

This beetle leaves a trail of dust in its wake as its larvae eat through the wood. They cause serious weakening in the timber because they can digest the cellulose in the cell walls of the wood. The adults can grow to 12 mm. They mostly feed on hardwood timbers.

● Powderpost beetle

The Life Cycle of a Wood Beetle

An understanding of this cycle can greatly help to prevent further infection. By treating the wood (see chapter 9) one can prevent adult insects laying eggs or feeding on the wood.

Fungal Attack

Fungus attacks wood and digests it, which causes it to rot. This can occur whether the tree is living or dead. Parasitic fungus attacks growing wood (**honey fungus**) while dead wood becomes susceptible to wet or dry rot. Fungal attack damages the strength of the timber.

● Wood rot

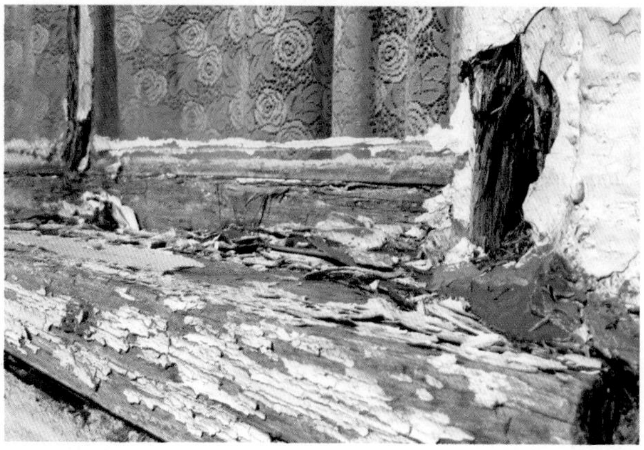

Wet rot

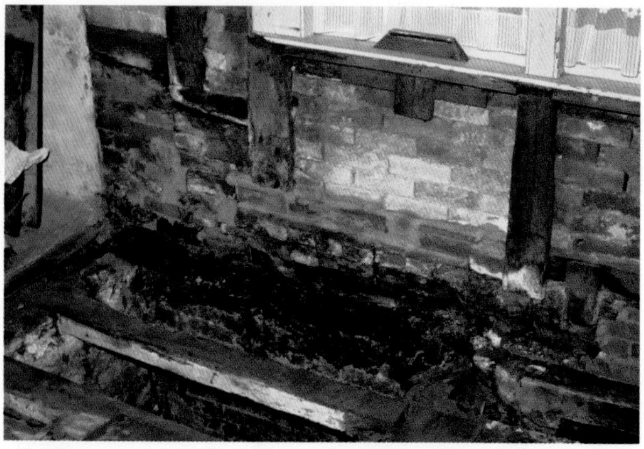

Dry rot

For a fungus to take hold, a number of environmental conditions must be present, such as:

- food (wood)
- moisture (damp wood)
- oxygen (air)
- heat (indoors)

Dry rot is often referred to as **brown rot**. This rot feeds on the cellulose in the wood leaving behind a brown residue. Infected wood is greatly weakened, and frequently this decay cannot be detected until collapse occurs. When this happens in sheltered areas (under floors etc.) any contact with the wood will cause it to crumble into dry dust. Dry rot is just a term used to describe the rot as any dry timber not infected cannot decay on its own.

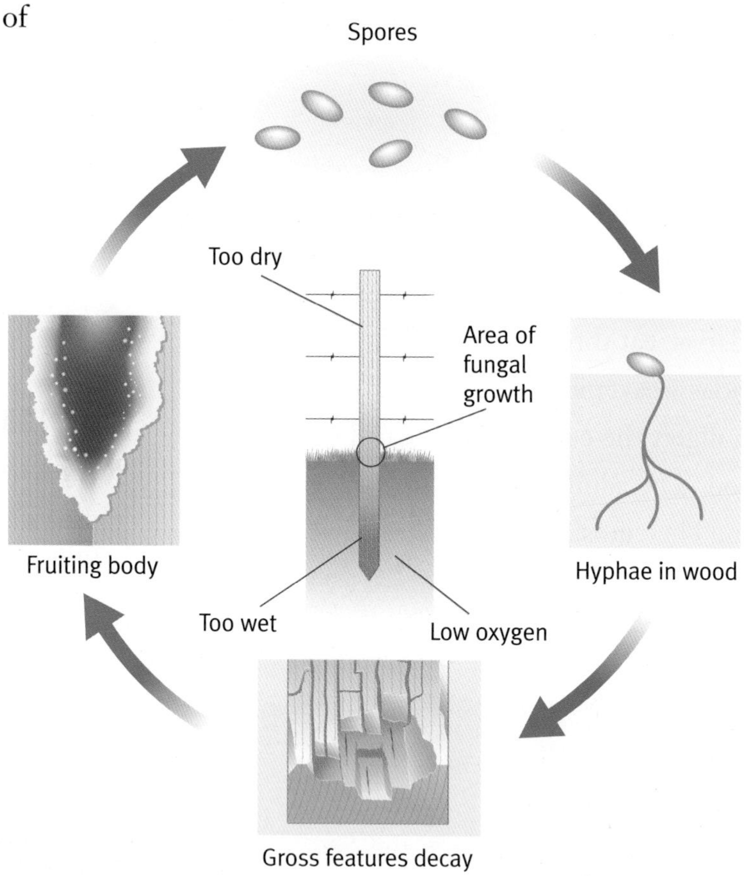
Spores
Too dry
Area of fungal growth
Fruiting body
Hyphae in wood
Too wet
Low oxygen
Gross features decay

Life Cycle of fungus

Wet rot is often referred to as **white rot**. This fungus breaks down the cellulose and lignin of the wood causing the wood to lose colour – hence the **white** name. The wood often feels spongy to the touch but the strength is not as badly affected as dry rot.

Hands-on Tasks

1 Using tracing paper, make a pencil rubbing of a **live** knot.

2 Using tracing paper, make a pencil rubbing of a **dead** knot.

3 Suggest a possible method to fill the space created by a resin pocket in any piece of wood.

4 Print off pictures from the Internet of any four defects from page 61.

5 Try to obtain spalted Beech from your local timber yard for use in a school woodwork project.

6 Make an A3 wall chart of the different **wood-boring** beetles.

7 Make a wall chart to show the life cycle of a fungus.

Homework Sheet on Defects and Diseases in Timber

1 Name two different types of defect.

2 Explain the difference between live and dead knots.

3 Where on the tree does a knot form?

4 What effect does a resin pocket have on the wood?

5 Make a neat sketch to show the difference between warping and cupping.

6 What type of product can be made from spalted Beech?

7 What is the name of the powder left behind when woodworm bore through wood?

8 Make a neat drawing of a deathwatch and a powderpost beetle.

9 What is the difference between dry and wet rot?

10 Draw the life cycle of a fungus.

INTERNET LINKS AND TASKS

Defects in timber

http://homepage.eircom.net/~woodworkwebsite

Images of defects in timber decks and floors

www.thedeckcentre.com

Company that deals with wood defects

www.handr.co.uk

SEARCH

Sample Exam Questions on Defects and Diseases in Timber

Ordinary Level | **2010**

Name the grain feature shown at **A**.

NAME _____

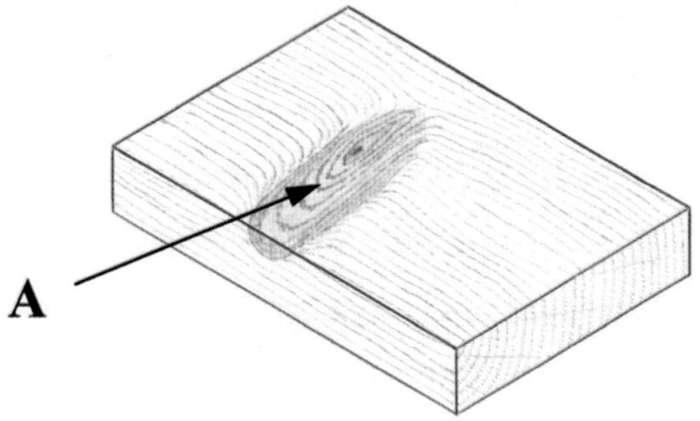

A

Ordinary Level 2007

The diagram shows an image of the common furniture beetle (woodworm).

(i) Describe, using notes and sketches, the life cycle of the common furniture beetle under the following headings:

(a) Eggs

(b) Larva

(c) Pupa

(d) Adult Beetle

(ii) Explain how to treat a piece of furniture that has been attacked by woodworm.

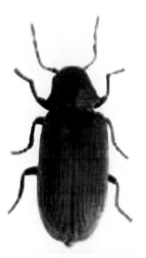

(3 mm)

Higher Level 2010

The diagram shows four stages in the lifecycle of a wood-boring beetle.

At what stage is most damage caused to the wood?

STAGE ______________________________

Higher Level 2010

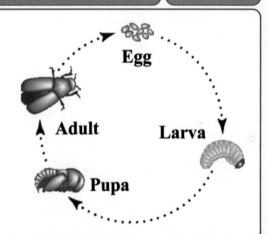

Dry rot is the most common form of decay in wood.

State **TWO** conditions necessary for its occurrence.

CONDITION 1 ______________________________

CONDITION 2 ______________________________

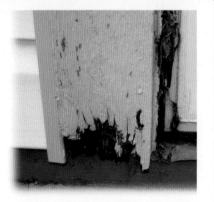

The diagram shows a common defect in timber.

(i)   Give the correct name for this defect.

   NAME _____

(ii) What is the most common cause of this defect?

   CAUSE _____

   _____

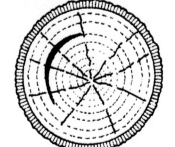

The diagram shows a common defect in timber.

(i)   Give the correct name for this defect.

   NAME _____

(ii) What is the possible cause of this defect?

   CAUSE _____

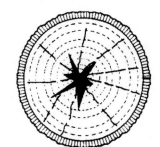

The board shown in the diagram has become distorted across its width.

(i)   What is this form of distortion commonly called?

   ANSWER _____

(ii) What causes a board to distort in this manner?

   ANSWER _____

Test Yourself
eTest.ie

CHAPTER 9

Preserving Timber

The Theory of Wood

Introduction to Preserving Timber

Preservatives are what we use to extend the lifespan of the wood. It is important to protect wood from elements such as wear and tear, weather damage and also insect and fungal infection. For Junior Certificate projects, applied finishes are used to enhance the appearance and feel of the work, but these finishes have the added effect of providing long-term protection, e.g. varnish.

Wooden artefacts placed outside need more durable preservatives to protect them from constant weather damage. Even on warm and sunny days the light can fade parts of the wood surface. Examples of preservatives and finishes we can see in everyday life include **creosote** on **telephone poles** and the common red colour of wooden fence finishes.

❋ Selection of preservatives

❋ Preservative application gun

❋ Telegraph pole treated with preservative

⚜ Applying water-based finish to shed

Why Use Preservatives?

If one wishes to prolong the lifespan of a timber product, it must be treated with a preservative. Preservatives protect the wood from the insect and fungal attack as discussed earlier. Preservatives also protect wood from weather (e.g. sun and rain). Wood is becoming more expensive and thus there is a need to make it last longer. So in the long run preservatives actually save money. Unfortunately there may be some damage to the environment if they are not used correctly.

Types of Preservatives

Water-based

These preservative contain toxic salts, which is carried into the wood. When the water evaporates the toxins remain and protect the wood. They are very effective against **insect** and **fungal** attack. The water base causes a rise in the moisture content and this must be accounted for in the final use of the timber.

Not as damaging to the environment as other treatments.

Uses: Structural timbers and furniture.

Advantages

* relatively safe to use
* easy to apply
* cheap
* easy on environment relative to other types

Disadvantages

* It is not great for outdoor use, salts can wash off.
* Protection is only for a few years indoors.
* Water content can cause defects as outlined in earlier chapters.

Solvent-based

This is a mix of toxins and white spirits. As above, the spirits evaporate leaving behind the toxins to protect the wood. This is the most common type of preservative for school use.

⚜ Solvent-based preservative on timber decking

Solvent-based preservatives are very effective against fungal attack.

Uses: Furniture and all external woodwork (e.g. gates, sheds, bird tables, play houses).

Advantages
* long-lasting protection
* very resistant to insect and fungal attack
* safe to animals around the home
* easy to apply

Disadvantages
* It is strong smelling after application and for a few hours after.
* It is costly for large applications.
* It stains clothes and hands if misused.

Tar Oil

These are normally dark liquids. They are mainly used in outdoor woodwork which will not come into human contact. Creosote (seen on telephone poles and farm fencing) is the most common variant.

Use: Telephone and electricity poles, fencing, wooden railway sleepers.

Advantages
* excellent outdoor protection
* cheap
* very toxic to insects and fungae
* capable of deep wood penetration
* It is an excellent water repellent.

Disadvantages
* It cannot be easily painted over.
* It stains and burns grass etc. on contact.

* Creosote used on railway sleepers

* It is difficult to work with treated wood (stains).
* It is strong smelling for weeks after application.

Application Methods
Woodwork Room
Brushing/Spraying

The easiest method in the MTW room is brushing or spraying – assuming that there are adequate facilities. Ensure that all the surfaces are coated well. Any gaps will allow attack from fungae, insects or weather. When spraying, apply as many coats as possible. When brushing, do not allow dripping of the preservative at the end grain. Whichever method you use, these forms of application will not penetrate below 5 mm (depending on the timber). Softwoods will allow deeper penetration due to the larger cells.

❂ Pressure treatment plant

> **Safety**
> Always wear a respirator and eye protection when brushing or spraying especially in confined areas.

Professional
Immersion

As its name suggests, the wood is dipped fully in a bath of the chosen preservative. The longer the wood can be left in the tank, the better the penetration.

❂ Readying poles for immersion in preservative

Pressure Treatment

The basic method here involves vacuuming out air and water from the timber in a special chamber. Then the preservative is flooded into the chamber and allowed to replace the areas taken up by the water and moisture. This allows for almost full penetration in high-tech chambers. This is an expensive process and can be used for important structural timbers such as laminated roofs and piers.

Hands-on Tasks

1 Examine projects in the MTW room and identify projects which have had a treatment applied.

2 Make a list of wooden items in the vicinity of your school which have had treatment applied.

3 Using small pine pieces, brush on different types of solvent-based preservatives to compare ease of application and colouring effect on wood.

4 Use the Internet to find photos of wood being treated by immersion.

5 Use the Internet to visit a pressure-treating company, e.g. Protim. Write a short essay on how they pressure-treat their woods.

1 Why do timbers need preservative finishes?

2 What damage could preservatives cause to the environment?

3 List two uses for each of the three types of preservative.

4 List the common advantages between all three preservatives.

5 Identify one use for each of the three preservatives.

6 In your opinion, state which is the best preservative to use in the MTW room on your everyday projects. Why is it the best?

INTERNET LINKS AND TASKS

DIY timber preservation

http://www.protim.ie/diy.htm

Common timber problems

http://www.ourproperty.co.uk/guides/timber_preservation.html

Treatability of different Irish timbers

http://www.woodspec.ie/iopen

SEARCH

Sample Exam Question on Preserving Timber

Higher Level	2009

The diagram shows a wooden garden bench.

(i) Suggest **TWO** suitable applied finishes for the bench.

FINISH 1 _____

FINISH 2 _____

(ii) Give **ONE** reason why these finishes are suitable.

REASON _____

Test Yourself eTest.ie

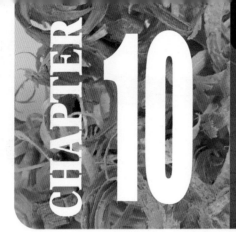

Introduction to Manufactured Boards

Where natural timbers do not meet the requirements of a project, manufactured boards with different properties may be substituted. These properties may be size, strength, cost or workability.

Manufactured boards are simply strips or pieces of wood glued together and pressed with a heat process to form larger boards, usually 2,400 mm × 1,200 mm.

The advantages over natural timber are:
* It is cheaper by volume to buy.
* It can produce larger projects from a smaller number of pieces.
* It can be covered in veneers from expensive woods.
* A constant thickness can be produced over large areas.

These can all be classified into three groups:
* laminate boards, fibreboards, particle boards
* hardboard, MDF, oriented strand board, plywood, edge
* laminated softwood board (pineboard), chipboard, melamine, blockboard

❋ Melamine worktop – a manufactured board

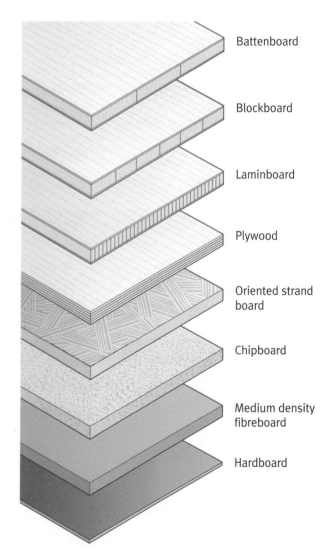

Battenboard

Blockboard

Laminboard

Plywood

Oriented strand board

Chipboard

Medium density fibreboard

Hardboard

❋ Various manufactured boards

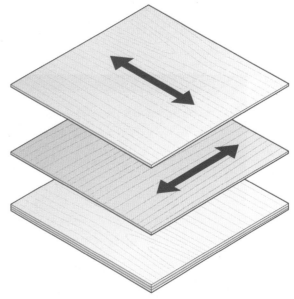

● Grain alignment for making plywood

Key Elements to Understand for Junior Certificate Course

* The various types of manufactured board.
* The manufacture of each type of manufactured board.
* The uses of each type of manufactured board.
* The properties of each type of manufactured board.

Laminate Boards

Generally speaking these are boards that are glued together to produce larger boards. These boards can be used as they are or covered in veneers to produce a more natural appearance.

Plywood

Veneers must be cut from trees to produce the layers required. Veneers are cut from logs of the required timber and these are glued and pressed to form the finished manufactured board. The thickness of the veneers can be changed but thicker veneers may break during cutting.

Plywood is used in everyday furniture such as table tops, in boat building and in hoardings.

There are three main types, **standard plywood** (interior use), **marine plywood** (boat building) and **WBP** (**water boil proof plywood**) for exterior use. All three are basically made in the same way but with different glues for different uses. Veneers are laid down in alternative directions to counteract any warping tendencies.

Pineboard

Strips of pine (**Red Deal**) are glued together, planed to thickness and squared to form sheets of 2,438 mm × 1,219 mm. These can then be sawn into various sizes to make handling easier. They can be used for making a variety of furniture and especially for table tops in the MTW room. They can be obtained in various thicknesses but with each increase in size it gets more difficult to handle because of the extra weight. The boards have good strength but tend to snap if too much compression force is applied, e.g. in a vice. This can be managed if the board is placed as

● Plywood

shown below with the joints running at ninety degrees to the vice.

🌸 Pineboard

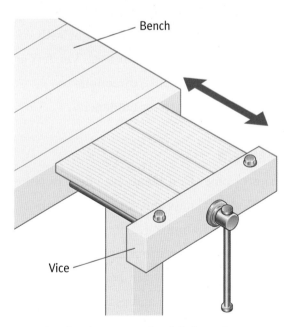

🌸 Securing laminate wood safely in a vice

Bench

Vice

Blockboard

Similar to the laminate board but covered in a layer of veneer (3 mm) to improve strength. Used in cheaper furniture and desktops. Can

be used as grounds for **marquetry** on a table top.

🌸 Blockboard

Melamine

Melamine is combined with **formaldehyde** to produce **melamine resin**, a very durable **thermosetting plastic**. This is then coated on chipboard, or a similar manufactured board, to make a durable and strong product. It is normally used in counter and desktop applications as well as in wardrobe sidings. It is not often used in the MTW room.

Particle Boards
Chipboard

Chipboard is a common sight in all homes. It is usually covered by more expensive veneers

🌸 Chipboard

or melamine. Its manufacture is by the gluing and compression of wood particles.

While chipboard saves the environment by recycling unwanted wood chips it is very weak – especially if it becomes wet.

It may be used for veneer grounds or small press assemblies in the MTW room.

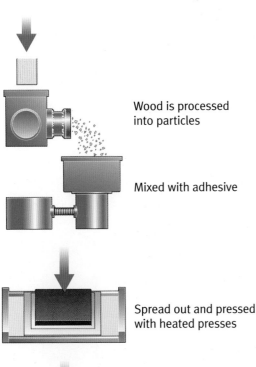

Wood is processed into particles

Mixed with adhesive

Spread out and pressed with heated presses

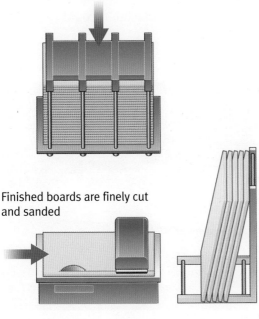

Finished boards are finely cut and sanded

❋ Manufacture of chipboard

OSB

Oriented strand board (OSB), is manufactured by a company called Louisiana Pacific here in Ireland. It is made by compressing wood chips with resin and wax. These are then cut into 2,438 mm × 1,219 mm boards. The wax makes the board almost impenetrable to moisture and it is therefore useful for outdoor applications such as hoarding or flooring in sheds.

In the MTW room it can be used as grounding for veneering or directly as a table top, which can be well varnished for an interesting appearance.

❋ Oriented strand board (OSB)

Fibreboard
MDF/HDF

Medium density fibreboard (MDF) and **high density fibreboard** (HDF) are made by compressing extremely small wood particles with resin glue. The boards were a common sight in the MTW workshop until concerns about the amount of suspended dust from the cutting of these boards was raised recently.

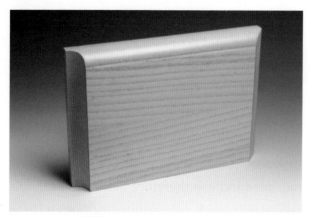
❋ Veneered MDF

The boards have a dark brown colour and are used to make furniture (which is normally covered in more expensive veneers).

The fibreboard materials are strong in all directions but moisture damage weakens them considerably.

Hardboard

A very common material in the home, hardboard comes in many different formats, most notably as the material in the bottom of the drawers in cabinets. It may be used as a backing for cabinets made in the MTW room. It is made by the heating and compression of small wood particles (waste), which are heated

to extract water thus leaving their natural resins in the wood to adhere to each other. The boards are then sanded (usually on one side only) and cut to length and width.

Edging Manufactured Boards

Most manufactured boards must be covered with a veneer to improve the appearance – see Chapter 22, Veneering. The edges of the boards may also be veneered or edged as shown below, to enhance the overall effect.

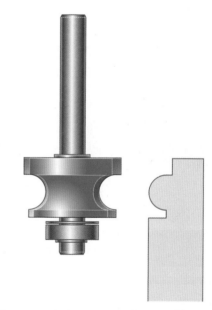
❋ Router edging a manufactured board

❋ Hardboard

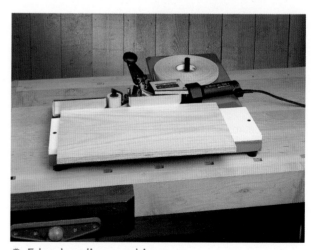
❋ Edge-banding machine

Strips of more expensive wood may also be tacked on, as may mouldings available from local hardware shops.

✸ Edge moulding for manufactured board

Hands-on Tasks

1 Can you come up with two more advantages and two disadvantages of manufactured board?

2 Gather some pictures of different wood veneers from the Internet.

3 Using a 12 mm piece of **laminate** pineboard, test out this method for securely holding wood in a vice. Wear safety goggles when trying this out.

4 Test a 3 mm piece of **ply** and a 3 mm piece of **blockboard** to compare strengths.

5 Gather some Internet photos of **chipboard** veneered tables and cabinets.

6 Apply different types of finish as outlined in Chapter 28 and see which is best for OSB.

7 Investigate the links between MDF dust and **respiratory disease**. Use the local library or the Internet.

8 Make sketches of five different mouldings available from your local hardware shop. Keep these for future project reference.

Homework Sheet on Manufactured Boards

1   Name the three main types of **manufactured boards**.

2   Make a small poster showing the different types of laminate boards beside each other.

3   What are the advantages of using **manufactured boards** over **natural timber** planks?

4   Design a moulding that could be used to enhance the edge of a **manufactured board**.

5   Use diagrams to describe the manufacture of MDF.

6   Suggest a suitable method for the **vertical** or **horizontal** storage of such large sheets of material in your MTW room.

7   Why are the grain patterns of veneers used in **plywood** glues at ninety degrees to each other?

8   Suggest a suitable **manufactured board** for the construction of a **half-pipe** for a skateboard park. Give a reason for your answer.

INTERNET LINKS AND TASKS

Visit the following or similar websites for more facts in relation to the manufacture and uses of manufactured boards.

Blockboard information

www.design-technology.org/Blockboard.htm

Working with OSB

www.osbguide.com/

Manufactured flooring systems

http://www.lpcorp.com/floorsystem/floorsystem.aspx

SEARCH

Sample Exam Questions on Manufactured Boards

Ordinary Level	2010

Three veneers of wood are to be glued together to form a sheet of plywood.

Show by using arrows the direction the grain should go in each layer.

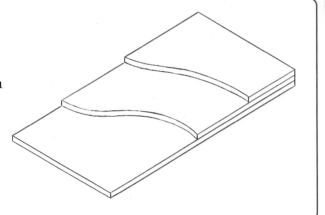

Ordinary Level	2009

Plywood is a manufactured board.
Name two other manufactured boards.

1. _____

2. _____

Ordinary Level	2008

The diagram shows **rotary cutting** of veneers.

(i) Explain what is happening in the diagram. (See chapter 22, Veneering.)

(ii) Plywood is made by gluing an odd number of veneers together.

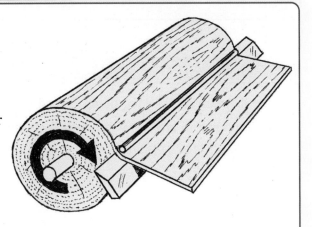

Draw a neat diagram showing the grain direction in each layer (veneer), in a piece of three-ply plywood.

Explain **one** advantage of this method of manufacture.

Ordinary Level — **2005**

The diagram shows a piece of chipboard.

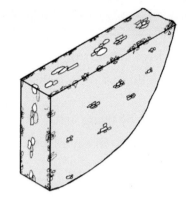

(i) Name **two** other types of manufactured boards. In the case of any **one** of these, describe using notes and sketches how the board is made.

(ii) Cut edges of chipboard look unattractive. Describe, using notes and sketches, a method commonly used to cover these edges.

(iii) List **three** advantages that manufactured boards have over solid wood.

Higher Level — **2010**

(i) Name the manufactured board shown on the right.

NAME _____

(ii) Give **TWO** advantages of using this board instead of solid wood.

ADVANTAGE 1 _____

_____

ADVANTAGE 2 _____

_____

Higher Level — **2010**

The diagram shows a log being peeled to produce a continuous thin layer of wood which is often used in manufactured boards.

(i) What is the layer called?

NAME _____

(ii) What is the name of this method of peeling?

METHOD _____

(i)   Name the **three** manufactured boards, labelled **A**, **B** and **C**, in the diagrams.

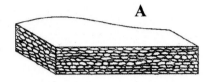   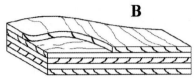   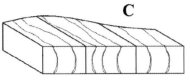

A   B   C

_____   _____   _____

(ii)   State **four** advantages of manufactured boards.

(iii) With the aid of notes and **neat freehand sketches** describe, in detail, the manufacture
       of **one** of the above boards.

In the manufacture of exterior grade plywood what do the letters **WBP** stand for?

W	B	P

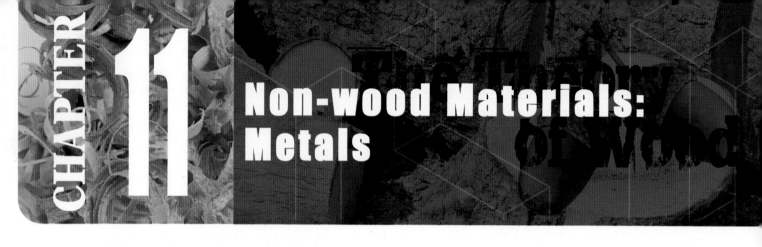

Non-wood Materials: Metals

Introduction to Metals

Metallurgy dates back to 6000 BC. Gold and copper were the first metals to be used almost exclusively to make jewellery and ornaments. Metals were mostly used in their singular

form but the Sumerians discovered that stronger metal could be formed by mixing metals such as tin and copper to form bronze. This was known as the Bronze Age. There were only twelve known metals before 1800 but this has grown to eighty-six today. Metals are known for their electrical and heat conductive properties. Each different metal has different properties which distinguishes them from other metals.

* Gold goblet

It may be possible for you to use some metals in your projects in the MTW room. Very often metals can be used from adjoining metalwork rooms and skills applied that have been learned in metalwork studies. If you have not studied metalwork there are a number of things you can do in the MTW room providing that the metal you need is available. Knowledge of basic metalwork is part of the MTW course and this must be covered even if you do not use metal in any of your projects.

Key Elements to Understand for Junior Certificate Course

* properties of metals
* classification of metals
    * ferrous and non-ferrous
* finishing metals

Properties of Metals

* high level of heat conductivity
* high level of electrical conductivity
* high lustre
* high density
* highly malleable
* ability to expand on heating

* Woodwork vice

Ferrous metals

Definition: Ferrous metal contains a certain amount of **iron**. All ferrous metals are magnetic.

Types of ferrous metals
Mild Steel

Tough low-carbon steel is used for nuts and bolts. This is the most common form of steel. It contains mostly iron with small amounts of other metals. It is also known as **carbon steel** but must contain no more than two per cent carbon.

⚙ Mild steel chain

High Speed Steel (HSS)

Hard medium-carbon steel is used for lathe chisels and cutting tools. It can withstand high temperatures without losing its hardness.

⚙ HSS lathe tools

Stainless Steel

Steel with added **chromium** and **nickel** is corrosion-resistant and used in cutlery. This steel must contain ten per cent chromium. It is the chromium which prevents rust from penetrating the steel.

⚙ Stainless steel Japanese basin

High Carbon Steel (HCS)

Hard and tough steel that is used in chisels and hammers. As the carbon content rises the steel becomes harder and stronger but is not as easy to weld or shape.

Cast Iron

Pig iron and scrap steel are used in vices and gears. It can be bought in white or grey colour formats. Iron makes up ninety-five per cent of

⚙ Cast iron fireplace

cast iron with silicon and carbon making up most of the rest. Cast iron is brittle with a low melting point.

Non-ferrous Metals

Definition: Non-ferrous metals are those which contain **no iron** and are less prone to rust.

Types of non-ferrous metals
Aluminium

Silvery white with high levels of ductility. It is the third most abundant element in the earth's crust after oxygen and silicon. It is made from a raw ore called **bauxite**. It has a high level of resistance to corrosion due to its low density. It is used extensively in the aircraft industry.

● Aluminium aeroplane fuselage

Copper

This is a reddish-brown ductile metal with very high electrical and thermal conductivity. Pure copper is very soft and must have other metals added to harden it before use. It is largely mined in the US and Chile. Copper used on roofs will turn green over a period of

● Copper roof

years. This green layer is copper carbonate (verdigris) and can be seen most notably on church roofs and on the Statue of Liberty.

Zinc

This is less dense than iron with a blue-white appearance. Zinc is hard and brittle at room temperature but when heated to 150°C it becomes workable. It is mostly used to form alloys with other metals due to its low melting point. The main sources of zinc are in Australia and China. Zinc is used to coat other metals due to its corrosive-resistant properties, in a process called **galvanisation**. It is also used in the negative terminals of batteries.

Tin

Tin is a malleable, ductile silver-white metal. When bending tin a cracking sound can be heard due to the brittleness of tin while it is cold. China and Malaysia are the largest suppliers of tin. Tin is mostly used as an alloy with copper to make brass. It can also be used nearly pure to make pewter plates and cups. Tin is also used to line steel drinks cans. Solder in your MTW room is an alloy of tin and lead.

Lead

Lead flashing on a chimney

Lead is a soft and malleable metal which is a dull grey in colour. It is widely used in construction on flashings for chimneys and flat roofs. It is also used in car batteries, bullets, solder, pewter and radiation shields for X-rays. Australia and China are the main suppliers of lead to the world.

Alloys
Types
Brass

Brass is an alloy (mixture) of copper and zinc. Brass is mostly used for decorative purposes, door knobs, candlesticks, hinges and screws. It

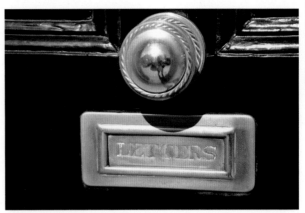
Brass door knob

has a yellow appearance which improves with polishing. Its malleability and acoustic properties make brass ideal for musical instruments. Brass is often used as a substitute for gold when it can be polished regularly.

Bronze

Bronze is an alloy – eighty-eight per cent copper and twelve per cent tin. It is famous for having given its name to the Bronze Age where it was extensively used to make utensils and weapons. It is a lot less brittle than iron and less susceptible to rust and corrosion. It is used today for sculptures and statues, electrical connectors, springs and church bells.

Using Metal in the MTW Room
Cutting Sheet Metal

Metal for your project can be bought in the correct size and cut in the adjoining metalwork room, or if it is thin enough it can be cut with a snips as shown. A hacksaw can be used for more precise cutting of thin sheet metal.

> **Safety**
> Heat is created in the process so be careful not to burn your skin on the heated metal. Care must be taken with the edges, as they can be sharp.

Chart Comparison between Various Metals – Fill in for any project work

Choosing Metals						
Name	Ferrous	Non-ferrous	Alloy	Properties	Uses	Make-up
Mild Steel						
HSS						
HCS						
Stainless Steel						
Cast Iron						
Copper						
Aluminium						
Zinc						
Tin						
Lead						
Brass						
Bronze						

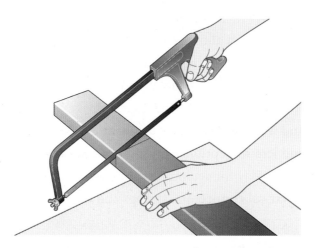

● Using a hacksaw

Filing Metal

A fine metal file should be used after cutting to soften the sharp edges. Filing should be with a fine-toothed metal file held at a forty-five degree angle – making sure to keep the file level with both hands in motion.

● Cutting tin with snips

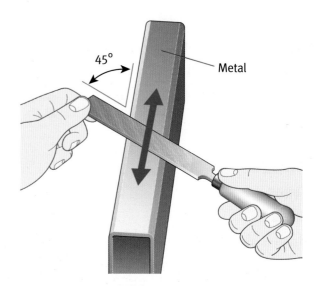
● Filing metal technique

Drilling Metal

The centre of the hole to be drilled must be marked with a dot punch to help centre the larger bit of the drill. Remove the chuck key from the drill and ensure that face protection/eye protection is worn. Pull the lever down slowly and drill small sections at a time allowing burr to clear the hole.

> **Safety**
>
> Care should be taken after drilling because a great deal of heat is generated in the bit and the metal during the process. Always wear goggles when drilling.

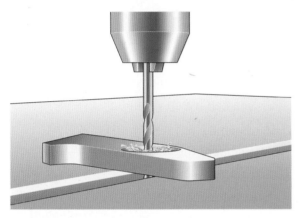

⬤ Drilling metal

Plaques

One of the most common uses of metal in MTW projects is on trophies and artefacts where engraved plaques are used to highlight the function of the design. Plaques can be made from small brass plates and engraved with an electric engraver set on a high speed. The lettering and/or designs should first be printed on the metal using carbon paper.

Joining Plates

There are two simple ways to join metal to wood in your projects. For plaques and non-structural elements, hot-melt glue and epoxy resins can be used to great effect. For metal supports and structural elements some form of mechanical fixing is required. This can be achieved by drilling the metal in the corner areas and then screwing round-headed matching screws to secure.

Finishing Metals
Polishing

In the MTW room, a wire brush can be attached to a power drill and used to polish up brass and aluminium plates. Following this a buffer pad can be used to achieve a fine finish. Products such as Brasso can then be applied to achieve a high-shine finish.

⬤ Brass plaque

JAMES WELLBELOVED
Naturally Healthy
**Proud to support
Bath Cats & Dogs Home.**

⬤ Polishing brass

Painting

You can also choose to paint any metal parts in your projects. The metal will have to be free of all contaminants such as rust and oil. The paint is applied in layers as shown.

Finishing coat(s)

Undercoat No. 2

Apply rust primer/eater

Remove grease, rust and dirt

Undercoat No. 1

❋ Painting metal in layers

Advanced Coatings

Whilst the following methods may not be available to you, metal can be bought in for a project with the following finishes applied.

❋ Galvanised shelving

Galvanised metal will prevent rust as it is plated in zinc (as described earlier).

Electroplated metal such as gold and silver is expensive but gives a high-quality appearance to any project.

Hands-on Tasks

1 Ask the metalwork teacher in your school to show you which metals and processes you can use in your project designs.

2 Make a chart for the MTW room to highlight the various properties of all metals.

3 Gather images from the Internet of **ferrous** metals and make a collage of them for the MTW room wall.

4 Use a digital camera to capture images of **aluminium** products around your home and school. Print the results and make a poster for your classroom wall.

5 Gather images from the Internet of **non-ferrous** metals and make a collage of them for the MTW room wall.

6 Take a piece of **mild steel** and file the edges to a fine finish. Shine up with some **wet and dry** paper.

7 Make a chart showing the correct layering of paints on metal.

Homework Sheet on Metals

1   List the six properties of a metal.

2   Explain any three of the six properties of a metal.

3   What is the main difference between **ferrous** and **non-ferrous** metals?

4   Name two examples of a **ferrous metal** and their use.

5   Name two examples of a **non-ferrous metal** and their use.

6   Name any item in the home which is made from **cast iron**.

7   What is the definition of an **alloy**?

8   Why is **aluminium** used in the manufacture of large aircraft?

9   Give two examples of **alloys** and their uses.

10 Describe a method for shining up **brass** plaques.

INTERNET LINKS AND TASKS

Recycling metal

http://earth911.com/metal/

Information on aluminium

http://www.world-aluminium.org/

Working with brass

http://www.doityourself.com/stry/brass

SEARCH

Sample Exam Questions on Metals

Brass is an alloy of two metals.
Name the **TWO** metals.

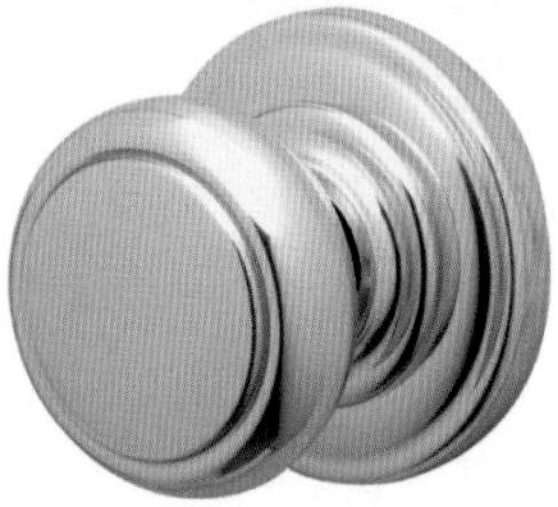

METAL 1 _____

METAL 2 _____

Identify, using a tick (✔), whether the following metals are **Ferrous** or **Non Ferrous**.

Metals	Ferrous	Non Ferrous
Brass		
Copper		
Steel		
Zinc		
Cast Iron		

CHAPTER 12

Non-wood Materials: Plastics

Introduction to Plastics

Plastic is a rather recent invention when compared to metals. It is used in every aspect of our daily lives such as iPods, buckets, pencil cases and bottles. The word plastic comes from the Greek word **plastikos**, meaning **fit for moulding**. Chewing gum (natural rubber) was one of the first plastics to be used in the 1800s. Most of the shapes made from plastic today are moulded to their final form. Plastic as we know it is not a renewable resource because not all plastics can be recycled. This is an important consideration for any designer thinking of a solution to a problem. When designing projects for MTW you need to know which are recyclable and try building these into your design. More and more companies are developing biodegradable plastics, which break down in sunlight over a short period. New **bioplastics** are being developed from the starch in plants and would be renewable and biodegradable.

Key Elements to Understand for Junior Certificate Course

* classification of plastics
  * thermosetting
  * thermoplastic
* glass reinforced plastic
* forming plastic in the MTW room
* plastic finishes

Thermosetting Plastics

Definition: A plastic that cannot be reformed into a new shape.

The thermosetting plastics have a 3-D molecular structure, which makes them very strong. This allows them to be used for applications such as tyre rubber, melamine kitchen worktops and the bodywork of jumbo jets (e.g. Airbus A380).

Examples of thermosetting
Epoxy Resin

High-performance glue used in aircraft and anywhere where a high level of adhesion is needed.

* Everyday uses of plastic

Bakelite

Hard plastic used for toys, camera bodies, plugs and cables due to its electrical non-conductive properties.

Melamine

High-durability plastic used in kitchen counter tops and school whiteboards.

Polyester

May be thermosetting or thermo – depending on the composition. The thermosetting versions are mostly used for making fabrics and tarpaulins to cover tennis courts and swimming pools.

✺ Polyester fabric

Thermoplastics

Definition: A plastic that can be melted and remoulded into a new shape.

The thermoplastics have a 2-D molecular structure. The ability to be remoulded makes thermoplastics highly recyclable. They are used in everyday objects such as drinks bottles, cup holders, bags and stockings.

Examples of thermoplastics
Acrylic

A clear glass-like plastic used because of its resistance to breaking under forces as normal glass would. It is used in shower doors, skylights and aquariums. Commonly known as **perspex** and readily available to MTW students.

✺ Acrylic notice board

Polystyrene

Easily recognisable by the number **6** printed on the recycling label. This plastic is used in many applications such as cutlery, Styrofoam™ insulation and product insulation in boxes containing items like TVs.

PVC (Polyvinyl Chloride)

The most valuable plastic in history due to its extensive use in the building industry – e.g. pipes, cladding and window frames (uPVC). It is also used in clothing and as insulation on electrical wires.

Polythene

A plastic used heavily in consumer products with over sixty million tons produced worldwide each year. Although it is recyclable, it does take many years to degrade in landfills. It is used for plastic bags, bulletproof vests, hip replacements and film wrap.

● Polythene bag

Nylon

Originally designed as a replacement for silk around the time of the Second World War it is now used for tyres, tents, gears and replacement parts in medicine.

Glass-reinforced Plastic (GRP)

Invented last century, GRP is one of the most widely used plastics today. We know it as **fibreglass** and it has many applications. It is used to make boats, helicopter shells and pond liners.

It is made by allowing plastic fibres to set in a resin in many different patterns. Multiple layers can be combined to increase the thickness and strength.

The layers are placed over a mould and brushed into place ensuring that there are no dry patches where resin is missing and no air voids.

● GRP canoe

Using Perspex (Acrylic) in the MTW Room

If you are planning to use plastics in your designs, then perspex will perform many of the operations you require. It is available in many sizes and should be ordered well in advance before making the final design.

Perspex can be cut, drilled, bent and formed into many shapes if the right equipment is available to you. It can often form part of a design and looks good when attached to wood-based designs.

Many of the techniques used to process perspex involve heating it, so care should be taken with hot surfaces. Also, be wary of sharp edges which have not been finished.

95

Leave the protective plastic coating on both sides until it is necessary to remove them in order to protect the surface during cutting and drilling. Heat operations will require the plastic protective layer to be removed.

Cutting

Straight cutting of perspex is best carried out by the teacher using the circular saw but it may also be cut with a fine-toothed saw or Scroll saw. Curved work can be carried out with a Scroll saw or Coping saw. (You may have a hot wire cutter in the MTW room, which is useful for cutting out delicate and intricate details especially in polystyrene. Using this on perspex can give off fumes and is not recommended.)

⬡ Cutting perspex to size

Drilling

The centre of the hole should be punched as with metal. A fine pilot hole should also be drilled to guide larger bits. Metal bits are adequate for drilling due to the softness of the perspex. It is best to drill from both sides slowly and to remove any burring after the plastic has cooled – five seconds or so.

Safety
Goggles should be worn at all times when drilling plastic.

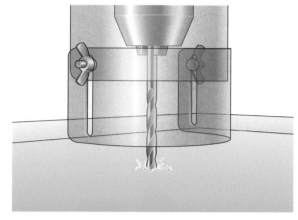

⬡ Drilling perspex on pillar drill

Bending

Perspex can be bent using the strip heater shown below. A line is drawn where the bend is required. Remember to take off the plastic protective layer on the heated side. After a couple of minutes remove the plastic and bend to the required angle set on a former as shown. For ninety degree bends, the edge of the bench is ideal.

⬡ Strip heater

Forming

Many MTW rooms will have a vacuum former available. With assistance you can create a mould from any timber (usually scraps of MDF). This is placed in the former and a thin coloured sheet of plastic placed over it. The former heats the plastic and in

● Vacuum former

Finishing

Most plastics can be painted in any colour or left in the colour in which they were originally bought. Acrylic paints are readily available, e.g. the paints used to colour plastic aeroplane models.

Most plastics do not take sanding well and the surface can be badly affected. Minor sanding using emery paper can be used at the edges to remove sharp edges.

Ultimately the best finish is achieved by keeping the protective plastic layer on as long as possible. This avoids scratches and blemishes on the surfaces.

turn the vacuum pump is turned on. This pulls the sheet over the mould creating the required design. The cooled plastic shape is then trimmed and altered to fulfil its final use.

Hands-on Tasks

1 Find the symbol used to indicate whether a plastic is recyclable or not. Make a large poster of it to display in the MTW room.

2 Search the Internet for examples of thermosetting plastics and compile a list in your copy.

3 Obtain a piece of **acrylic** from the MTW room and test it for bending strength, compressive strength and torsion strength. Record your results.

4 Search the Internet for examples of thermoplastics and compile a list in your copy.

5 Make a list of other objects made from GRP that we use everyday.

6 Design and make a pen holder made from a wooden base and a plastic holder using the equipment outlined in this chapter.

Homework Sheet on Plastics

1 What is the name of a plastic which will break down over time if exposed to sunlight?

2 What is a **thermosetting** plastic?

3 Where are **epoxy resin** and **polyester** used?

4 What is a **thermoplastic**?

5 Where are PVC and **nylon** used?

6 What does GRP stand for?

7 Name the piece of equipment used to form plastic into complex shapes.

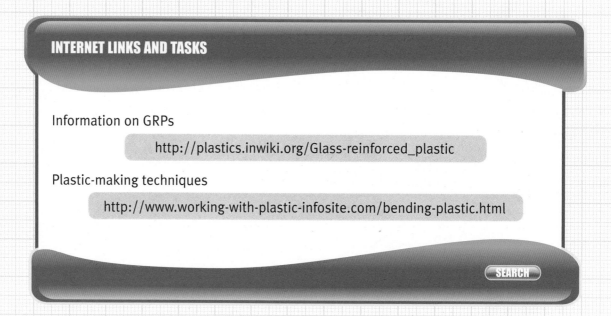

INTERNET LINKS AND TASKS

Information on GRPs

http://plastics.inwiki.org/Glass-reinforced_plastic

Plastic-making techniques

http://www.working-with-plastic-infosite.com/bending-plastic.html

SEARCH

Sample Exam Questions on Plastics

Ordinary Level   2010

The diagram shows a toothbrush holder.

(i)   Describe, using notes and sketches, how the acrylic sheet is bent to a 90° angle, as shown at **A**.

(ii)   Using notes and sketches, describe a method that would prevent the acrylic from shattering when drilling the holes.

(iii)   The back board is very plain. Using notes and sketches, suggest **two** design changes you would make to improve the appearance of this back board.

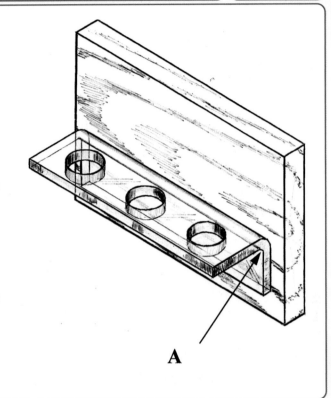

A

Higher Level   2010

The diagram shows a cook book stand which is made from acrylic.

(i)   Using a *neat freehand sketch*, draw the development that would be marked out on the acrylic sheet in order to manufacture this stand.

(ii)   With the aid of *neat freehand sketches* describe, in detail, the steps you would follow to **CUT OUT** and **FORM** the holder.

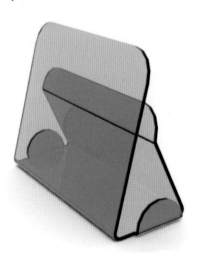

(iii)   It is proposed that the stand would be fixed to a hardwood base. With the aid of *neat freehand sketches* suggest a suitable design for the wooden base.

(iv)   The stand is to be fixed to the hardwood base using screws. With the aid of notes and *neat freehand sketches*, describe how you would drill the appropriate holes in both the acrylic and the hardwood base for the insertion of the screws.

(i)   Plastics are divided into two main categories.
     Name the categories.

     CATEGORY 1 _____

     CATEGORY 2 _____

(ii) Which category of plastic can be moulded and remoulded
     many times?

     ANSWER _____

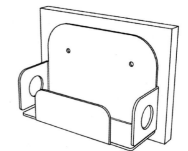

The diagram shows an acrylic letter holder with a hardwood back.

(i)   Draw the development that would be marked out on an
      acrylic sheet in order to manufacture the letter holder.

(ii)   With the aid of notes and **neat freehand sketches**
      describe the steps involved in drilling the two small holes
      in the acrylic.

(iii) Using notes and **neat freehand sketches** describe how
      the large holes at the sides of the holder could be formed.

(iv)   Suggest an appropriate modification to the design of the hardwood back which would
      improve the appearance of the unit.

CHAPTER 13

Alternative Materials of wood

Introduction to Alternative Materials

The subject MTW encourages the use of many different materials. The goal is to select materials suitable to your design, renewable where possible and ones for which there is the required tooling in your MTW room.

Selecting other materials as part of the design will add to the aesthetics of the design and set it apart from a lot of all-wood projects.

The list of other materials is exhaustive so we will be looking at those which are easily available in Ireland and which can be processed using standard equipment found in the MTW room.

* Mixing material for better designs

Key Elements to Understand for Junior Certificate Course

* different examples of each material
* processing these materials
* joining materials to wood

Ceramics

Ceramic comes from the ancient Greek word for **pottery**. It is no surprise to learn that the ceramics we use are made from clay heated to a high temperature where they harden. The kiln used to make the ceramics can be over 1,000°C. They are so hard that they are now used to replace steel ball bearings because they last three times longer. Other properties include being brittle and a non-electrical conductor.

Ceramics we use in the MTW room can be matt finish or **glazed** finish (shiny) depending on your requirements.

* Ceramic chess pieces

Ceramics must be bought to the correct size, as cutting in the MTW room can be dangerous due to the glass-like edges.

Ceramics can be bonded to wood using epoxy resin.

Textile/Fabric

Fabrics are soft materials such as your uniform jumper. They are mostly used for making seat covers in MTW. There are two main groups you can choose from:

* Natural – wool, cotton, linen
* Synthetic – acrylic, polyester, nylon

You may also consider the use of leather for covering your seats.

1. Cut foam to the size required for the top of the seat base.

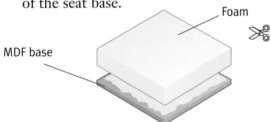

Foam

MDF base

2. Place the fabric over the foam and base.

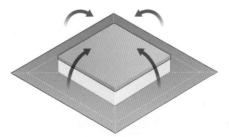

3. Turn over and tack on the fabric, pulling in all the time.

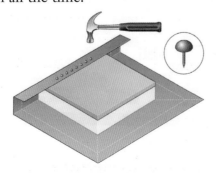

4. Fold over materials at the corners.

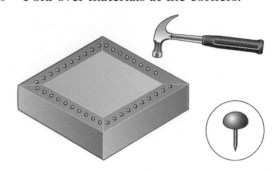

* Upholstering a seat base

Slate and Stone

Slate and stone can be used to give a very natural and rustic look to your designs. Although they are heavy this suits some applications such as bases for trophies and awards as well as teapot stands.

* Where possible they must be cut by the seller before you take delivery.
* Examples of such material you can readily obtain include natural black slate, Liscannor stone offcuts, granite, marble and sandstone.

Epoxy resins are the best for adhesion to wood.

* Liscannor stone

Glass

Glass is easily available and can be used in many applications in MTW. It is a hard, brittle and transparent material that we see in everyday use. It is made from a combination of **soda** and **lime** melted at temperatures over 1,500°C. Lead can be added to make crystal, or iron to make the UV-resistant glass used in many car windows.

Glass used in MTW can be cut at the shop where purchased or cut using the glasscutter below.

❋ Glass cutter

> **Safety**
> Mirror glass is best cut in the glass shop as it shatters easily.

For applications where the glass could be impacted (e.g. a glass door) in your project, select toughened glass which will not shatter. Satin glass is freely available – it is toughened and semi-transparent.

Categories of Glass

❋ **Drawn Glass** – Glass pulled from the furnace, melted and then drawn into sheets of varying thickness.

❋ **Toughened Glass** – Glass with enhanced thermal properties that shatters into small fragments rather than large, sharp dangerous pieces. Pyrex® dishes are an example and are used in high-temperature ovens without cracking.

❋ **Laminated Glass** – Layers of glass stuck together with glue that holds together even when the outside layer cracks. This is very useful in applications such as window panes in public places as well as car and aircraft windows.

❋ **Plate Glass** – Strong polished glass used in mirrors.

All glass can be attached using epoxy resins, but not hot-melt glues because the glass may separate from the wood when the hot-melt glue hardens.

Cement/Concrete

If you wish to make a heavy (but formed) shape for the base of a trophy, a former can be made to the correct shape and filled with a cement, sand and water mixture. Allow to set before removing the oil-lined mould.

Hands-on Tasks

1 Make and keep a list of materials other than wood which are available to you in the MTW room and locally in your shops and elsewhere.

2 Using air-dry clay, available from the Art room, make a 3-D sculpture of any item you wish which could be mounted on top of a natural piece of timber and presented to someone as a gift.

3 Print off examples of **stained glass** windows from the Internet for display in the MTW room.

Homework Sheet on Alternative Materials

1 What temperature can a clay-drying oven reach?

2 Name two natural and two synthetic examples of textiles.

3 What is the term used to apply a covered cushion to a seat?

4 Name one advantage and one disadvantage of using stone in your projects.

5 What is laminated glass and where can it be used to good effect?

INTERNET LINKS AND TASKS

Information on ceramics

http://ceramics.org/?p=5535

How to use air-drying clay

http://www.wikihow.com/Use-Air-Drying-Clay

Stained glass techniques and samples

http://art-of-stained-glass.com/

SEARCH

Sample Exam Questions on Alternative Materials

No relevant whole questions in previous years.

Test Yourself
eTest.ie

Introduction to Material Properties, Forces and Structures

In order to design a project correctly (apart from the obvious considerations of function and aesthetics) other factors must be considered to allow the project to operate and function safely. These other factors take into account the kind of pressures that the project will undergo and allow the designer to build in a safety margin for overuse and/or overexposure to loads.

Hand in hand with these forces goes a requirement to understand different mechanisms, which may make the operation of any design more user-friendly. Mechanisms generally allow operations to be carried out

which would not normally have been possible, e.g. lifting heavy goods with cranes.

It is also important to understand the different properties of materials you wish to use – enabling you to select the best material for the job. If you can understand the meaning of different properties you should be able to analyse your timber, for example, to judge if it will do the task required.

Key Elements to Understand for Junior Certificate Course

* forces acting on projects
* structures
* gears and pulleys
* lever and linkage mechanisms
* material properties

* Wood clamped in sash clamps – compression force

* Tug-of-War rope under tension force

Forces

Tension

Tension is any force which tries to pull an object apart. Holding your fingers together and pulling in the opposite direction is a tension force. Examples of tension force in MTW include the force applied to Scroll saw and Coping saw blades as shown.

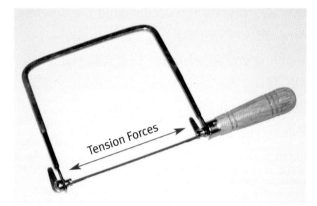

● Coping saw blade in tension

Compression

Compression force is any force which pushes on an object. Pushing your hands together is a compression force. Examples of compression in the MTW room include clamping operations and veneer pressing.

● Clamping wood – wood in compression

Torsion

Torsion is any force which causes an object to twist. These forces are used in operations such as screwdriving and putting lids back on bottles.

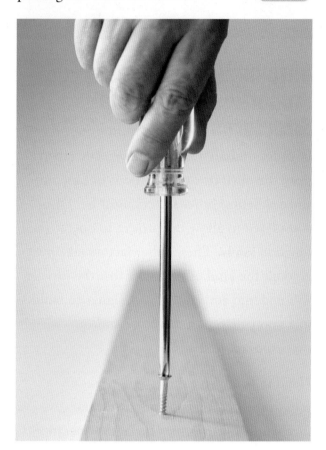

● Screwdriver showing torsion

Shear

Shear is any force which causes objects to move apart in opposite directions. In the MTW room we use nails and screws to hold materials together which will undergo shear stress.

● Shear pin

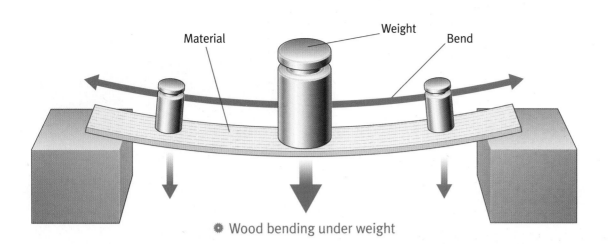

Material   Weight   Bend

❁ Wood bending under weight

Bending

A bending force is any force or weight which causes the material to deflect, usually leading to breakage of the material. Wood used on its edge, as opposed to its face, (as shown) will be stronger under bending forces.

Structures

Structures occur naturally in nature and animals, birds and insects use them to make homes.

❁ Honeycomb structure

Materials may not be strong enough in their natural form to perform the task at hand. We can modify or design projects to perform tasks which would not otherwise be possible by the use of a structure.

❁ Crane

❁ Arch bridge

❁ Roof

By use of triangulation, small members (sections) of material as in the crane, can be used to support greater loads. The members of a structure will undergo many of the forces described above.

Gears and Pulleys
Gear

A gear is a mechanism used to slow down, or speed up, rotary and linear motions. The most common use is for car gears but we can use gears in the MTW room to make movements possible in conjunction with small motors.

✹ Rack and pinion

It is important to understand the way one gear affects another gear it is attached to and also to know the different types of possible gear linkages.

Most gears involve gear cogs, which rotate against each other as in diagrams below.

✹ Car gears

✹ Bevel gears

✹ Worm gears on guitar head

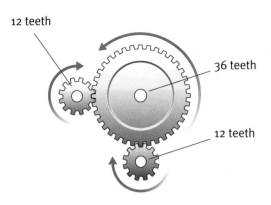

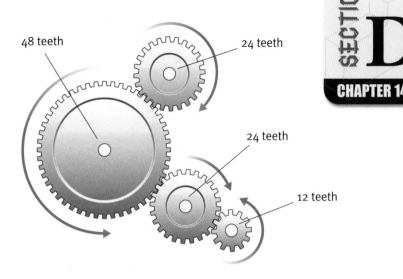

● Gears in different configurations

The rotation of each circular gear causes the gear wheel to which it is attached to rotate in the opposite direction. Larger gear cogs will make a smaller cog rotate faster and vice versa.

It is also important to be able to calculate the **velocity ratio** (VR) of gear cogs for use in projects. This figure is simply a relationship between the number of teeth on the driven gear and the number of teeth on the driver gear.

Formula

$$VR = \frac{\text{No. of teeth on driven gear}}{\text{No. of teeth on driver gear}}$$

● Gear calculations

Pulleys

Pulleys are belt systems used to speed up or down mechanisms, or to reduce the load of lifting heavy objects.

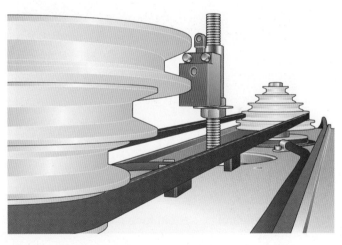

● Pulley mechanism on a pillar drill

Pulleys are used in everyday applications such as car engines, pillar drills and washing machines. Pulleys are also used in manual lifting operations. By adding more wheels in the system (shown below) the load on the operator is reduced as the system takes some of the load.

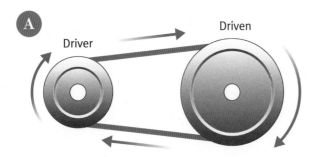

● Pulleys in different configurations

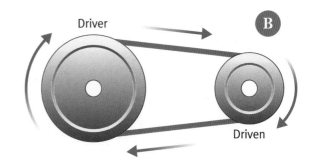

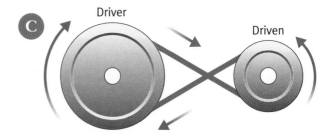

● Double pulley system for easy lifting

The velocity of the driven wheel should be known for any design. This will allow you to control the output of a motor, e.g. in a toy car.

First one must calculate the VR.

$$VR = \frac{\text{diameter of driven wheel}}{\text{diameter of driver wheel}}$$

This leads to the **output** speed rating which

$$= \frac{\text{input speed}}{\text{velocity ratio}}$$

RPM = revolutions per minute

A A small wheel on the drive end of a pulley will cause the larger wheel on the drive to rotate slowly.

B A large wheel on the **driver** will cause a small wheel on the **driven** to rotate faster.

C Crossing the belts will cause the direction of the **driven** to rotate counter to the **driver** wheel.

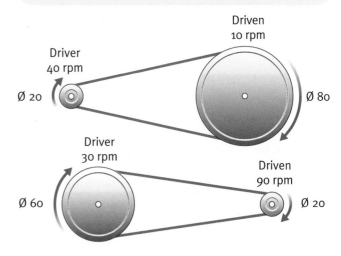

● Pulley sample calculations

Lever and Linkage Mechanisms

Levers and linkages are mechanisms used to make tasks easier.

A **lever** is a length of material which rotates around a fixed point called a fulcrum, as shown. The longer the arm the easier the effort required to lift the load.

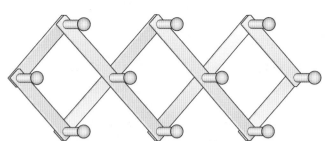

⚙ Coat hanger linkage mechanism

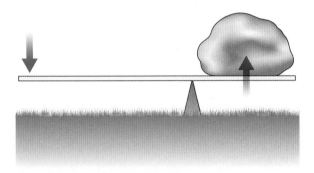
⚙ Lifting boulder with lever

A **linkage** is a series of levers connected by movable joints, e.g. the coat hanger shown above.

Material Properties

The following is a list of properties which must be considered for any material before selecting that material for use in your designs. Firstly, establish the likely loads and uses of the design when completed. Secondly, try to use materials which match your requirements under the following properties. They are listed in no specific order so choose the type of material property which is relevant to your design and fill in the **material selection chart** (MSC) as below.

Material Selection Chart									
Property	Hardness	Strength	Durability	Density	Ductility	Malleability	Elasticity	Insulation	Colour
Material Name									

Hardness

The hardness of the material is its ability to resist denting. In the MTW room we rely on this property for chiselling as the hard steel easily removes the soft wood. To test the hardness of various woods, push the corner of one into the other to see if it dents the other wood and vice versa.

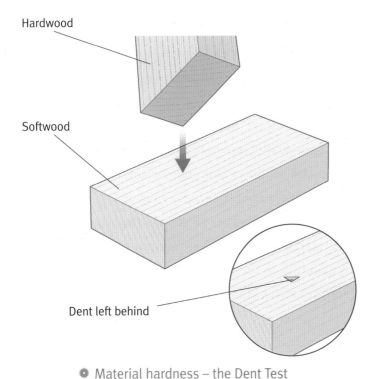

Hardwood

Softwood

Dent left behind

❋ Material hardness – the Dent Test

Strength

The strength of the material is its ability to resist breakage. To test the hardness of a wood sample, cut thin strips of different wood species and subject them to the forces described earlier in the chapter.

Durability

Durability refers to the material's ability to resist the effects of use, and the weather if outside over a period of time. The selection of material is of utmost importance if the project is designed to be used outside.

❋ Bird house to demonstrate durability

❋ Material strength – crossing a plank

Density

The density of a material refers to the relationship between its mass and volume. Different materials of the same size have different masses. Can you imagine playing hurling with a steel hurley instead of a wooden hurley? The density of materials for your projects can be calculated by dividing the **weight** of the material by the **volume** of the material.

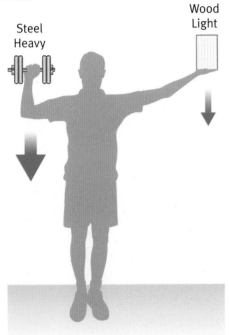

Steel Heavy

Wood Light

⚙ Material density – steel heavier than wood

Ductility

Ductility refers to a material's ability to stretch without breaking. Some materials have a higher ductile value than others. Copper is an example of a highly ductile material which can be stretched to form wire in a cable.

⚙ Copper wire showing ductility

Malleability

This refers to the material's ability to change shape under force. Copper can be hammered into various shapes to make items such as plates and vessels.

⚙ Copper shaping showing malleability

Elasticity

Elastic is found in everyday items such as socks and tracksuits. It has the ability to return to its original state as long as it is not overstretched. Wood and other materials also have the ability to return to their original state. Wood that has good elastic properties is even used to build the chassis of cars, see below.

⚙ Morgan car chassis – timber with great elastic properties

Insulation

The ability of a material to resist heat loss is important in many applications such as insulating a house. This ability to resist heat loss is the material's insulation quality. Wood is generally a good insulator of heat.

🌼 Timber frame houses – good insulators

Colour

The colour of any material is important in the overall design so that the project looks good and fits in with the intended area of use. Test the material to be used in the project by

🌼 Pine colour matching its surroundings

bringing it to the intended place of use to see if it fits the furniture already there.

Hands-on Tasks

1 Test small pieces of wood for any project you are making to see if it will last over the life of the project.

2 Identify another tool in the MTW room which may undergo tension forces.

3 Test three equal size strips of different woods in a vice to obtain the best material under torsion force.

4 Test strips of different wood species between two blocks of wood to test for bending strength. Use weights from a science laboratory for accuracy and record your results.

5 Obtain images from the Internet of different structures in the world and make a poster called 'Structures from Around the World' for the classroom wall.

6 Draw two gears with as many teeth as you want and use the formula to calculate the **velocity ratio** for your design.

7 Draw (design) a pulley system for the transfer of large sheets of timber from one woodwork bench to another in your classroom.

8 Test four woods of your choice for all the properties listed on the MSC chart.

Matthew Ó Cadhla

Homework Sheet on Material Properties, Forces and Structures

1   What is meant by the term **tension**. Give an example of tension in the MTW room tools.

2   What is meant by the term **torsion**. Give an example of torsion from the MTW room.

3   Name one naturally occurring structure in nature.

4   What is a gear?

5   Indicate the direction of the driven gear in the samples below.

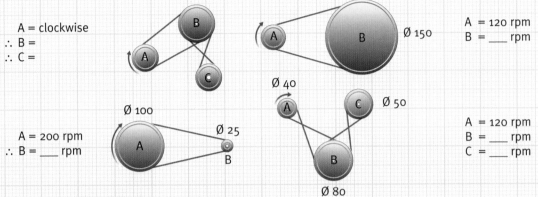

A = clockwise
∴ B =
∴ C =

A = 120 rpm
B = ___ rpm

Ø 150

Ø 40

Ø 50

Ø 100

A = 200 rpm
∴ B = ___ rpm

Ø 25

A = 120 rpm
B = ___ rpm
C = ___ rpm

Ø 80

6   Calculate the **velocity ratio** for the sample below.

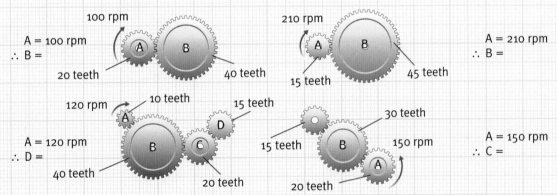

100 rpm

A = 100 rpm
∴ B =

20 teeth   40 teeth

210 rpm

A = 210 rpm
∴ B =

15 teeth   45 teeth

120 rpm   10 teeth   15 teeth

A = 120 rpm
∴ D =

40 teeth   20 teeth

30 teeth

15 teeth   150 rpm

A = 150 rpm
∴ C =

20 teeth

7   Why do designers need to know the velocity of the driver and driven gears?

8   Give four examples of where levers are used in everyday life.

9   How would you test the hardness of one wood material against another?

INTERNET LINKS AND TASKS

Visit the following (or similar) websites.

Structures for students

http://www.technologystudent.com/struct1/struindex.htm

SEARCH

Sample Exam Questions on Material Properties, Forces and Structures

Ordinary Level — 2007

The blade of a Coping saw is held in place with which of the following forces?

(a)   Compression   ☐

(b)   Tension   ☐

(c)   Torque   ☐

Ordinary Level — 2002

Pulley **C** is a drive pulley.

Which of the other two rotates fastest, **A** or **B**?

ANSWER _____

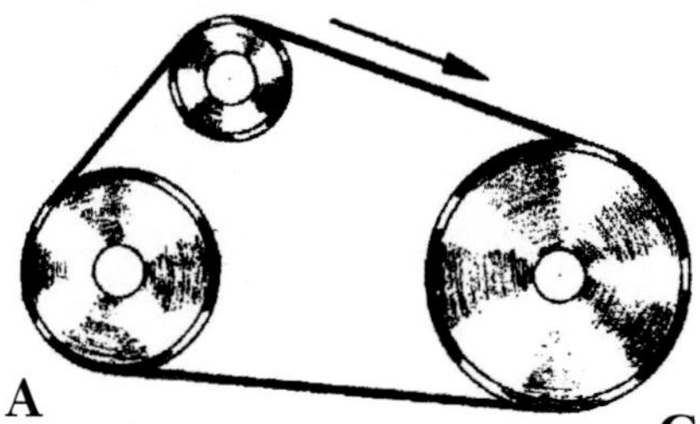

Ordinary Level — 2000

Pulley **A** and pulley **B** are connected with a belt.

Which pulley spins faster?

ANSWER _____

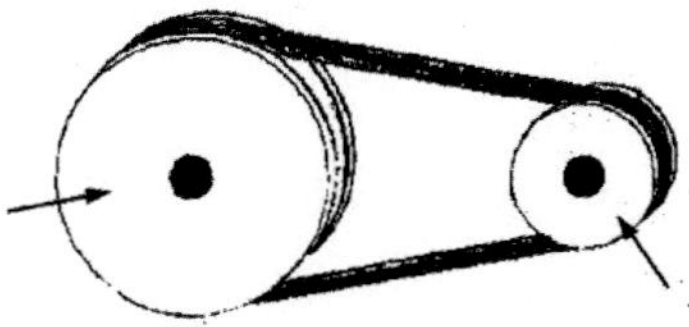

Higher Level | 2010

The diagram shows a coping saw. Using a tick (✔), identify the force which is acting on the blade.

COMPRESSION ☐

TENSION ☐

TORSION ☐

Higher Level | 2010

The diagram shows a pulley mechanism which is used to change the speed of a pillar drill.

On the diagram indicate the position of the belt which will achieve minimum speed.

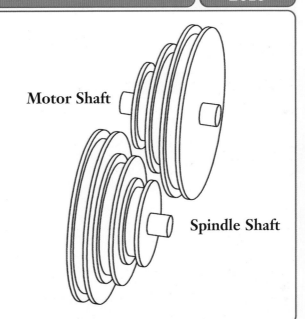

Motor Shaft

Spindle Shaft

Higher Level | 2009

The diagram shows a piece of wood securely held in a wood working vice. What is the correct name for the force applied to the piece of wood in the vice?

TORSION ☐

COMPRESSION ☐

TENSION ☐

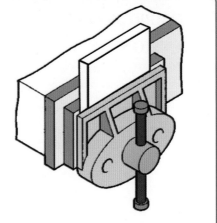

(i)　If pulley **A** rotates clockwise, indicate by ticking the box, the direction in which pulley **C** will rotate?

CLOCKWISE ☐ or **ANTI-CLOCKWISE** ☐

(ii)　The small pulleys are 100 mm in diameter and the large pulley is 200 mm in diameter.

If pulley **A** rotates at 180 revolutions per minute (rpm), what is the rotational speed of pulley **C**?

SPEED OF C _____ **rpm**

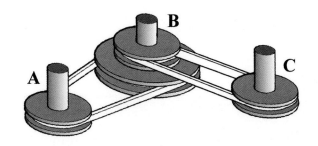

The diagram shows a screwdriver being used to insert a screw.

Using a tick, identify the force which is being applied to the screw.

COMPRESSION　☐

TORSION　☐

TENSION　☐

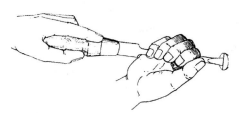

The diagram shows a gate. What is the correct name for the force acting on member **A**?

TORSION　☐

COMPRESSION　☐

TENSION　☐

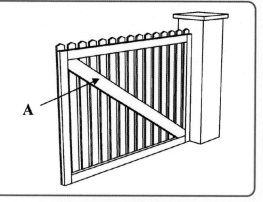

CHAPTER 15
Basic Electronics for MTW
The Theory of Wood

Introduction to Basic Electronics for MTW

Electronics have formed much of the technical developments for the past 100 years. Electronics form part of our everyday lives – from watching TV to cooking food in microwaves. Electronics can form a very important part of your designs in MTW as many of the available electrical components can be attached to, and used with, wood and other materials.

Although not strictly part of the MTW course you are studying, it is essential to have an understanding of the basics so you can bring your designs and projects to life. In fact, some basic projects (e.g. lamps) require you have the skills to wire a lamp holder and the plug.

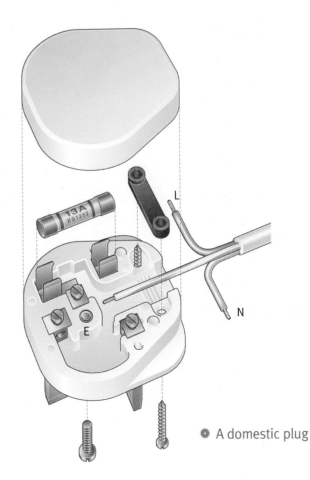

* Electric lamp

* A domestic plug

The Plug

The **three-pin plug** is the most common electrical component available. Wiring it is simple with the correct tools. Incorrect wiring will prevent the electronic device operating and it may also trip the fuse on your fuse board. Wiring should be carried out as follows.

Wiring a Plug

1. Open the main casing with a screwdriver.

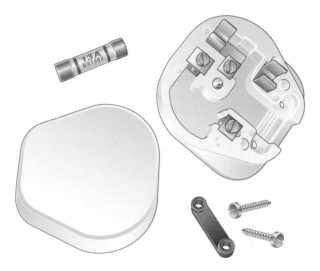

2. Open the hold screws for the cable at the rear of the plug. Remove one screw completely and swivel the other around to the side, out of the way.

3. Undo the small brass screws for each pin.

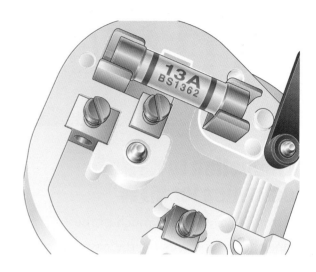

4. Strip the wire on the plug (as shown) so that the copper part of wire sits in the pin slots.

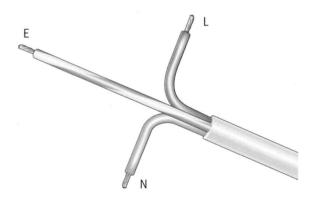

5. Tighten each pin screw carefully but firmly.

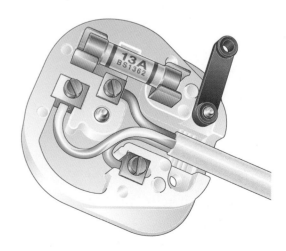

6. Ensure that the correct fuse (3–13 amp) is inserted correctly into its holder at the live wire.

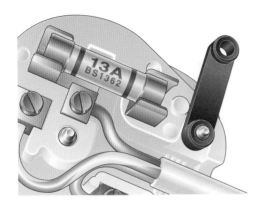

7. Push all the pins in tight, swivel the flex holder round, then screw into place.

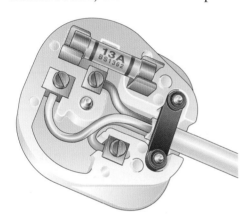

8. Replace the outer casing with the screw provided.

Test by plugging into the socket to see if the appliance operates.

Basic Components for MTW

9V Battery

Used to power the operation with the snap providing the link between the battery and the stripboard.

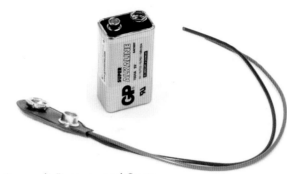

❀ 9 volt Battery and Snap

Breadboards and Stripboards

Breadboard is used to test the operation of the circuit before committing to soldering the wires in place on the **stripboard**. The stripboard is used to attach components to wiring in the final project. Current flows along each track separately.

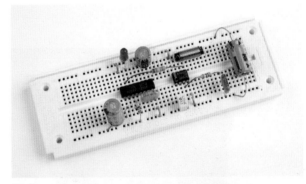

❀ Breadboard

❀ Stripboard

Single Core Wire

Comes in a variety of colours. Use different colours for positive and negative applications for clarity of operations and soldering. The end of the wire must be stripped with the pliers (as shown) to expose the inner metal wire.

◉ Solid Core Wire

Solder

Solder is a metal alloy which melts at 90°C. Where possible use a lead-free solder with a substance called **flux** already contained in the solder. This flux will remove impurities from the surfaces to be joined leading to a better bond.

◉ Solder

Soldering Iron

The soldering iron is used to melt the solder, which acts as a connection between the wires and the components.

◉ Soldering iron

Safety
This tool gets very hot, so care should be taken not to burn your hands.

Hold the solder in one hand, the iron in the other, and allow the solder to drip onto the wire or component to be soldered.

Safety
Do not inhale the fumes from the solder.

Switches

There are a number of switches available and choice depends on the application. In most cases a single-pole, single-throw switch will suffice. These can be obtained with a light indicator if required.

● Switches

Bulb

Bulbs and their holders are easy to use, as no soldering is needed. The wires are wrapped around the screws at the edges and tightened. They are available at different voltages with 9 volt being the most commonly used in MTW.

● Bulb holder

LED Coloured

Light Emitting Diode (LED). These are very bright lights mostly used as indicators or for visual effect. They can also be obtained in

● LEDs

super-bright or flashing formats. They work on low voltages and therefore need the protection of a resistor.

Resistors

A resistor is a component used to control the flow of power and they are available in many strengths. Their value is measured in ohms and this can be determined from the colour chart below. They are often used in conjunction with LEDs as above.

● Resistor

First band	Second band	Number of zeros Third band	Tolerance Fourth band
Brown	Black	Black	No band
Red	Brown	Brown	Silver
Orange	Red	Red	Gold
Yellow	Orange	Orange	Red
Green	Yellow	Yellow	Brown
Blue	Green	Green	Green
Violet	Blue	Blue	Blue
Grey	Violet	Silver	Violet
White	Grey	Gold	Grey
	White		

● Resistor colour coding

Black	0	
Brown	1	
Red	2	
Orange	3	
Yellow	4	
Green	5	
Blue	6	
Violet	7	
Grey	8	
White	9	
Gold	+/- 10%	accuracy of value
Silver	+/- 5%	accuracy of value

10 Ω 12 Ω 15 Ω 18 Ω 22 Ω 27 Ω 33 Ω 39 Ω 47 Ω 56 Ω 68 Ω 82 Ω

● Sample resistor values

Buzzers

Buzzers come with many different sounds and tone choices and are used as indicators such as a BUZZ OFF game.

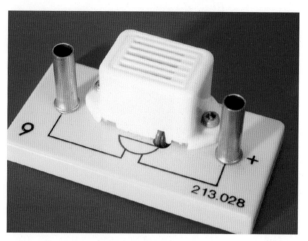

● Buzzer

Motor

Motors are used to power mechanisms and are commonly used in MTW in conjunction with a gearbox to slow down the rotation.

● Motor

Light-dependent Resistor (LDR)

This works by measuring the amount of light available and allows current to flow through the wires depending on the brightness.

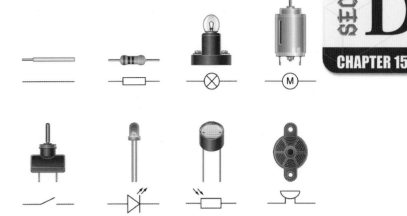

● Components and symbols for circuit diagrams

● Light-dependent resistor

Thermistor

Uses the amount of heat available to determine the rate of current flow through the wires. Can be used to control a window in a greenhouse.

Soldering to Stripboard
How to Solder

1. Try out the circuit on a board first.

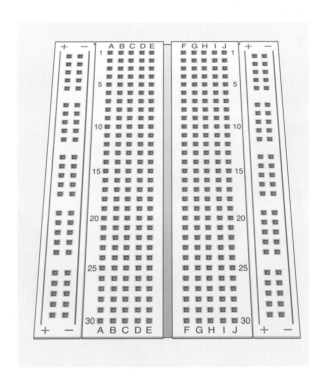

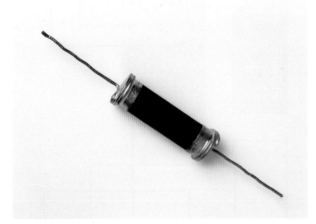

● Thermistor

2. All components should allow about 2 mm of wire to protrude through the back of the stripboard.

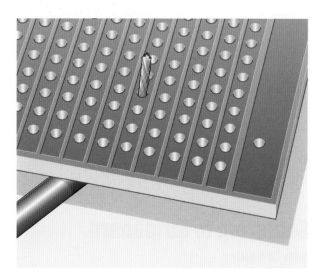

3. Using solder and the soldering iron, allow a small droplet to fall on the wire and the track it is in. Do not let the solder run onto the next track.

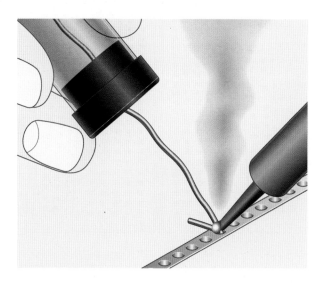

4. Blow on the solder to get it setting straight away.

Circuits for MTW

Motor Circuit

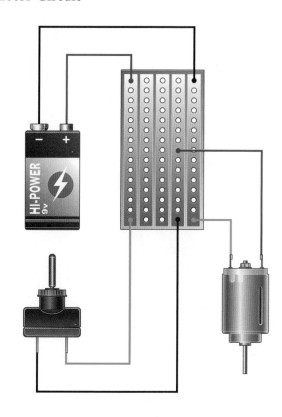

Light Circuits – Parallel Circuit

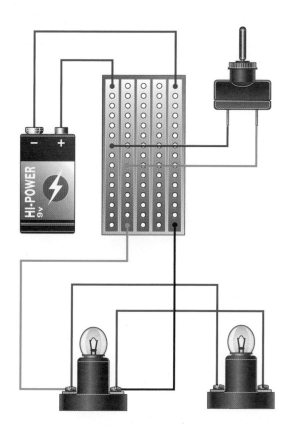

Buzzer Circuit

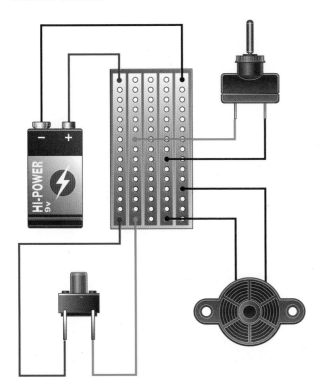

Heat Sensor Circuit

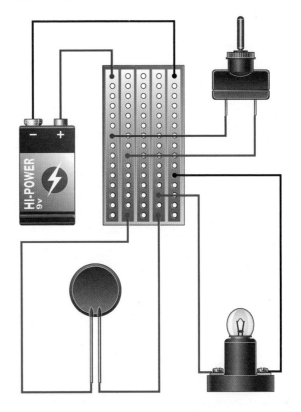

LED Circuit

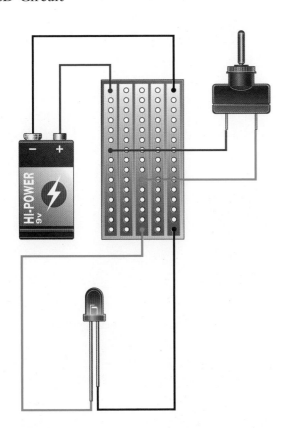

Fitting a Clock Mechanism

Although a simple electronic circuit combined with a mechanism, clock movements look attractive in suitable projects. Here is how we fit them into wood projects.

1. Locate and drill a 12 mm hole in the wood for the centre of the clock.

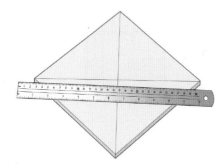

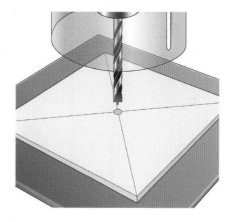

2. Mark the outline of the clock back on the rear of the wood.

3. Mortise out the back of the clock, leaving 10 mm of material to the front of the clock.

4. Insert the clock back and any rubber spacers as needed.

5. Screw on the front holding nut and tighten with a screwdriver.

6. Push on the small hand and then the big hand.

7. Secure with locking nut.

8. Insert the battery and set the time.

● Ohm's Law triangle

Voltage = current × resistance

$$\text{Current} = \frac{\text{voltage}}{\text{resistance}}$$

$$\text{Resistance} = \frac{\text{voltage}}{\text{current}}$$

Calculations for Current and Voltage

Ohm's Law: For students who want more information on their circuits, Ohm's law can be utilised to calculate different **voltages**, **currents** and **resistances**. The famous triangle as shown here demonstrates how to remember the different formulae. Currents (and other values) can be read from your circuits using a **multimeter** as shown.

● Multimeter

Hands-on Tasks

1 Make a list of all the **electrical** appliances in your kitchen and home and identify ways that their use can be reduced to save on energy bills.

2 Make an A3 rendered and coloured sketch of the inside of a plug for your classroom wall.

3 Make a chart to show the value of resistors based on their colour coding.

4 Use some scrap wood to practise the fitting of a clock mechanism into the wood before trying it on a more expensive selection of wood.

Homework Sheet on Basic Electronics for MTW

1 Name the three wires which are in a plug.

2 Name the device in a plug, connected to the live wire, which prevents the plug from overheating.

3 What is the correct process for soldering a wire to a stripboard?

4 What do the letters LED stand for?

5 What does the gold band on a resistor stand for?

6 What does a violet line on a resistor mean?

7 What do the letters LDR stand for?

8 Finish this equation:

Voltage = _____ × _____

INTERNET LINKS AND TASKS

Visit the following (or similar) websites for more facts in relation to electronics.

Working with electricity safely

http://www.esb.ie/esbnetworks/safety-environment/wire_a_plug.jsp

Electronic build projects

http://www.kpsec.freeuk.com/

Soldering techniques

http://www.mediacollege.com/misc/solder/

SEARCH

Sample Exam Questions on Basic Electronics for MTW

Ordinary Level — 2008

Using an arrow, indicate the **earth** terminal on the diagram.

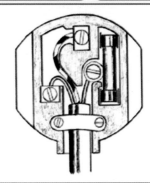

Ordinary Level — 2005

What colour is the wire that goes to the fused terminal of a plug, indicated at **A** in the diagram.

ANSWER _____

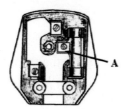

Ordinary Level — 2003

Using an arrow, indicate the **neutral** terminal on the diagram.

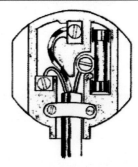

Ordinary Level — 2002

Using an arrow, indicate the **earth** terminal on the diagram.

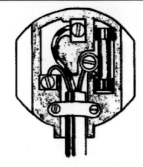

Higher Level   **2009**

The diagram shows the interior of a three pin plug.

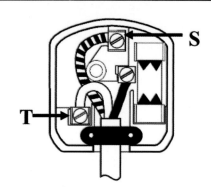

(i)   Name the plug terminals **S** and **T**.

S   _____

T   _____

(ii) What is the function of the **FUSE** in the plug?

FUNCTION _____

Higher Level   **2006**

Shown in the diagram is a plug top.

(i)   Name the plug terminals labelled **P** and **Q**.

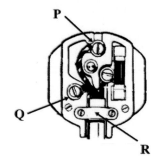

_____

(ii) What is the function of the component labelled **R**?

FUNCTION _____

Higher Level   **2003**

The diagram shows the wiring terminals in a three-pin plug.

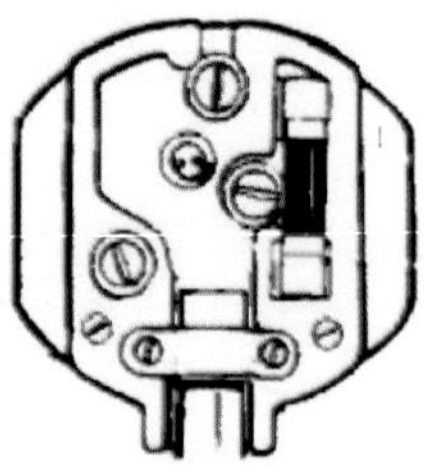

(i)   Indicate, using an **X** the **earth** terminal, and state what is the correct colour coding for the wire connected to it.

COLOUR CODING _____

(ii) Most electrical devices are **earthed**. Why is this?

ANSWER _____

UNIT 2: PRACTICAL WOODWORK

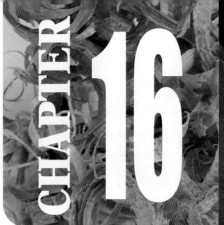

CHAPTER 16

SECTION E
Health and Safety in the MTW Room

Introduction to your Health and Safety in the MTW Room

Before any practical work can be undertaken in the MTW room, you must understand that your safety and wellbeing is the number one priority. The teacher can show you all the safety rules in the world, but unless you are willing to listen and understand these rules and procedures, you may put yourself and your classmates at risk of serious injury.

There are general rules, which must be followed in order for the class to run safely, and then there are more specific rules relating to the use of different tools and machines. It is important to note that not all machines in the room are for your use and these should be clearly marked by the teacher.

Key Elements to Understand for Junior Certificate Course

* personal safety
    * protection of sight and hearing
    * masks, gloves, muffs etc.
    * effects of inhalation of glues and solvents
* workplace safety
    * tidiness in the workshop
    * storage of equipment
    * safety with the use of tools
    * safety with electrical equipment
    * code of practice for the safe use of power tools
    * safety signage
    * safety in design and finish

Safety equipment for the MTW room

Clean MTW room

Personal Safety

The main areas, which require protection in the MTW room, are the **eyes**, **ears**, **lungs** and **fingers**. If you understand when to protect each of these, and how, you will be able to enjoy your woodwork and be able to work in safety and comfort.

Eyes

Eye protection is required whenever there is a chance of material passing into the eyes. Goggles must be worn if there is any concern that this may happen. Chiselling, sanding, woodturning and drilling are examples of such occasions where eye protection is required. Many experienced woodworkers wear eye protection glasses at all times.

✹ Eye protection glasses

Ears

Ear protection is required whenever there is a chance that loud noise will hurt and damage the eardrums. Normally this will only occur when using percussion tools (e.g. a hammer) or when using machinery such as Scroll saws, bandsaws and jigsaws. Earmuffs or earplugs may be used.

✹ Ear defenders

Lungs

Dust is common in the MTW room, especially during project finishing time. Over a period of time this dust can clog the lungs

✹ Dust mask

leading to breathing problems. Whenever you are sanding, especially by using a belt sander, you should wear a simple dust mask.

Hands

Damage to the hands makes up most of the accidents in the MTW room. Simple precautions such as keeping hands behind cutting edges and safe around saw blades will reduce the number of cuts you receive. Hands may also be damaged by accidentally hitting them against bench vices etc., so be careful and stay alert.

✹ Keep two hands behind cutting edge of chisel

General Safety

Wear gloves when using applied finishes and always wash hands upon completion of coatings. Do not inhale any vapours from glues or preservatives etc. as inhalation can cause serious damage to lungs – in severe cases inhalation may cause death. Other steps such as removing your tie when drilling or woodturning, tying up long hair, removing jewellery and removing loose clothing will reduce the risk to you in the room. Poor behaviour is unacceptable in the MTW room.

Workplace/MTW Room Safety

1. Tidiness in the Workshop

A neat woodwork room can reduce the risk of injury to those using it and also has the added bonus of being easier and more inspirational to work in. Keys to a tidy room are clean floors and desk. It is everyone's responsibility to keep their desks neat and clean and also to clean up at the end of class. Always put away tools which are not in use. There should be no cutting tools on your desk when marking out and vice versa.

✹ A tidy workbench is a safe place to work

2. Storage of Equipment

It is important to return all tools to the place they belong as others will expect them to be in certain locations. It also makes it easier for the teacher to count equipment at the end of class. Important and expensive power tools should be locked away after each class.

❋ Store all tools neatly

Always keep hands behind the leading edge of the blade and never in front (as shown in the diagram). Keep the thumb up when sawing to prevent the saw from running across the back of your hand.

Each hand tool and power tool has its own safety rules and these can be viewed in the chapter relating to each of these tools.

4. Safety with Electrical Equipment

Your teacher should supervise you when using power tools and explain all the risks involved. The power cable should always be kept clear, especially if using jigsaws. Never overload plugs or use plugs/equipment with faulty/stripped cables. Always stand clear of others using electrical equipment.

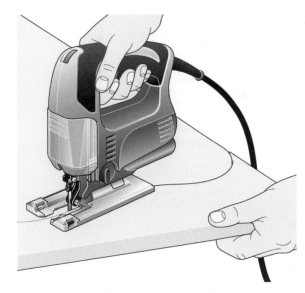
❋ Keep cords clear of cutting edges

3. Safety with the Use of Tools

All of the tools described in other chapters of this book have potential dangers. The major cause of damage to hands in the MTW room occurs through the misuse of the chisels.

❋ Keep thumb up when using the Tenon saw

5. Code of Practice for the Safe Use of Power Tools

1. Read and understand all instructions from the manual, or from your teacher, regarding the tool to be used.
2. Remove all loose clothing and jewellery.
3. Note the position in the room of emergency stop buttons.
4. Keep hands clear of moving parts and blades.
5. Wear eye and ear protection.
6. Keep clear of electric cables and use 110 volt power if available.
7. Always work under the supervision of the teacher.
8. Do not interfere with others using power tools.

6. Safety Signage

Ear wear warning sign

Hand danger warning sign

Corrosive warning sign

Irritant warning sign

Eye-wear warning sign

Electricity warning sign

Take note and understand all the safety signs shown here. Some signs warn of danger and others advise you to wear personal protective equipment. This advice should always be followed. If you are in doubt about any sign, ask your teacher for advice on its meaning.

Safety in Design and Finish

When designing any project, especially for your Junior Certificate, the design itself can include safety features for the final user. These features will often add to the aesthetics of the design, e.g. fillets and arris to an edge will soften the appearance and remove the danger of any sharp edges, e.g. on a coffee table top.

The shape and form of the design will always impinge on the stability of the project. Freestanding objects should be very stable in their design to prevent injury due to them falling over. This is not so important if the project is to be fixed to the wall.

✸ Relatively unstable hall table due to height

Weight is a serious concern to the designer in terms of safety. It is common for a project to fall from the desk top, for example, so keep the weight down to a minimum. Remember you will have to carry your material for storage at the end of class.

To avoid getting splinters in your hands, all surfaces should be sanded to a smooth finish and sealed at the end of construction. Another consideration is the type of finish to be used. Whether you use paint or varnish, all finishes should be non-toxic and odours kept down to a minimum.

✸ Rounding to edge of table top

✸ Stable low coffee table

Hands-on Tasks

1. Identify four areas of this room where there could be potential for injury.
2. Make a poster for the MTW room outlining the main areas of safety.
3. Make a poster for the MTW room outlining the dangers to different areas of the body from accidents in the room.
4. Discuss the differences between a tidy and an untidy work bench.
5. Sketch another design for the layout of tools in your locker or on your bench.
6. Make a poster to highlight the requirements of good design to make a project as safe as possible.

Homework Sheet on Health and Safety in the MTW Room

1. List the parts of the body which could be injured by working in the MTW room.
2. What type of tools from the following chapter (Chapter 17, Hand Tools) would you suggest require eye protection to be worn?
3. What type of operations in the MTW room would require a dust mask to be worn?
4. List three steps one could take to protect hands in the MTW room.
5. Make your own code of practice for the safe use of hand tools in the MTW room.
6. Why is it important to pick up all loose pieces of timber from the MTW room floor?
7. List the design consideration required to ensure that any design is safe to use.
8. Identify the hazards in the following:
   (a) An overloaded plug drawing.
   (b) An untidy desk.
   (c) A chisel at the edge of the bench.

INTERNET LINKS AND TASKS

Safety equipment

http://www.needlepointers.com/ShowArticles.aspx?NavID=863

Safety in the use of hand tools

http://woodworking.about.com/od/safetyfirst/Using_your_Woodworking_Tools_Safely.htm

Basic workshop safety

http://woodzone.com/shop-safety.htm

SEARCH

Sample Exam Questions on Health and Safety in the MTW Room

Ordinary Level	2010

List **two** safety precautions that should be observed when carrying a chisel across a room.

1. _____

2. _____

Ordinary Level	2010

When using power tools it is safer to use the type that plug into a transformer rather than those that plug directly into a mains socket.

Why is this?

ANSWER _____

_____

Ordinary Level | **2009**

List **two** safety precautions that should be observed when using sharp tools.

1. _____

2. _____

Ordinary Level | **2007**

List **two** safety precautions that should be observed when using portable electric power tools.

1. _____

2. _____

Higher Level | **2009**

Identify **THREE** safety features that are found in MTW school workshops.

FEATURE 1 _____

FEATURE 2 _____

FEATURE 3 _____

Higher Level | **2008**

State **two** specific safety precautions that should be observed when using wood chisels.

PRECAUTION 1 _____

PRECAUTION 2 _____

Higher Level | 2007

State **two** specific safety precautions that should be observed when using a pillar drill.

SAFETY 1 _____

SAFETY 2 _____

Higher Level | 2007

State **two** appropriate safety precautions that should be observed when using an electric drill, as shown.

PRECAUTION 1 _____

PRECAUTION 2 _____

Higher Level | 2005

The diagram shows a spray gun that is used to apply cellulose-based finishes. State **two** safety precautions that should be observed when applying such finishes.

PRECAUTION 1 _____

PRECAUTION 2 _____

Introduction to Hand Tools

Hand tools will vary from classroom to classroom, but most rooms will have the basic set of tools in a locker for each student. Some of the tools will be easy to use from the start but others will require some practice to obtain a high degree of skill. There is an almost endless list of tools which can be bought in most hardware shops or online, but they all fit into one of a small number of tool families. Here we will look at the standard tools available in the MTW room in terms of their components, safe use and maintenance. A number of other specialised tools will be covered, as they may be available to you in a limited number in the classroom or at home.

Key Elements to Understand for Junior Certificate Course

* the design concepts behind tools
* safe use of tools
* making jigs to help in the use of hand tools
* tool families
  * boring
  * cutting
  * paring
  * shaping
  * setting-out tools
  * fastening

Setting-out Tools
Rules
Steel Rule

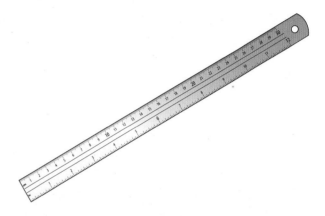

This is the standard measuring instrument used in woodworking today. Measurements begin at the very edge of the rule as shown. One error to be avoided is known as **parallax error** where the user does not look at the rule correctly as shown. Measurements are normally in millimetres, which allows for very accurate woodworking.

Steel Tape

This is used for longer measurements and is not as accurate as the steel rule. When using the **body** as part of the measurement one must remember to add the length of the body to the final measurement.

To check the squareness of wood, place the Try square against the wood and hold up to the light. No light should come in under the blade if the wood is square.

Safety
The steel tape can retract at a fast speed. Be careful of cuts to the skin if this happens and use the brake (stop) mechanism on the top of the tape.

Sliding Bevel

The sliding bevel is used to mark angles on wood. It has a pointed blade, which is stored in the stock for safekeeping. The wing nut must be loosened to remove the blade and the angle is then set using an adjustable set square as shown. The stock must always be kept firmly against the wood for accuracy.

Try Square

The Try square is used to mark straight lines on wood at ninety degrees to the edge and also to check the wood for squareness. The Try square has a steel blade, which holds its shape better, a rosewood stock for quality and a brass strip to maintain the precise ninety degree angle.

To use the Try square correctly, the stock must always be pressed firmly against the wood. Use of the face side and the face edge when marking, will ensure that your lines meet when marked all the way round.

⚬ Sliding bevel

Safety
The sharp end of the blade is dangerous and must be avoided. It must also be stored in the closed position after use.

⚬ Try square

Marking Gauge

The marking gauge is used to scribe and indent lines on wood before any cutting takes place. The stock (Beech) has two brass strips to prevent distortion. The stock can be locked in place anywhere along the stem (Beech). The spur is sharp and will have to be sharpened from time to time.

The stock must be pressed against the wood at all times and the spur should be angled to the wood as shown, for ease of use. A stop hole should be placed at the end of the line to be scribed to prevent damage to the wood as shown.

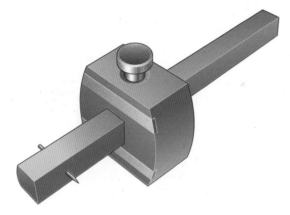

● Marking gauge

Safety
When storing the marking gauge, the stock should be locked next to the spur to prevent the next user from getting stabbed. Care should be taken at all times around the spur area.

Mortise Gauge

The mortise gauge is used to mark parallel lines onto the wood for the removal of trenches called mortises. It is also used to mark parallel lines for the creation of tenons as in the diagram.

It is made from hardwood (Mahogany) and has two brass strips for stability. The distance between the pins is set by loosening the thumbscrew and then moving the pins using the end wheel. The thumbscrew is then locked in position and the lines scribed as shown. Again, as in the marking gauge, pinholes can be made at the end of the desired mortise, to stop the gauge at the correct point.

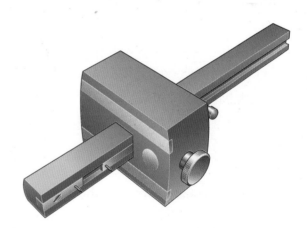

● Mortise gauge

Safety
Close the spurs when finished and be careful not to get injured from the two spurs. Some gauges have a single spur on the underside and this must be avoided when in use.

Thumb Gauge

The thumb gauge is used to mark parallel distances from the edge of the wood. These lines are most often used to mark the edge of chamfers, as shown. They simply slide along the wood edges and the woodworker uses a pencil or knife to follow it.

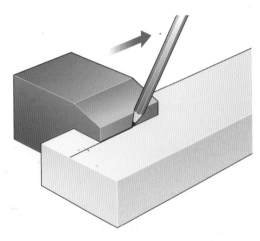

❋ Thumb gauge

Cutting Tools

Bench Hook

Although not a cutting tool itself, the bench hook greatly aids hand sawing and other operations. Made from Beech, it is held in the vice and the wood is held against it to aid straight sawing.

Tenon Saw

The Tenon saw is the most widely used saw by MTW students. It is small but very strong in design. The handle is designed to be comfortable and should be held as shown. The blade has many teeth and they saw on the forward stroke. The teeth alternate left and right if viewed end-on. The teeth must be sharpened regularly and the correct gaps can be set using the saw set shown. A sewing needle can be run down the teeth to test for imperfections. The needle should glide down the teeth with ease. The brass rib on the back adds strength to the Tenon saw and keeps the blade stable.

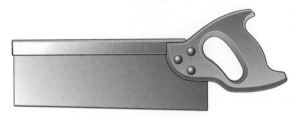

❋ Tenon saw

Safety
Keep hands clear of the teeth and hold up the thumb when sawing to prevent the saw from skidding across the back of the hand.

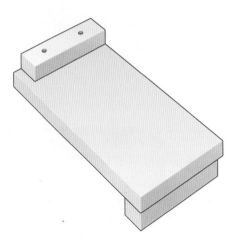

❋ Bench hook

Sawing using the Tenon Saw

1. Having marked out the wood to be removed place the wood vertically in a vice as low down as possible to avoid vibration.

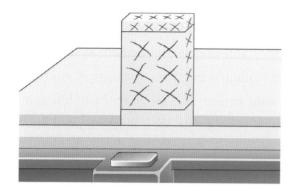

2. Hold the saw (as shown below).

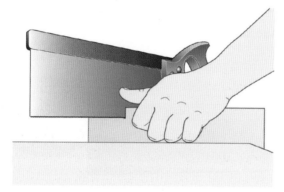

3. Draw the saw back 3-4 times on the waste side of the line to start the cut.

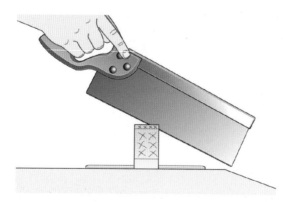

4. Saw straight to the waste line.

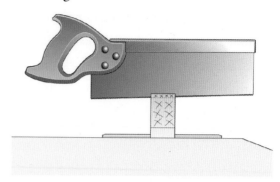

5. Remove timber and slope it forward to forty-five degrees.

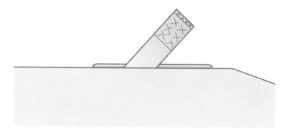

6. Continue to cut until the waste line stopping point.

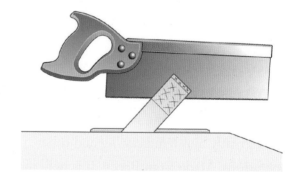

7. Remove the wood and saw at forty-five degrees to the waste line on the other side.

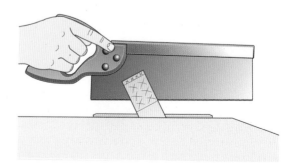

8. Place the wood vertically again and cut straight down to remove the V-shaped remaining wood.

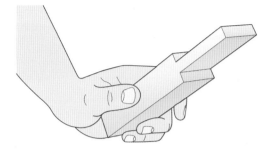

Hint: Spray silicon spray on the blade to ease the sawing action.

9. Place the wood on the bench hook to remove waste.

Panel Saw

The Panel saw is much larger than the Tenon saw and is used to cut larger boards to size. It is especially adapted to large, but thin, boards such as plywood and hardboard. The teeth are small and cut on the forward stroke.

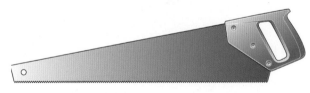

❋ Panel saw

Cross Cut Saw

This saw is used to cut larger pieces of wood across their grain. It is sometimes recognisable by the curved blade on the top edge of the saw. Due to its large size, Cross Cut saws can bend easily in use so care has to be taken.

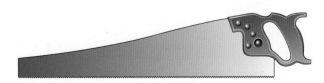

❋ Cross Cut saw

Dovetail Saw

This saw is a smaller version of the Tenon saw and is used for delicate work such as dovetail joints. Its teeth pattern is similar to that of the larger rip saw as it rarely has to cut across the grain.

❋ Dovetail saw

> **Safety**
> Keep hands clear of the teeth and hold up the thumb when sawing to prevent the saw from skidding across the back of the hand.
>
>

Coping Saw

This small saw is used for curved sawing of thin material. The teeth cut on the backstroke as this tensions the frame and blade making it stronger and last longer. The Coping saw has two pins to help in the alignment and changing of the blade.

To use the Coping saw, place both hands on the Beech handle and gently it move back and forth. Remember that the teeth cut on the way back so do not put a lot of pressure on the forward stroke. This will cause the blade to snap.

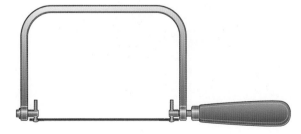

❋ Coping saw

To Change the Blade

1. Hold the first pin and the frame with the same hand.

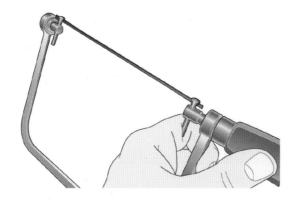

2. Unscrew the wooden handle with the other hand until the frame loosens considerably.

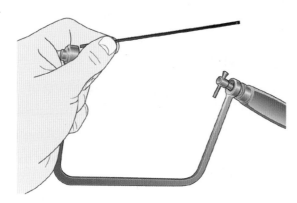

3. Carefully remove the blade by popping it out of the pin holders.

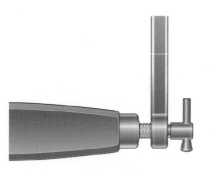

4. Place the new blade in the pin holders as shown, ensuring that the teeth point to the handle.

5. Hold the pin and the frame again and tighten the handle.

Pad Saw

This saw is used to cut holes in wood. A small drill hole is required inside the desired hole for this saw to work. The blade can be lengthened by loosening the screw and moving the blade.

❋ Pad saw

Safety
Tighten the screw well because the blade can come through the handle when the saw is under pressure.

Hacksaw

The Hacksaw is used to cut metal and plastic in the MTW room. It has a hollow frame and works in a similar manner to the Coping saw. The teeth are very fine and this allows small amounts of material to be removed at a time. The wing nut is used to tighten the blade.

❋ Hacksaw

> **Safety**
> The blade and the material being cut become very hot so allow them to cool before touching them.

Percussion Tools

Mallet

The woodworker's mallet is made from Beechwood, as this wood is highly shock-absorbent. The handle is tapered at the top to stop the head from coming off. The mallet is used to strike chisels when removing trenches, or to gently tap joints together with a scrap

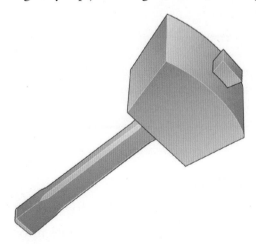

❋ Beech mallet

piece of wood between as shown. More power can be delivered to the head if the mallet is held low down on the handle as shown.

> **Safety**
> Keep fingers clear of the head when striking chisels.

CHAPTER 17

Carver's Mallet

This mallet has a round head and is made from Beech or Mahogany. The round head allows the carver to make fine blows to the carving gouges. The short handle means that only small amounts of force can be applied and this suits the carving process.

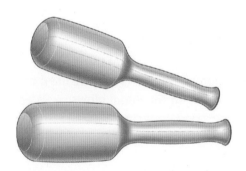

❋ Carver's mallet

> **Safety**
> Keep fingers clear of the striking face as the carver's mallet rolls off the wood very easily.

Claw Hammer

The claw hammer is one of the most recognisable tools in the workshop and home. The handle can be wooden or steel with a soft grip and the head is made from very durable steel. This hammer is used to drive nails into wood and also to remove nails with the claw at the rear of the hammer.

☀ Claw hammer

It is very important to strike the nails in the centre of the face, as this will prevent bending the nails and wearing the face unevenly. When removing nails, tap the nail through the wood as far as possible and then use a scrap piece of timber to lean the claw against.

> **Safety**
> Wear goggles when driving nails in and when removing nails. Keep thumb and fingers clear of the head when in use. Pliers may be used to hold the nail for the initial blows.

Warrington Hammer

This is a smaller hammer with a slender back face, as shown. It can be used for light hammering such as driving in panel pins. It is lightweight to help with delicate operations such as putting pins in picture frames.

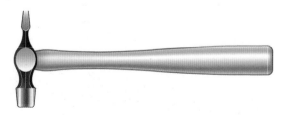

☀ Warrington hammer

Nail Punch

The nail punch is a round piece of hard steel used to drive nails below the surface of the wood before sanding commences. It has a square head for ease of striking with the hammer and a knurled pattern on the shank for grip. The punch must be hit gently to keep it on the nail head centre.

> **Safety**
> Wear goggles to prevent eye damage from flying nails.

Pliers

Pliers are used for many jobs from the removal of small nails to the cutting of thin wire. In the MTW room they are very useful for holding nails when hammering. The long nose plier is especially useful for this type of job. The shorter flat head plier is useful for cutting, as shown.

☀ Pliers

> **Safety**
> Be careful not to trap your skin between the arms of the pliers when squeezing.

Screwdrivers

There are many types of screwdrivers but they all do the same task of driving screws into wood and other materials. Most have plastic

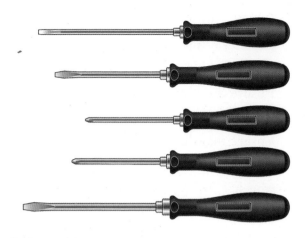

🔹 Screwdrivers

🔹 Bradawl

Mark the location of the screw with a pencil and make an indentation. This allows the screw to take hold easily. This is a great tool for putting screws in melamine boards, as in your kitchen cabinets at home.

> **Safety**
> Keep your other hand away from the area where the bradawl is to be used. They easily slip and can pierce the skin.

handles but some in the MTW room will have wooden handles, e.g. the large cabinet screwdriver has a flat head. The most common screwdriver used in the MTW room today is the Phillips head screwdriver. There is also a pozidrive version which is more common in power screwdrivers.

The screwdriver has a handle, a blade and a point (or head). A simple rule for screwdrivers is to match the screwdriver to the screw being used (see p. 293 Types of Screw). Also, the longer the screwdriver, the more power is delivered to the head. This is called **torque**.

> **Safety**
> Be careful of screwdriver heads because they are sharp.

Paring Tools
Planes

A plane is a cast iron or metal body with a sharp, wide blade which removes wood (shavings) by passing it across the surface of the wood. To use the plane, one hand rests on the front knob and the other on the back handle. Always plane with the grain for ease of use. Holding the plane at a slight angle will help the plane to glide, as shown. Always support the end of the good timber piece with

Bradawl

The bradawl is a small pointed piece of steel with a plastic handle and is used to make a starter hole for operations such as drilling, but especially for starting holes for screws.

🔹 Jack plane

a bad timber piece. This will prevent any breakout of the good wood.

Safety

Always be careful of the blade on the underside of the plane and always rest the plane on its side on the bench – this prevents damage to the blade and desk. Planes are generally heavy so do not allow them to drop on the floor or your foot.

It is important to know how to dismantle a plane so that it can be kept working at maximum efficiency.

How to Remove and Clean the Blade

(See also the information in this chapter on sharpening.)

1. Stand the plane up at the back with scrap wood.
2. Loosen the locking screw.
3. Undo the lever cap (lever or screw).
4. Remove the cap iron and blade assembly.
5. Remove the screw from the assembly and clean away any shaving.
6. Have the blade sharpened if necessary.
7. Ensure that the frog is in alignment with the blade exit point of the sole.
8. Ensure that the Y lever is vertical to the sole and can be turned by the adjustment wheel.
9. Screw the blade and cap iron back, as shown, leaving only 1–2 mm of blade protruding.
10. Replace the blade assembly with the screw facing downwards.
11. Replace the lever cap and lightly screw on the locking nut.
12. Adjust the depth of the blade with the brass wheel and the angle of the blade to the sole, using the lateral adjustment lever.
13. When satisfied, lock the locking screw tightly using the cabinet screwdriver.
14. Take test shavings on scrap wood first and then proceed to work on the good wood.

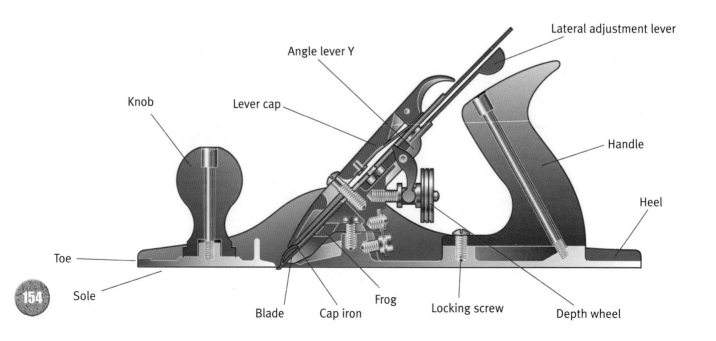

Lateral adjustment lever

Angle lever Y

Knob   Lever cap

Handle

Heel

Toe

Sole

Blade   Cap iron   Frog   Locking screw   Depth wheel

Types of Planes
Block
Small handheld plane for planing small wooden pieces.

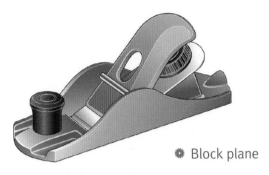

❋ Block plane

Jack
Normally used in the MTW room, it is useful for removing uneven surfaces. It is a medium-sized plane but is heavy in use.

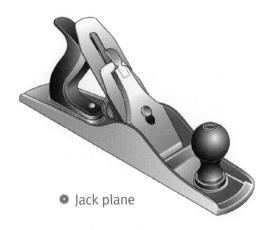

❋ Jack plane

Smoothing
This is shorter than the Jack plane and is used for a finer finish before sanding as it takes smaller and cleaner shavings from the wood.

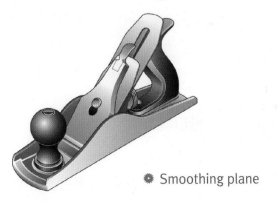

❋ Smoothing plane

Rebate
This unusual looking plane can be used to plane out a rebate on the edge of wood for holding glass etc.

❋ Rebate plane

Plough
This is used to plane away a groove in the timber to hold a panel or glass. The width of the trench is determined by the choice of blade installed in the plane.

❋ Plough plane

Spokeshave
Spokeshaves are cast-iron planes with two wings for holding. They are used to plane curved surfaces. The flat-bottomed version

🌸 Spokeshave

known as a **convex** spokeshave is used to plane external curves, as shown. The round-bottom version known as the **concave** spokeshave is used to plane internal curves.

Both are held between the thumb and the fingers and pushed away from the body. The depth of the cut is set using the two adjustment screws. They are best used in the direction of the grain.

Cabinet Scraper

The Cabinet scraper is a metal plate which is flexible and scrapes away at the timber surface. It removes small amounts of wood at a time but gives a very smooth finish. It is especially good on curved pieces of wood after they have been spokeshaven.

They are held between the fingers and can be pushed away or drawn to the body. Great strength is required to hold the plate in the curved position, as shown.

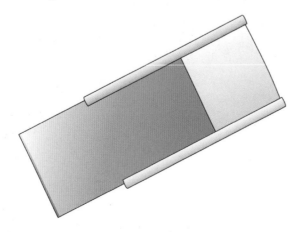

🌸 Cabinet scraper

Chisels

There are a variety of chisels available in the MTW room and each one has a separate role to play. The key to working with chisels is that they are kept sharp at all times. This produces better quality work and is safer because the chisel will not need to be pushed too hard, which may cause it to slip. All chisels are made from three basic parts: the handle, the tang and the blade. The tang is the area where the chisel's handle meets and is joined to the blade.

Bevel

This chisel has a slender profile and is useful for paring in dovetail joints. It is the weakest of the chisel family and must not be abused.

🌸 Bevel chisel

Firmer

This chisel has a rectangular cross-section and can take some abuse, as it is strong. It is an excellent chisel for the removal of material from trenches and shoulders. The correct way to remove a trench is shown later.

🌸 Firmer chisel

Mortise

The mortise chisel has a squarer section and is useful for removing material to greater depths than the other two chisels. The handles have a steel ferrule to strengthen the handle. The correct method to remove a mortise is shown using this chisel.

> **Safety**
> * Always keep hands behind the cutting edge of the blade.
> * Always hold the chisel firmly by the blade especially when walking around.
> * Do not leave the chisel at the edge of your bench as the circular handle makes it easy for the chisel to roll off.
> * Wear goggles when removing waste material, especially when mortising.

Removing a Mortise by Hand

1. Mark out the mortise with a mortise gauge and scribe the top and bottom.

2. Hold the Mortise chisel vertically and hit it with the mallet three times.

3. Repeat, moving along the mortise site until you reach the other end.

4. Repeat this process in the opposite direction.

5. Remove waste with the chisel in reverse but do not damage the good wood at the upper and lower edges of the mortise. Use a steel ruler to lean on (as shown in the diagram).

6. Continue until you have reached the required depth which can be set on the reverse of the chisel with a pencil.

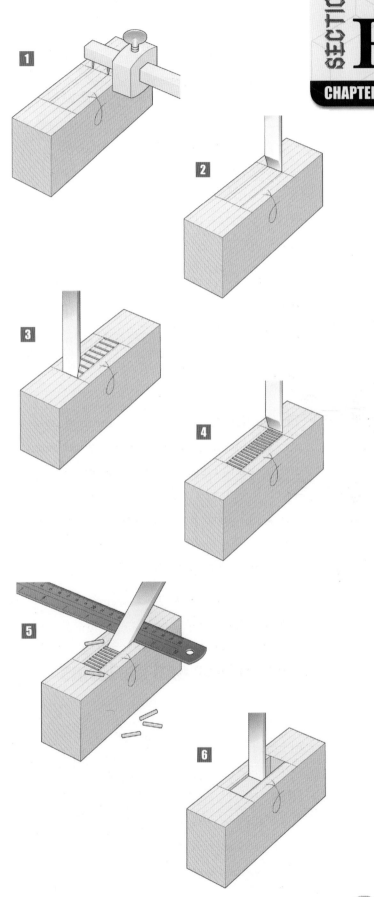

Removing a mortise by hand

Sharpening Chisels

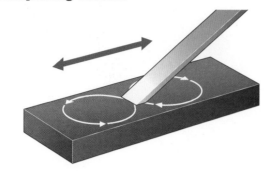

❋ Sharpening a chisel – honing

Damaged chisel blades at the tips must be ground straight by your teacher. Following this, and any time you feel that the chisel is loosing its sharpness, you can sharpen and hone your chisel using the oilstone in your classroom.

The initial grinding is carried out by holding the chisel with the flat side up and rubbing it in a figure of eight on the stone.
Metal filings will gather on the tip of the chisel and these are removed by rubbing the flat back of the chisel on the smooth side of the stone.

Gouges: see Chapter 21, Carving

Files, Rasps and Surforms

These are used to tear away small amounts of wood usually to reduce bumps on the surface of non-linear surfaces.

Files

They allow a variety of hard-to-reach places to be smoothened, e.g. acute corners, and round holes. A large selection of profiles is available. Sanding is nearly always required after the filing process.

File Types: flat rectangular, circular, half round, triangular.

The files are made up of a handle, ferrule, tang and blade (or face). The face has lots of sharp edges, which need to be cleaned constantly to prevent clogging. A file brush with its steel wire face can clean the file easily. Most woodwork files do not come with a handle and must be used with care. When using a file, one hand holds the tang and the other lies flat on the face and moves at the same rate as the filing action to prevent damage to the hand. Alternatively, handles should be made or bought to prevent damage to the hands at the tang area.

Rasps

The rasp has a rougher face than a file and can remove more material at a time. They clog easily and must be constantly cleaned. They are used in the same way as the files.

❋ Rasp

Surforms

The surforms are easy to hold and use rasps. They remove a lot of material relative to a file but do not clog due to the voids between the teeth, as shown. The shavings enter the chamber and can be easily dumped when the process is finished.

Surforms can be flat or round. Blades can be replaced as needed as they regularly snap and wear away due to their light construction.

❋ Surform

❋ Hand drill

> **Safety**
> ❋ Buy and fit handles for files and rasps with a bare tang.
> ❋ Do not rub against the skin.
> ❋ Clean the teeth as often as possible.

Boring Tools

Drills are used to remove a circular section of material from the wood. All have the facility to change the drilling device (bit) to a more suitable bit for the operation. Most holes will require a centre point to be punched to aid accuracy in drilling. It is also important not to allow the bit to break out the other side. This can be prevented by drilling from both sides or by placing waste wood at other side.

Hand Drill

The hand drill is used for delicate drilling operations. The drill resembles a whisk and is used in a similar fashion. It is an excellent drill for boring thin plastics and manufactured boards.

The bit is changed by holding the chuck and winding back the handle.

Ratchet and Brace Drill

This is the most common boring hand tool in the MTW room and its operation can be tricky. It is comprised of a frame handle, a rotating hand piece, gear mechanism and a chuck.

The bits are changed by holding the chuck in one hand whilst rotating the frame with the other hand. Ensure that the gear is in the correct position. The forward and reverse gear is selected by rotating the knurled knob, as shown. The gears work on a ratchet and pawl mechanism as outlined in Chapter 14, Material Properties, Forces and Structures.

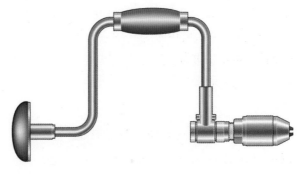

❋ Ratchet and brace drill

Bits
Brace Bits

These have a screw mechanism to engage the bit in the wood. They may have single or double twists on the shank. They must be kept sharp for ease of use. Modern versions have an adjustable leading edge.

❋ Brace bit

Forstner Bits

Available in a number of sizes, they are use to remove wood in larger amounts leaving a high-quality finish. They are mostly used on the pillar drill as they require a high speed of operation.

❋ Forstner bit

Countersink Bits

This is used to drill a small cone-shaped hole at the top of a pilot hole allowing the screw head to sit flush against the surface. Modern versions incorporate the pilot bit with the countersink bit, as shown.

❋ Countersink bit

Flat Bits

These may be used by either a brace or an electric drill and remove wood effortlessly. A dot punch must be used to set up the centre of the drilling area, as this bit has no screw mechanism for accuracy.

❋ Flat bit

Hole Saws

Must be used with a power drill, these are used to remove very large holes in the timber. The edge of the bit is comprised of saw teeth and it cuts the wood away as in a sawing operation. They are available in many sizes.

❋ Hole saw

Safety
- Always wear goggles when drilling.
- Keep hands away from the bit tips.
- Keep hands clear of underside of drilling area.
- Reduce pressure on the drill when the bit emerges from the other side of the wood as the bit can burst through suddenly.

Shaping Tools: see Chapter 21, Carving and Chapter 20, Woodturning

Fastening Tools or Clamping Tools: see Chapter 26, Adhesives and Clamping Wood

Hands-on Tasks

1 Make a list of the hand tools you have at home and practise with them under supervision – after you have learned all the basics from your teacher.

2 Use a steel tape to measure and draw the outline of your classroom.

3 Practise using a **Try square** to check the squareness of scrap pieces of timber in the classroom.

4 Mark lines on scrap pieces of wood with the marking gauge, trying to keep the stock against the edge at all times.

5 Mark out and practise sawing straight with the Tenon saw using scrap pieces of timber.

6 Remove and replace the blade from a Coping saw and get the teacher to check that everything is correctly positioned.

7 Make a chart of different screwdriver tips and hang it on the wall of the MTW room.

8 Take a Smoothing plane apart noting the sequence in which each part was removed. Then replace all the parts in the correct order.

9 Use a ratchet and brace drill to practise drilling from both sides of scrap wood.

10 Obtain a flat bit for a cordless drill from your teacher and practise drilling through scrap timber. The goal is to get a clean circle on each side of the hole.

Homework Sheet on Hand Tools

1 List two uses for a Try square in woodwork.

2 Make a neat, rendered 3-D sketch of a sliding bevel.

3 Why is it important to put a stop punch hole at the end of the area to be scribed with the marking gauge?

4 How do you change the distance between the pins of a mortise gauge?

5 Make a neat, rendered 3-D sketch of a **Tenon saw**.

6 Make a neat sketch to show the direction of the teeth in a **Coping saw**.

7 What feature in the design of a mallet keeps the head in place during operation?

8 How could you protect the good wood when removing a nail with a claw hammer?

9 What force acts on a screwdriver when in use?

10 Label the parts of the plane and brace drill.

INTERNET LINKS AND TASKS

Hand tool safety

http://www.toolboxtopics.com/Gen%20Industry/Hand%20Tool%20Safety.htm

Using tools safely

http://www.kidscanmakeit.com/woodworking_tips.htm

SEARCH

Sample Exam Questions on Hand Tools

Ordinary Level   **2010**

Name the tool labelled **A** in the diagram and give its use.

NAME   _____

USE   _____

_____

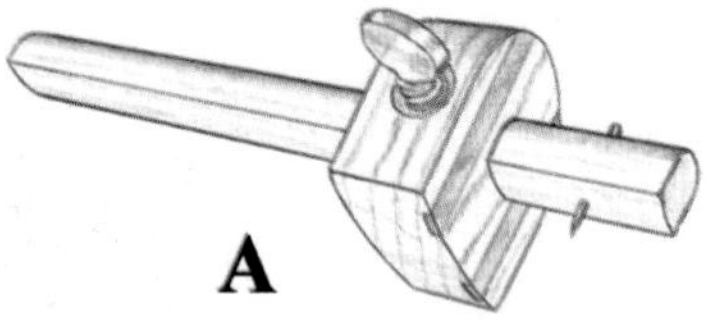

A

OR

Name the tool labelled **B** in the diagram and give its use.

NAME   _____

USE   _____

_____

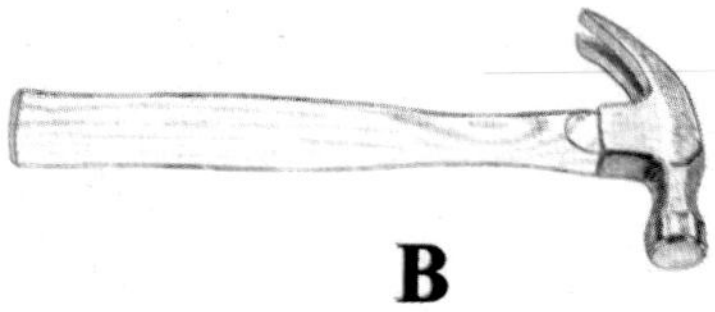

B

Ordinary Level — 2010

How could a plane blade get damaged as shown in the sketch?

ANSWER _____

_____

Ordinary Level — 2010

Saws can be divided into two categories, saws for straight cuts and saws for cutting curves. Show by means of a tick (✓) into which group each of the following saws fit.

	Straight Cuts	Curved Cuts
Coping Saw		
Dovetail Saw		
Compass Saw		
Scroll Saw		
Tenon Saw		

Ordinary Level — 2009

Name the tool labelled **A** in the diagram and give its use.

NAME _____

USE _____

_____

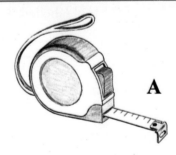

OR

Name the tool labelled **B** in the diagram and give its use.

NAME _____

USE _____

_____

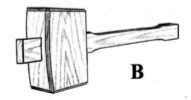

Ordinary Level 2009

What makes shavings curl when planing?

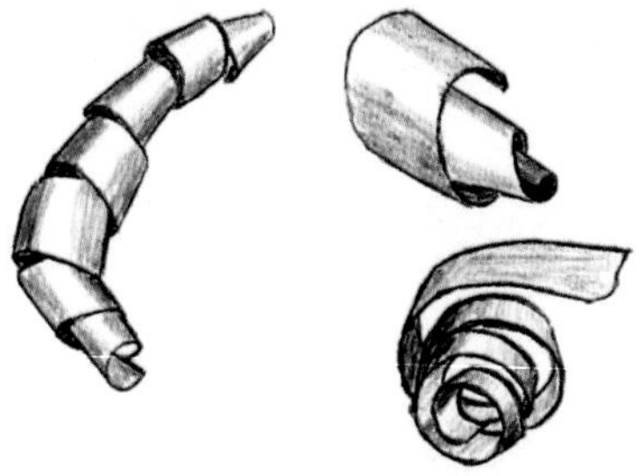

ANSWER ______________________________

____

Ordinary Level 2009

When sharpening the blade of a plane or chisel, angle **A** is called the grinding angle.
What is angle **B** called?

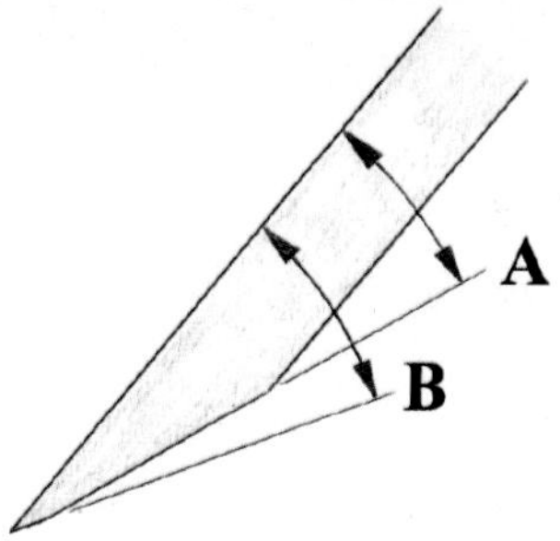

NAME ______________________________

Ordinary Level 2008

Name the tool labelled **A** in the diagram and give its use.

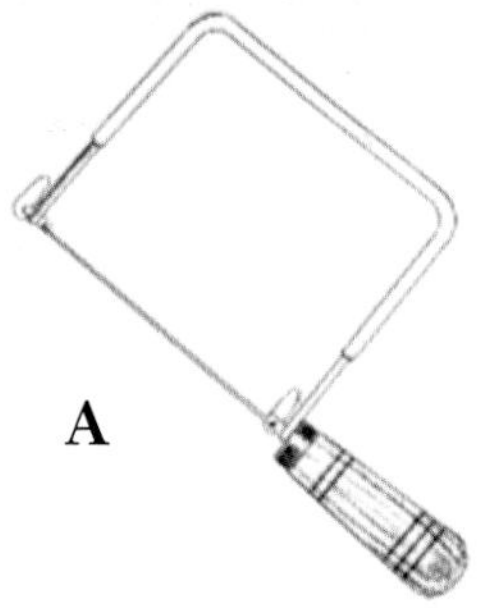

NAME ______________________________

USE ______________________________

OR

Name the tool labelled **B** in the diagram and give its use.

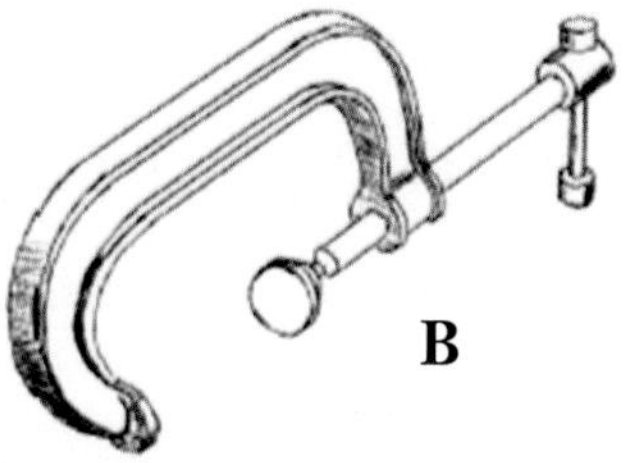

NAME ______________________________

USE ______________________________

Ordinary Level 2008

List **two** safety precautions that should be observed when carrying a chisel in the classroom.

1. ______________________________

2. ______________________________

Ordinary Level 2008

What is the bottom surface of a plane, shown at **A**, called?

ANSWER _____

A

Ordinary Level 2008

How do you prevent a drill bit from damaging a board when drilling through the board?

ANSWER _____

_____

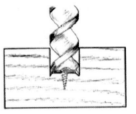

Ordinary Level 2008

What is the name of the object shown in the diagram?

_____

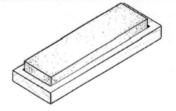

Higher Level 2010

(i) Name the woodworking tool shown in the diagram.

NAME _____

(ii) Give one specific use for this tool.

USE _____

_____

(i)   Name the tool shown in the diagram.

NAME _____

(ii) State an appropriate use for this tool.

USE _____

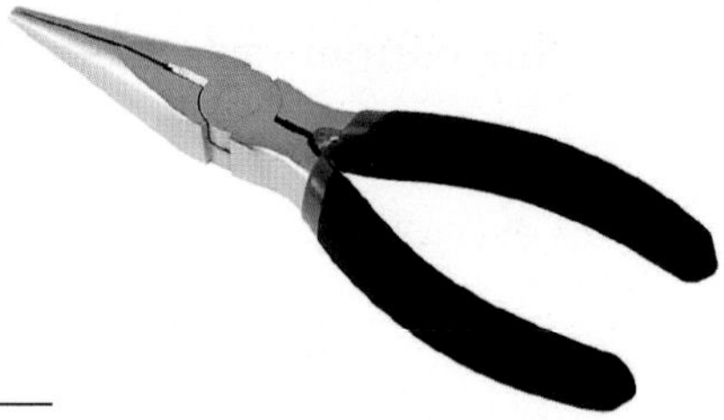

Identify, using a tick (✓), which of the following saws are more suitable for curved or straight cuts.

Saws	Curved	Straight
Dovetail saw		
Band saw		
Scroll saw		
Circular saw		
Rip saw		

(i)   Name the woodworking tool shown in the diagram.

A →

NAME _____

(ii) State the function of the part **A** of this tool.

FUNCTION _____

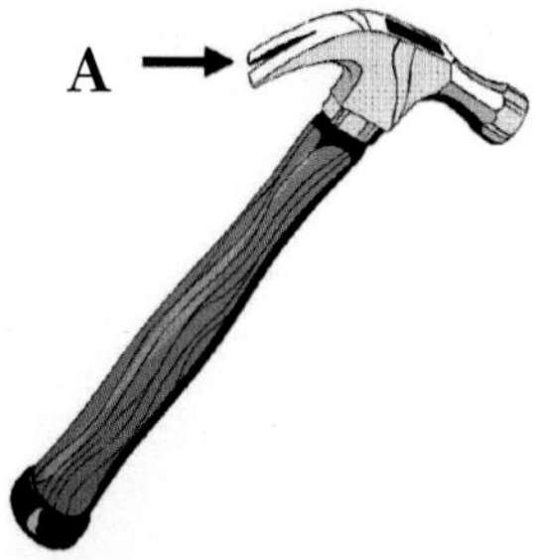

(i)   The diagram shows a tenon saw and a close up view of its teeth. Every second tooth is bent left and right. What is this feature called?

FEATURE _____

(ii) Why is this feature necessary?

ANSWER _____

_____

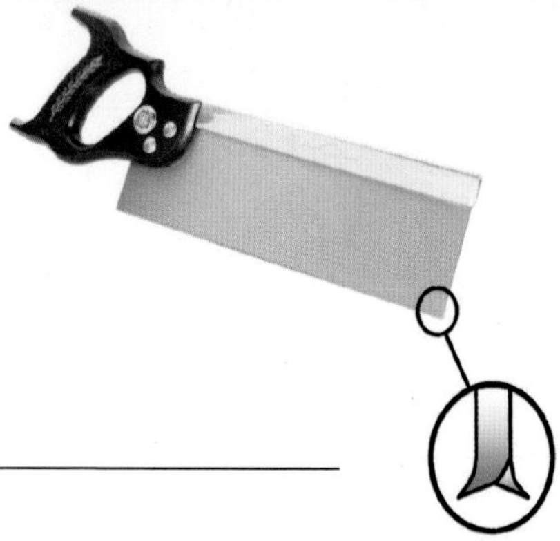

Higher Level | **2008**

(i) Using a tick (✓), identify the woodworking tool shown.

Marking Gauge ☐

Cutting Gauge ☐

Mortise Gauge ☐

(ii) Give one specific use for this tool.

USE _____

Higher Level | **2008**

(i) State the correct name for each of the planes labelled **A**, **B** and **C** below.

A    **B**    **C**

_____   _____   _____

(ii) Select any **two** of the planes shown and describe their appropriate use.

_____   _____

(iii) The diagram shows the cutting assembly of a plane.
Name the parts labelled **X** and **Y** and state the function of each.

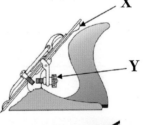

X _____

Y _____

(iv) The blade of the plane, as shown, has been badly damaged. Describe, **in detail**, with the aid of notes and **neat freehand sketches**, the steps involved in resharpening the cutting edge of the blade.

Higher Level 2007

The blade of a chisel has become damaged and needs to be sharpened.

Using the numbers 1, 2 and 3, place the following steps in the correct order.

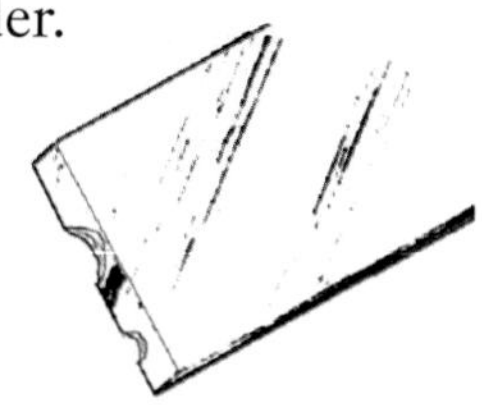

HONING ___

BURR REMOVAL ___

GRINDING ___

Higher Level 2007

Make a 3-D sketch of a Try-square on the given isometric axes.

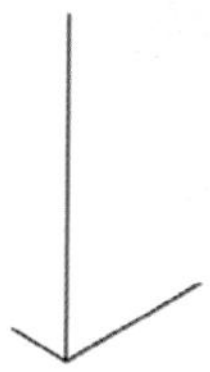

Higher Level 2007

(i) Name the tool shown in the diagram.

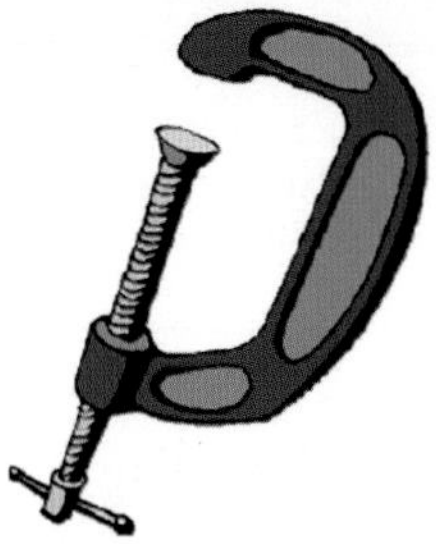

NAME ______________________

(ii) State an appropriate use for this tool.

USE ______________________

Higher Level 2006

(i) Name the woodworking tool shown in the diagram.

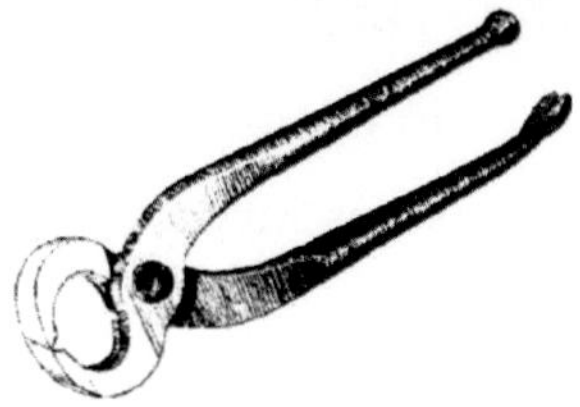

ANSWER ______________________

(ii) For what purpose is this tool used?

PURPOSE ______________________

Higher Level — 2006

(i) Name the tool shown in the diagram.

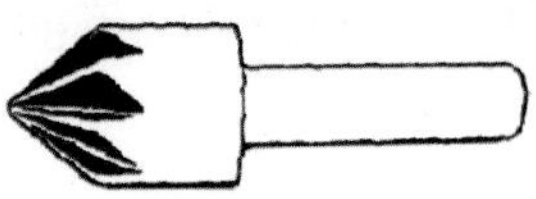

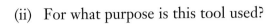

ANSWER _____

(ii) For what purpose is this tool used?

PURPOSE _____

Higher Level — 2006

(i) Name the tool shown in the diagram.

ANSWER _____

(ii) State an appropriate use for this tool.

PURPOSE _____

Higher Level — 2006

(i) State the correct names for the tools labelled **L**, **M** and **N**.

L

M

N

_____ _____ _____

(ii) What is the correct angle, **A**, for the cutting edge of a chisel when resharpening it?

A _____

(iii) Describe, **in detail**, using notes and **neat freehand sketches**, how you would resharpen a chisel that has a badly damaged cutting edge such as that shown in the diagram.

(iv) With the aid of notes and **neat freehand sketches** describe, **in detail**, the steps you would follow to cut out the trench shown in the diagram.

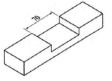

169

Higher Level — 2005

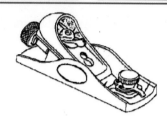

(i) Name the plane shown in the diagram.

ANSWER ______________________________

(ii) Where would you use this type of plane in preference to a Smoothing plane?

ANSWER ______________________________

Higher Level — 2005

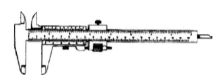

(i) Name the tool shown in the diagram.

NAME ______________________________

(ii) State an appropriate woodworking use for this tool.

USE ______________________________

Higher Level — 2004

(i) State the correct names for the marking-out tools labelled **A, B** and **C.**

A

B

C

______________ ______________ ______________

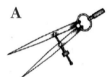

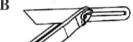

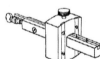

(ii) The diagram shows a small storage unit for DVDs made from Cherry. The top is inlaid with a decorative strip of boxwood. With the aid of notes and **neat freehand sketches** describe, **in detail**, the steps you would follow in order to insert the boxwood strip.

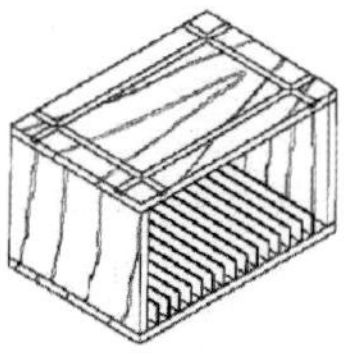

(iii) With the aid of notes and **neat freehand sketches** describe, **in detail**, the steps you would follow to mark out the stopped dovetail housing joint shown in the diagram.

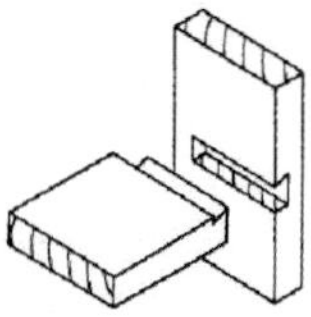

(i)   The diagrams show three wood-boring tools. State the correct names for the implements labelled **A**, **B** and **C**.

A

B

C

_____   _____   _____

(ii) With the aid of notes and **neat freehand sketches**, describe how you would bore the following holes:

   (a)   A hole of 2·5 mm diameter through a piece of hardwood 40 mm thick.

   (b)   A hole of 20 mm diameter to a depth of 40 mm in a piece of hardwood 100 mm thick.

   (c)   A hole of 12 mm diameter through a piece of acrylic 6 mm thick.

(iii) Cordless drills are often used in woodwork. State **two** advantages and **two** disadvantages associated with the use of cordless drills.

(iv) Give the correct names for the drill bits labelled **P**, **Q** and **R** shown in the diagrams, and state which of the drill bits are suitable for use with a cordless drill.
Give reasons for your answer.

P

Q

R

_____   _____   _____

Higher Level **2003**

(i) Name the woodworking tool shown in the diagram.

ANSWER ________________________________

(ii) State an appropriate use for part **A** of this tool.

USE ________________________________

____

Higher Level **2003**

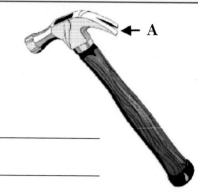

The diagram shows part of a curved mirror frame that is to be shaped with spokeshaves.

With the aid of arrows, indicate the correct directions in which the curves should be worked.

Higher Level **2003**

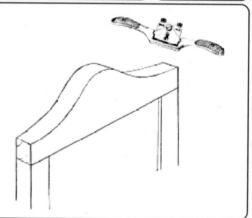

The diagram shows two boards being edge-jointed with the aid of sash clamps.

(i) What is the correct name for the force applied by the sash clamps to the boards shown in the diagram?

ANSWER ________________________________

(ii) What force acts on the pin, **P**, when the clamp is in use?

ANSWER ________________________________

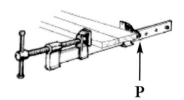

Higher Level 2003

(i) Name the metalworking tool shown in the diagram.

ANSWER _____

(ii) State an appropriate use for this tool.

ANSWER _____

Higher Level 2003

(i) The diagrams show three different types of saw. State the correct names for the saws labelled **A**, **B** and **C**, and give an appropriate use for each.

A	B	C

_____   _____   _____

(ii) The diagram shows the **tenon** portion of a mortise and tenon joint.
With the aid of notes and **neat freehand sketches**, describe the steps that should be taken in **marking out** and **cutting** the tenon.

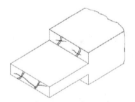

(iii) Explain what is meant by the term **saw-kerf**.

(iv) Shown in the diagram is a close up view of the teeth of a saw. The teeth are bent alternately to the left and right of the centreline of the saw blade. What name is given to this feature, and what function does it serve?

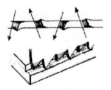

CHAPTER 18

Power Tools and Machines

Practical Woodwork

Introduction to Power Tools and Machines

The invention of power tools and machines in the past couple of centuries has greatly influenced the way we make things. Where power tools can be used benefits such as increased speed, accuracy and comfort of work are produced.

Power tools and machines can be more dangerous than hand operations, but when proper safety precautions are taken they can be very safe.

It is important to know and understand the parts and workings of all the power tools in order to make the correct choice for a given task. Knowledge of each tool's parts and workings will also help the operator determine whether or not they can fix any faults. In any case, knowledge of how to change blades, bits and sandpapers etc. will help to reduce the operational costs of using power tools and machines. Also, it is good practice to learn the correct procedure for changing a broken plug.

It is important for the student to understand that not all the power tools and machines in the MTW room are available for use, so check with the teacher first. Only use tools for which you have been given instruction and permission to use.

Key Elements to Understand for Junior Certificate Course

* The safe use of each tool.
* The parts of each tool.
* The selection of the correct tool for the operation.
* The making and use of jigs.

* Selection of power tools

Power Tools

Cordless Drill

The cordless drill is one of the easiest tools to use and is very helpful in executing projects. It can serve to drill holes or drive in screws, both of which will have a different setting to select on the drill. Always ensure that there is a spare battery charging while you are using the battery in the drill.

The drill can be set in forward or reverse by the selection switch. The power can be set by the switch which normally has the numbers **1** and **2** on it. Select **1** for screwing and **2** for drilling. There is also a torque setting facility which allows the drill to stop turning at a set level of pressure. If you are putting small screws in wood, the setting would be close to **5** or if you were drilling thick wood it would be set closer to the maximum indicated on the drill. Some drills even have a hammer action setting to drill light brickwork.

Parts of a cordless drill

To remove or place a drill bit in the drill, hold the chuck as shown and select forward to lock and reverse to open the chuck. Squeeze the power button gently until the chuck opens or closes.

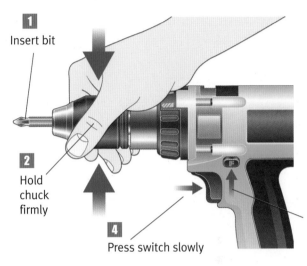

1 Insert bit

2 Hold chuck firmly

4 Press switch slowly

3 Select forward to hold bit (reverse to remove)

Installing and removing bits from a cordless drill

Safety
* Do not place hands in front of drill bits when they are turning.
* Do not burn your hand when locking or opening the chuck.
* Rest the drill on its side as they can fall over easily.
* Always clamp down material when drilling.

Hand Power Tools

One of the basic things to know in relation to hand power tools is how to change the plug if it gets damaged, if the flex is cut or if the fuse blows. The diagram below shows the correct placement for the internal parts of a three-pin plug **containing only a Live and Neutral wire**.

Changing a Plug

1. Unscrew the casing and the flex clamps.

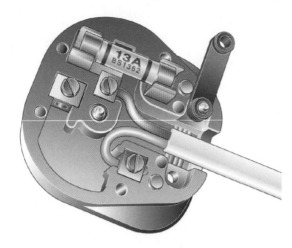

2. Undo the wires from their fixing points labelled **L** and **N**.

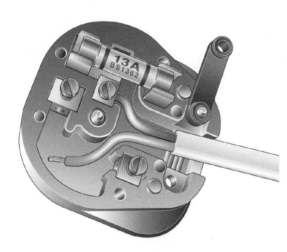

3. Place the **L** and **N** wires into the correct pins on the new plug and tighten.

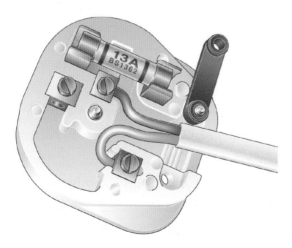

4. Lock down the flex with the clamp.

5. Replace the plug cap securely.

Orbital Sander

● Orbital sander

The orbital sander is used to sand wood to a good level of finish. They can be rectangular or circular in shape and the sanding pads are obtained to suit your own sander. The sanding pads are changed by ripping them off and sticking on the replacement (which has a Velcro backing). Ensure that the holes in the pad match up with holes in the sander base as these allow dust to be blown away. Always use the sander with the dust extraction bag attached to allow for easy collection of dust.

The sander is used by placing one hand on the unit and moving it to the areas to be sanded. The orbital action of the sander helps this process. Not only does the sander move the pad from side to side as in a conventional sander, it also rotates the pad to give a better finish with fewer scratch marks.

Safety
* Ensure that the pad is fitted properly as any pad sticking out can cut you.
* Keep the power cord away from the working area to prevent it getting cut.
* Wear a dust mask where possible.

Belt Sander

🌸 Belt sander

The belt sander is used for heavy sanding of wood that has a poor surface already. In the home it is often used to sand wooden floorboards. The sander must be kept even over the surface of the wood as it can cause hollows to form in the wood. Even pressure must be applied to the front and rear. The dust collection bag should be used or preferably a vacuum cleaner can be attached to the dust outlet. It is vital to wear a dust mask, as the amount of dust given off can be considerable. The belt is changed by opening the levers at both sides and slipping on the new belt. The lever is then closed and locked in position.

Safety
* Do not hit the power cord with the moving belt.
* Wear eye, ear and dust protection.
* Do not use worn or torn belts as they may fly off.

Electric Drill

🌸 Electric drill

The electric drill can be used to drill many surfaces. One only has to change the settings on the drill and change the drill bit type to drill different materials. The bits are generally changed by unlocking the chuck using a key and then tightening when the correct bit is inserted. In the MTW room this drill is often held in a drill press to ensure a precise angle of drill hole. The speed of the drill is adjusted by the level of pressure applied to the ON/OFF switch.

> **Safety**
> * Ensure that the chuck key is not in the drill when turning it on.
> * Keep the electric cord away from the moving chuck.
> * Wear eye and ear protection.

port, a facility to allow the blade to rock back and forth (this makes cutting faster but rougher and with more damage to the blade), a laser to make following of lines easier and an easy release mechanism to change the blades. The jigsaw can be used to drill out circles by using a drill hole to start off the process.

> **Safety**
> * Keep the cord away from the cutting edge of the blade.
> * Keep fingers away from the moving blade.
> * Allow the saw to stop prior to removing it from a material halfway, as it may jump from your hand.

Jigsaw

⚬ Jigsaw

The jigsaw is used to cut curves in large sections of timber, especially manufactured boards such as plywood and MDF. The blade reciprocates by the use of cams in the jigsaw housing. The speed of the cutting action can be adjusted by use of the ON/OFF switch. The correct blade must be chosen for the material, e.g. a metalwork blade will have finer teeth than a woodwork blade. Most modern jigsaws will have a dust extraction

Planer

⚬ Planer

This is used to remove large quantities of wood from the surface of rough timber down to the required line on the wood. It consists of a rotating drum with two blades, which tear away the wood. It leaves a pattern on the surface. These arcs have to be removed by sanding or scraping. The planer generally rotates at one constant high speed. This tool must not be used unless you have the teacher's permission.

Router

This is used to apply decorative edges to the wood but can be used to make joints, grooves and mortises. It is available in the MTW room but should only be used by the teacher, as it is highly dangerous. A motor spins any one of a number of bits at very high speeds and cuts away the wood. The finish is often of a very high quality due to the sharp bits and high speeds. It is ideal to soften the edges of tables or to enhance the appearance of the design.

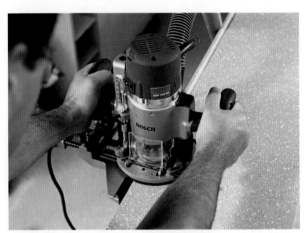

* Router

Biscuit Joiner

The biscuit joiner is used to join pieces of timber together by cutting a slit in the two opposing pieces of wood. The woodworker then glues in an oval-shaped **biscuit** and then the woods are clamped together as in diagram below. The joiner allows the depth of the biscuit to be set using a dial. Other parameters for different thickness of wood can be set using the face plate.

* Biscuit joiner

The Procedure for Joining a Frame

1. Mark the width of the wood against the adjoining piece using a Try square.

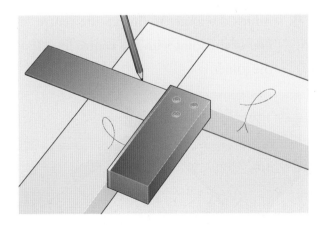

2. Scribe the centre of the adjoining faces with a marking gauge.

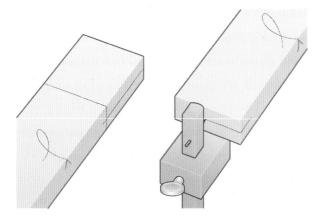

3. Mark a line perpendicular to the scribed line with a Try square.

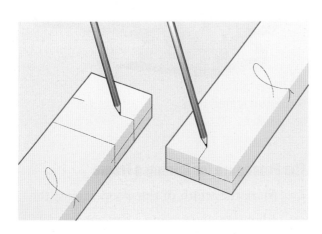

4. Adjust the joiner to line up the centre line of the joint with the centre line of the joiner.

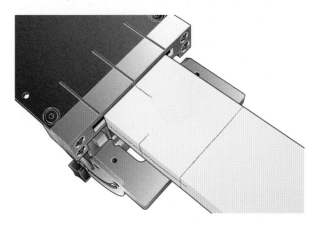

5. Select the biscuit depth on the side of the joiner.

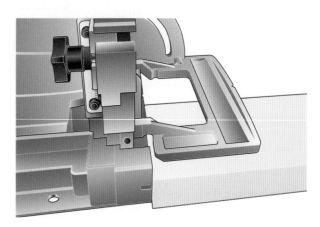

6. Line up the joiner, turn on and press into the wood.

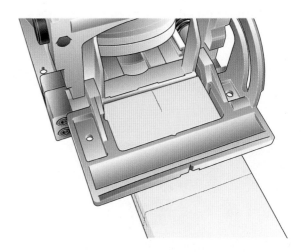

7. Repeat for the opposing face.

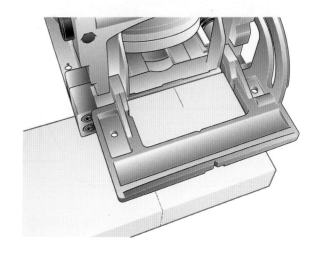

8. Pump glue into both hollows, insert the biscuit and clamp.

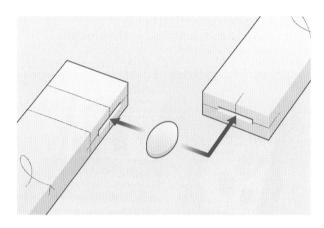

> **Safety**
> * Do not run the cutter in the open without the guard fully extended.
> * Keep the cord and the fingers away from the rotating blade.
> * Fit dust extraction where possible.
> * Wear ear, eye and dust mask protection equipment.

Multi Toolkit

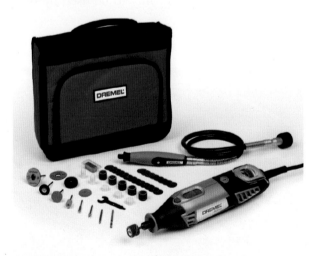

❋ Multi toolkit

Most MTW rooms will be equipped with a Multi tool. This is a kit, which includes a motor unit and a vast array of cutters, files, saws and engravers. They are especially good for cutting circular holes in plastics and thin woods. The kits also come with an extension cord which allows one to work some distance away from the power supply.

Spray Gun

This is an applied finish applicator which can be electric-powered or pneumatic. The finish is filled into the chamber and then applied in even coats to the wood. It is always better to apply a number of light coats than one heavy coat as this reduces drips. It is important to clean out the sprayer with white spirit after each use to prevent clogging.

❋ Spray gun

> **Safety**
> * Wear a respirator, eye protection and clothing protection.
> * Work only in a ventilated area devoid of airborne dust.

Nail Gun/Stapler

The nail gun is used to drive nails and staples into wood. Various size nails can be used depending on the operation. The gun must be switched on at the safety switch and pressed down into the wood before it will fire. It can be powered by gas or electricity.

✸ Nail gun

Veneer Iron

This iron is a simple design with a steel body and a heat control dial. The pointed end makes it easier to get into tricky corners. It is used to heat iron-on veneers as described in Chapter 22, Veneering.

✸ Veneer iron

Safety
* Always store in an upright position.
* Do not burn hands when in use.
* Keep cord away from the heated base.

Pyrograph

This is a pen-like tool which heats up and allows patterns to be burned into wood. For more detail see Chapter 24, Pyrography.

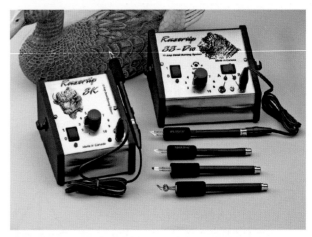

✸ Pyrography machine

Circular Saw

Mostly used to cut large boards to a rough size. Can cut more accurately with the small fence which is attached to the base of the circular saw. Generally only to be used by the teacher.

✸ Circular saw

Machines

Planer

Also located in the machine preparation room is the planer. This has a rotating drum with blades attached to smooth the surface of the wood. It also has a facility to pass wood through it allowing the wood to be shaved down to a desired thickness.

G0675

✹ Planer thicknesser

Bandsaw

The bandsaw is used to cut straight lengths of wood or very subtle curves. It has a rotating blade as shown and the teeth point in a downward direction. The width of the cut can be set using a fence to the left of the blade. The guard must always be kept as low to the wood as possible to prevent cutting of fingers. Only used at the discretion of your teacher.

> **Safety**
> - Wear eye protection at all times.
> - Keep fingers well away from the blade.
> - Know how to use the emergency stop.
> - Do not push the timber in too quickly as the blade can break or shear.

G0457

✹ Bandsaw

Scroll Saw

This machine is used for delicate work where curves and patterns are required. The blade revolves around a cam producing the cut, but also vibration. Consequently you must hold onto the wood firmly. The guard must be kept down and the air tube blowing at the work area for accurate results. Internal curves may be cut if a small drill hole is made and then the blade is removed and replaced to make the cut required.

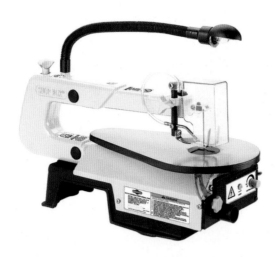

⚙ Scroll saw

> **Safety**
> ⚙ Wear goggles at all times.
> ⚙ Keep the guard in the down position.
> ⚙ Hold onto the wood firmly.
> ⚙ Keep the fingers away from the blade.

Belt Sander

The belt sander is used to sand large surfaces quickly. Most also come with a drum sanding facility, as shown. Wood is placed against the rotating belt for a short period as it sands away quickly. It is excellent for sanding end grain. Internal curves are sanded on the drum side

and external curves sanded on the flat side, as shown. This machine must be connected to a dust extraction system when in use.

> **Safety**
> ⚙ Wear dust and eye protection.
> ⚙ Keep hands away from the belt or bobbin.
> ⚙ Hold the wood firmly when in use.
> ⚙ Never use this machine on small sections of wood as it will grab them and fire them across the room.

Sharpening Wheel

This machine is used to grind chisels prior to honing by hand. (See Chapter 17, Hand Tools, for more information on sharpening.) The chisel sits in the holder at the desired angle and the rotating stone wheel (lubricated by oil) grinds down the leading edge of the chisel.

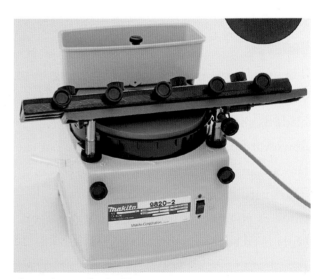

⚙ Horizontal grinder

⚙ Belt sander

Lathe

The lathe is described in detail in Chapter 20, Woodturning.

❋ Lathe

Mortise Machine

The mortiser is used to remove material from wood in a square pattern. A rotating drill inside the square chisel does most of the removal and the sharp chisel edge squares up

❋ Mortise machine

the hole. These chisels are available in standard sizes like your mortise chisels. Wood is held in place by the locking wheel. The depth of the mortise is set using the depth stop lever to the left. The material moves along by rotating the adjustment handle. The same handle is pulled out toward the operator to enable the wheel adjustment for the wood backwards and forwards, as shown. Normally the depth is set to just over half way and the mortise is finished by turning the wood over and mortising from the other side.

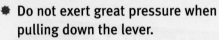

Safety
* Keep fingers away from the chisel.
* Do not exert great pressure when pulling down the lever.
* Eye protection should be worn.

Strip Heater

The strip heater is used to bend plastic sheets up to 12 mm thickness. The **tungsten** strip heats up very quickly. The plastic to be shaped is placed squarely over this and allowed to heat up. When the plastic appears to be softening. It is removed and bent on a former, or the edge of your bench if a ninety degree angle is required. Further information may be obtained in Chapter 12, Non-wood Materials: Plastics.

❋ Strip heater

Safety

* Do not touch the heater strip area when in use.
* Do not inhale the fumes of the heating plastic.

CNC Router

This machine is controlled by a computer. It is used to carve or rout intricate and stylish designs such as football club and family crests. A drawing is sent from the computer to the machine, which used a small router to carve out the design from the desired material. The teacher's assistance will be required to operate this machine.

 Pillar drill

* CNC router

Safety

* The work piece must be clamped in place.
* Eye protection must be worn and long hair/sleeves tied up.
* Ensure that the drill bit will not drill into the table before you use it.
* Ensure that the chuck key is removed before switching on.

Pillar Drill

The pillar drill is used to drill holes in larger depths of material and of greater diameter. The bit is held in the chuck and the depth is set using the gauge on the side of the drill. For ease of use, the table can be lowered and lifted using the release and wheel mechanism at the rear of the table.

Edge Bander

This machine is used to apply veneer to the edges of manufactured boards such as chipboard melamine. A heater with a fan blows hot air toward the joining area and the user pushes the edge of the wood against the veneer. A left-to-right motion at a slow pace allows the veneer to attach. Any protruding veneer can be removed with a sharp knife.

❋ Edge bander

Safety
* Do not touch hot surfaces.
* Allow to cool for fifteen minutes after use.

Hands-on Tasks

1 Search the Internet for photographs of common **power tools** and machines and make a collage of the ones that interest you.

2 Practise the safe installation and removal of different drill bits with the cordless drill.

3 Ask your teacher for a loose plug and practise fitting a three-core wire and changing a fuse. Do not plug into a socket.

4 Examine samples of different mouldings from the router in your MTW room and select the best three for use on the edge of a coffee table. State the reasons for your choice.

Homework Sheet on Power Tools and Machines

1   What does the **torque** facility on a drill allow the drill to do.

2   Describe how to connect wires to a plug correctly.

3   Name three safety precautions, which must be taken with an **orbital sander**.

4   Name two methods of dust collection from a hand-held **belt sander**.

5   What part of the drill holds a bit in place?

6   List three operations that a router can perform.

7   Why is the underside of a planer so dangerous when in use?

8   Outline the procedure for joining two lengths of wood with a **biscuit joiner**.

9   What safety equipment should you wear when using a **spray gun**?

10 What is used to set the depth on the **mortise machine**?

INTERNET LINKS AND TASKS

Making strong wood joints

http://www.mortiseandtenon.net/specialty_tools.html

Scroll saw operations

http://www.craftideas.info/html/scrollsaw.html

Parts of cordless drill

http://www.ultimatehandyman.co.uk/1cordlessdrill.htm

SEARCH

Sample Exam Questions on Power Tools and Machines

Ordinary Level — 2010

Name the power tool shown in the diagram.

NAME _____

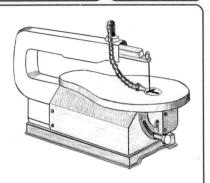

Ordinary Level — 2009

Name the power tool shown in the diagram.

NAME _____

Ordinary Level — 2008

Name the power tool shown in the diagram.

NAME _____

Ordinary Level — 2008

Name the power tool shown in the diagram.

NAME _____

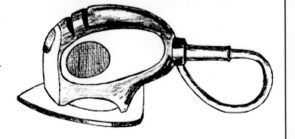

Ordinary Level **2007**

List **two** safety precautions that should be observed when using portable electric power tools.

1. _____

2. _____

Ordinary Level **2006**

Name the power tool shown in the diagram.

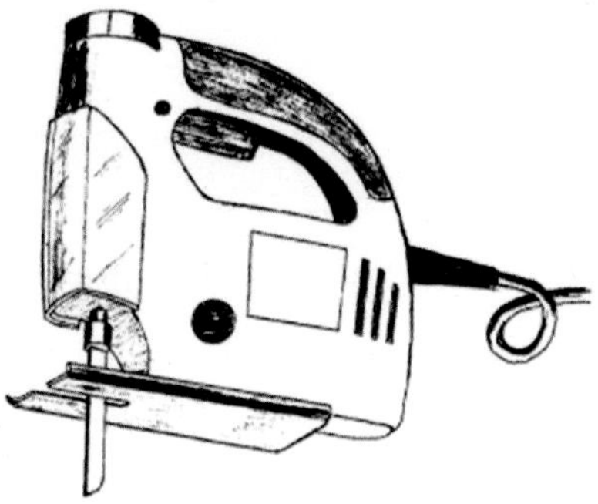

NAME _____

Ordinary Level **2005**

Name the power tool shown in the diagram.

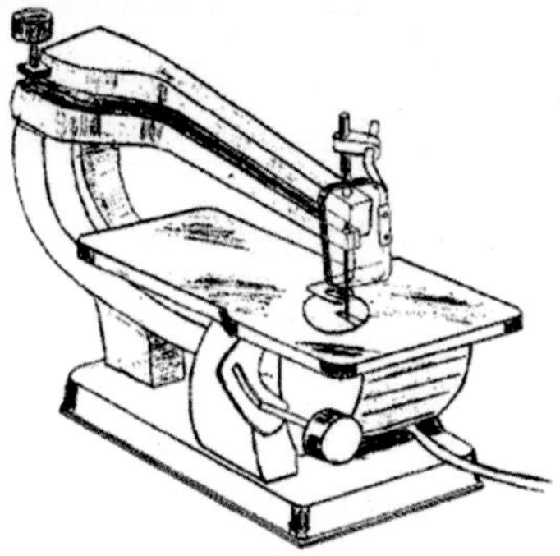

NAME _____

Ordinary Level **2004**

Give one **advantage** and one **disadvantage** of a cordless drill.

ADVANTAGE _____

DISADVANTAGE _____

The diagrams show three handheld power tools. State a specific safety precaution that should be observed when using each power tool.

Higher Level 2010

(i)   Name the power tool shown in the diagram.

ANSWER _____

(ii) For what purpose is this tool used?

ANSWER _____

_____

_____

_____

(i) State the correct name for the wood boring tools labelled **A**, **B** and **C**.

A 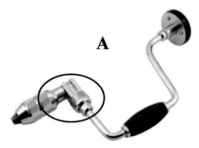 B  C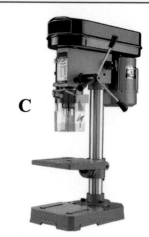

(ii) The diagram below shows a part of tool **A** enlarged. Name the part and describe how it functions.

(iii) The bit shown on the right is used with tool **A** to bore holes. Using notes and *neat freehand sketches*, describe the stages involved in boring such a hole **through** a piece of wood using this tool.

The diagram shows a machine controlled by a computer. State **TWO** advantages of controlling machines in this way.

1 _____

_____

2 _____

_____

Introduction to Woodwork Joints

Woodwork joints have been in use since the craft of woodwork began. They are the traditional method for joining two pieces of wood together. Joints are used in all forms of wood design from tables to chairs to toys. Joints are designed to give the maximum amount of strength to the joint with the minimum amount of material being removed.

Jointing will be a part of nearly every class you do for MTW and therefore it is important to understand how to select, make and join different joints together.

Joints are broken down into different families with each family of joints containing different variations to suit the joining task to hand. You may become competent enough over time to develop joints to suit your own needs.

Key Elements to Understand for Junior Certificate Course

* principles of joint design
* joint types and technique
    * butt and mitre
    * halving and housed and finger
    * bridle
    * mortise and tenon
    * dovetails
    * dowelling
* adhesives on joints (see Chapter 26, Adhesives and Clamping Wood)
* practice joints before final joints

* Sample woodwork joints

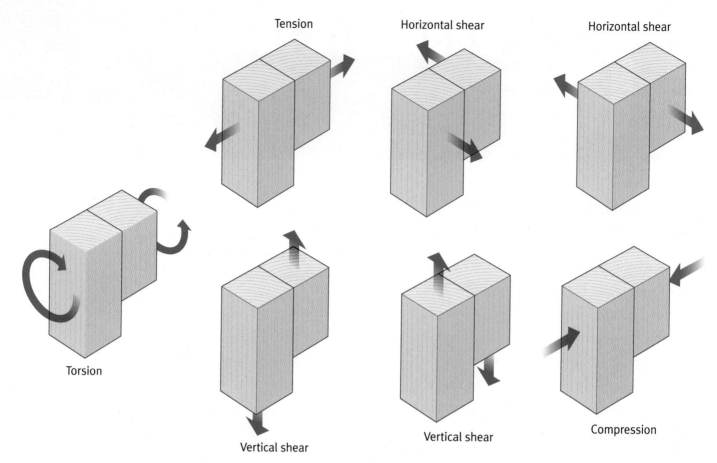

Tension   Horizontal shear   Horizontal shear

Torsion

Vertical shear   Vertical shear   Compression

✹ Forces acting on joints

Joint Design

Joints are designed to hold pieces of wood together, and resist the forces to which the joint will be subjected over time.

(See more detail in Chapter 14, Forces and Structures, Mechanisms and Material Properties)

Joints can be pulled apart under the following forces:

- ✹ tension
- ✹ compression
- ✹ torsion
- ✹ horizontal shear
- ✹ vertical shear

The joints you select for your project design must take these forces into account, and what pressures the joints be subjected to. There are a number of joints that will suit your needs – these are discussed below. To make your selection easier, each family of joints below contains a chart to show how effective those joints are under different forces.

Butt and Mitre

The quickest of the joints to produce but they have limited applications. The wood is simply glued together and to be effective they must have additional strengthening such as a dowel or biscuit inserted, as shown.

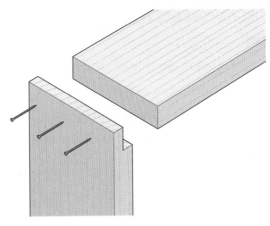

● Edge butt joint

Force \ Joint	Tension	Compression	Torsion	Horizontal Shear	Vertical Shear
Edge	✗	✓	✗	✗	✗

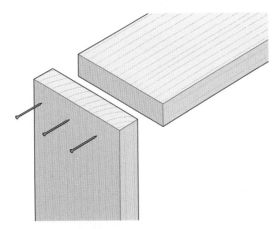

● Corner butt joint

Force \ Joint	Tension	Compression	Torsion	Horizontal Shear	Vertical Shear
Corner	✗	✓	✗	✗	✗

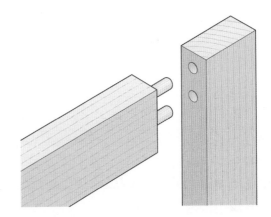

● Dowelled butt joint

Force \ Joint	Tension	Compression	Torsion	Horizontal Shear	Vertical Shear
Dowel	✗	✓	✓	✓	✓

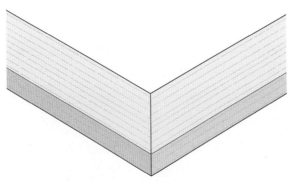

● Mitre butt joint

Force \ Joint	Tension	Compression	Torsion	Horizontal Shear	Vertical Shear
Mitre	✗	✓	✗	✗	✗

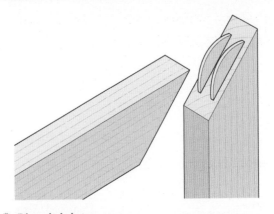

● Biscuit joint

Force \ Joint	Tension	Compression	Torsion	Horizontal Shear	Vertical Shear
Biscuit	✗	✓	✓	✓	✓

Halving, Housed and Finger Joints
Halving

Halving joints are capable of holding themselves together in certain applications. As the name suggests the joint is made by crossing over the two pieces of wood, and joining them by removing half of the material from one side and half from the other piece of wood (as shown). They must be glued together for added strength. Mostly used for small toys and projects.

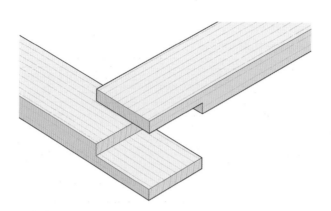

❋ Corner halving joint

Joint \ Force	Tension	Compression	Torsion	Horizontal Shear	Vertical Shear
Corner	✗	✓	✓	✗	✗

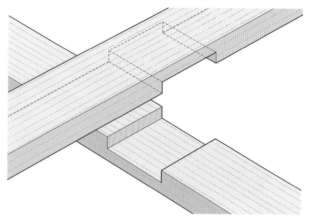

❋ Cross-halving joint

Joint \ Force	Tension	Compression	Torsion	Horizontal Shear	Vertical Shear
Cross	✗	✓	✓	✓	✗

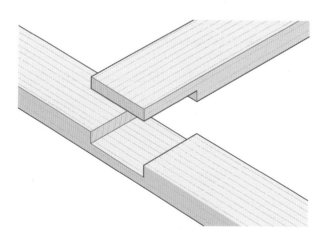

❋ Tee-halving joint

Joint \ Force	Tension	Compression	Torsion	Horizontal Shear	Vertical Shear
Tee	✗	✓	✓	✓	✗

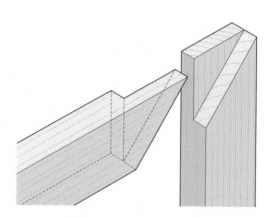

❋ Mitre halving joint

Joint \ Force	Tension	Compression	Torsion	Horizontal Shear	Vertical Shear
Mitre	✗	✓	✓	✗	✓

Housed

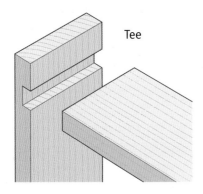

Tee

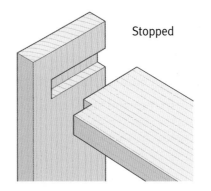

Stopped

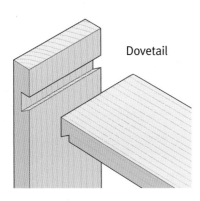

Dovetail

* Housing joints: tee, dovetail, stopped

Force\nJoint	Tension	Compression	Torsion	Horizontal Shear	Vertical Shear
Tee	✗	✓	✗	✗	✗

Force\nJoint	Tension	Compression	Torsion	Horizontal Shear	Vertical Shear
Dovetail	✗	✓	✗	✗	✓

Force\nJoint	Tension	Compression	Torsion	Horizontal Shear	Vertical Shear
Stopped	✓	✗	✗	✗	✓

Finger

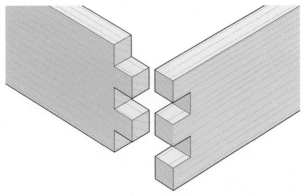

* Finger joint

Force\nJoint	Tension	Compression	Torsion	Horizontal Shear	Vertical Shear
Finger	✗	✓	✓	✗	✓

Bridle

The bridle joint involves the removal of one-third of the material from one piece and two-thirds of the material from the other to give more surface area in contact for a better joint. Mostly used for frames and small table legs.

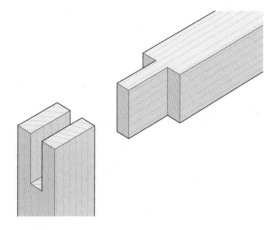

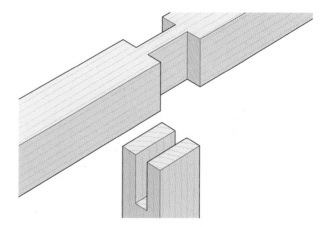

✹ Corner bridle joint

✹ Tee bridle joint

Force / Joint	Tension	Compression	Torsion	Horizontal Shear	Vertical Shear
Corner	✗	✓	✓	✗	✗

Force / Joint	Tension	Compression	Torsion	Horizontal Shear	Vertical Shear
Tee	✗	✓	✓	✓	✗

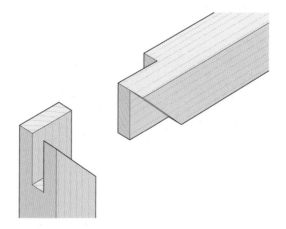

✹ Mitre bridle joint

Force / Joint	Tension	Compression	Torsion	Horizontal Shear	Vertical Shear
Mitre	✗	✓	✓	✗	✗

Mortise and Tenon

One of the strongest joints known is the **mortise** and **tenon** joint. A pin (tenon) is created in one piece of the material and this slots into the hole (mortise) of the other piece. Mostly used for the corners of tables and chairs.

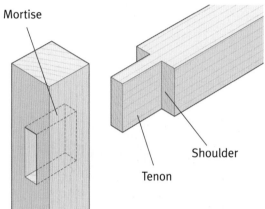

Mortise

Shoulder

Tenon

● Through mortise and tenon joint

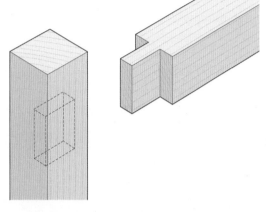

● Stopped mortise and tenon joint

Force / Joint	Tension	Compression	Torsion	Horizontal Shear	Vertical Shear
Through	✗	✓	✓	✓	✓

Force / Joint	Tension	Compression	Torsion	Horizontal Shear	Vertical Shear
Stopped	✗	✓	✓	✓	✓

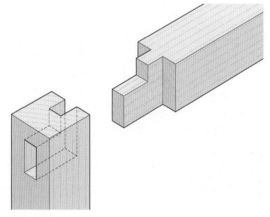

● Haunched mortise and tenon joint

Force / Joint	Tension	Compression	Torsion	Horizontal Shear	Vertical Shear
Haunched	✗	✓	✓	✓	✓

Dovetails

Dovetail joints are used to stop wood joints
from pulling apart, e.g. drawers. The angle of
the dovetail depends on the type of timber but
as a general rule a slope of 1:6 for **softwood**
and 1:8 for **hardwood** is acceptable. There is
a lot of work involved but the results are a
strong joint which has an attractive finish.
This is most often used in high-quality
cabinet-making.

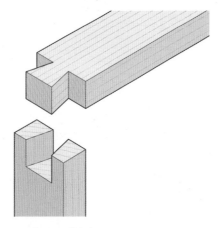

❋ Corner dovetail joint

Joint \ Force	Tension	Compression	Torsion	Horizontal Shear	Vertical Shear
Corner	✓	✓	✓	✓	✗

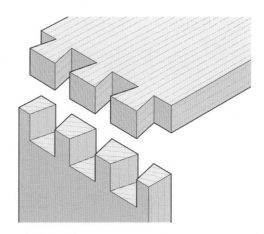

❋ Boxed dovetail joint

Joint \ Force	Tension	Compression	Torsion	Horizontal Shear	Vertical Shear
Boxed	✓	✓	✓	✓	✗

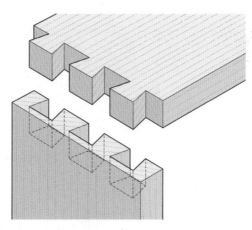

❋ Lapped dovetail joint

Joint \ Force	Tension	Compression	Torsion	Horizontal Shear	Vertical Shear
Lapped	✓	✓	✓	✓	✗

Dowelling

Round sections of timber are used to strengthen butt joints. Matching holes are drilled in opposite pieces of timber and a dowel inserted between them to give added strength. Mostly used in small tables and trophy bases.

Screwing

Screws are used to join wood quickly and can be used in almost any location as long as the head of the screw is covered where it is not required to be seen. (See Chapter 27, Fixtures and Fittings.)

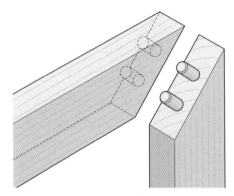

❋ Dowel joint

Force Joint	Tension	Compression	Torsion	Horizontal Shear	Vertical Shear
Dowel	✗	✓	✓	✗	✗

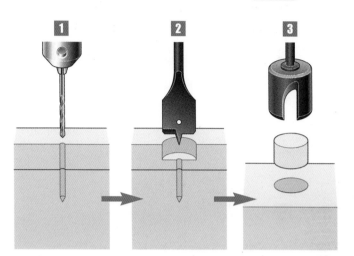

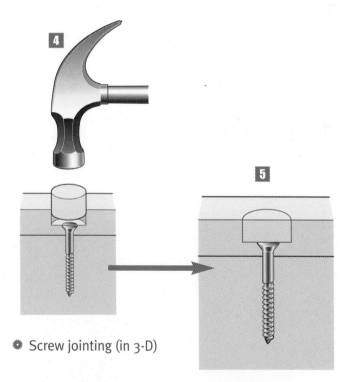

❋ Screw jointing (in 3-D)

Force Joint	Tension	Compression	Torsion	Horizontal Shear	Vertical Shear
Screw	✓	✓	✓	✓	✓

Where These Joints Can Be Used

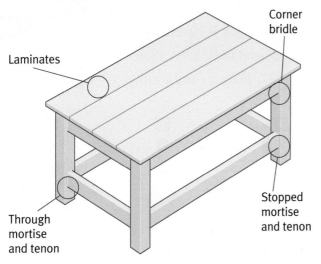

Laminates

Corner bridle

Through mortise and tenon

Stopped mortise and tenon

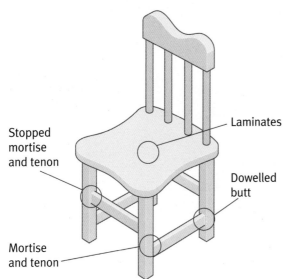

Stopped mortise and tenon

Laminates

Dowelled butt

Mortise and tenon

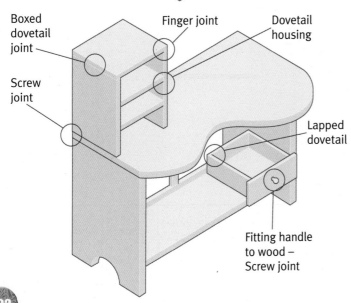

Boxed dovetail joint

Finger joint

Dovetail housing

Screw joint

Lapped dovetail

Fitting handle to wood – Screw joint

● Everyday use of common joints

Making Joints
Cross Halving
Marking Out

1. Mark face side and face edge on the wood.

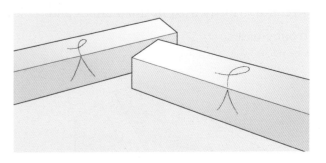

2. Mark 10 mm waste at both ends of the wood.

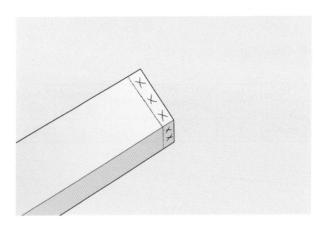

3. Draw line around the halfway point of the wood.

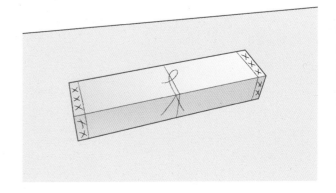

4a. Measure half the width of the wood out from the centre line and draw a line all around the wood with a Try square. Place the Try square on this line and mark the full width of the wood.

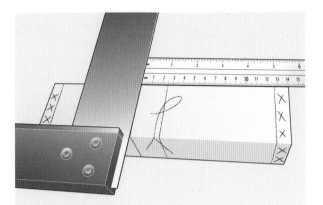

4b. Draw a line all around the wood remembering to use only the face side and edge to rest the Try square on.

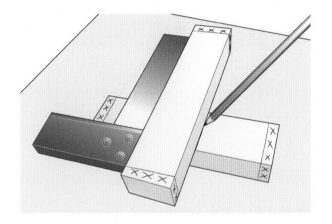

5. Set the marking gauge to half the depth of the wood and scribe lines between the maximum widths.

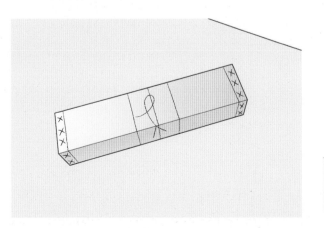

6. Mark the waste on the wood and scribe around the edges with a knife or chisel.

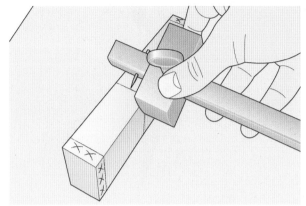

7. Repeat exactly for the other piece of wood.

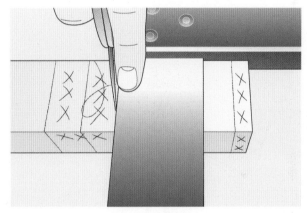

Processing

8. Cut the edges of the trench with a Tenon saw, staying inside the waste lines.

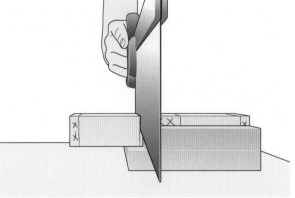

9. Add a third cut to ease the chiselling section.

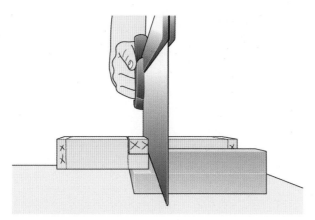

11. Repeat for the other piece of wood and fit together.

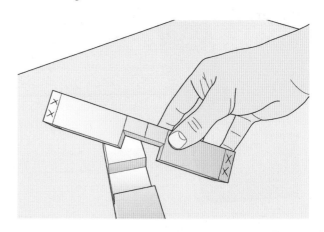

10. Chisel out the waste, working from both sides, and level the base of the joint with a rasp.

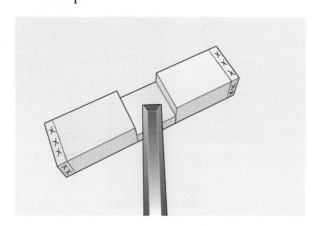

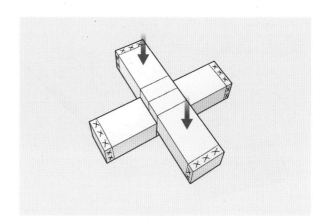

✹ Making a cross-halving joint

Corner Bridle

Part 1 – Male
Marking Out

1. Mark the face side and the face edge.

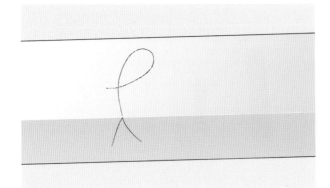

2. Mark a 10 mm waste line at the end and mark the width of the wood from the female piece.

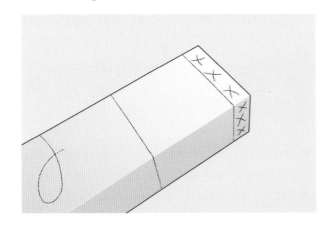

3. Draw lines all around using a Try square.

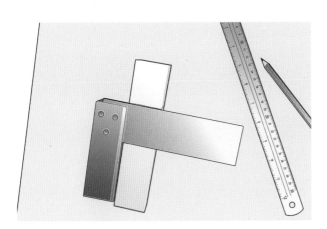

4. Set the mortise gauge to one-third the width of the wood between the pins and the stock.

5. Scribe a double line around the edges and the top of the wood.

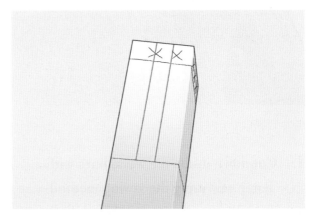

6. Mark the waste to the outside of these lines.

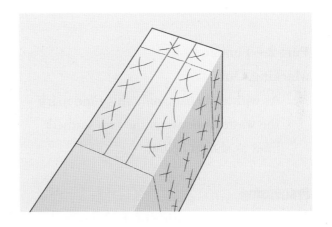

7. Scribe around the waste areas to be removed.

Processing

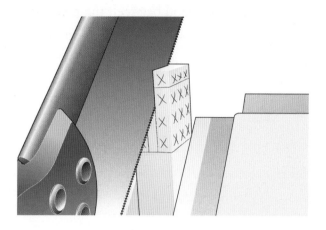

8. Cut down inside the waste lines with a Tenon saw using the sawing method described in Chapter 17, Hand Tools.

9. Remove the outside wood using a Tenon saw and a bench hook.

Part 2 – Female
Marking Out

10. As with male part, only this time mark the waste in between the two scribed lines as shown below.

Processing

11. Cut down the inside of the lines with a Tenon saw.

12. Remove waste with a Coping saw.

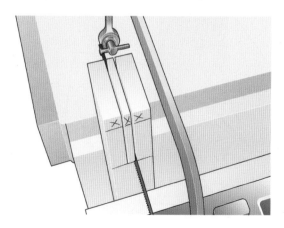

13. Square-off the bottom of the trench with a mortise chisel.

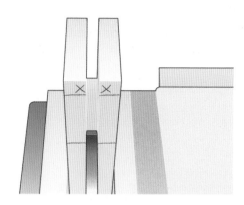

14. Fit two parts together, filing off sides of the female piece where needed.

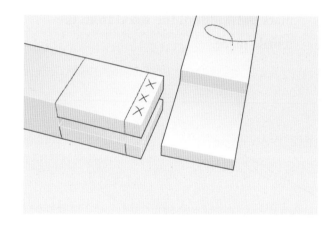

Stopped Mortise and Tenon

Part 1 – Male
Marking Out

1. Mark the face side and the edge on the wood.

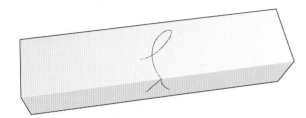

2. Mark 10 mm waste on the end of the wood and mark one-half of the width of the female piece from this.

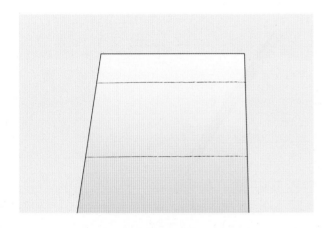

3. Draw lines around the wood.

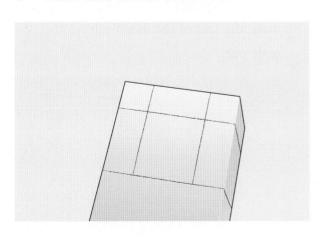

4. Mark the limit of the tenon by marking a line one-quarter of the width of the wood from the waste line and one-quarter of the width from the second width line.

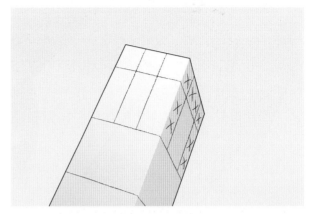

5. Set the marking gauge to one-third of the width of the wood and scribe between the limit lines.

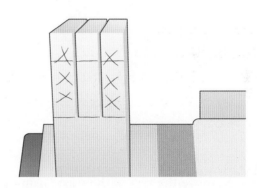

6. Scribe around the waste to be removed.

Processing

7. Saw down the outside of the waste lines as far as the second waste line.

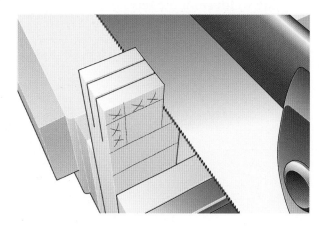

8. Saw down the side of the waste lines.

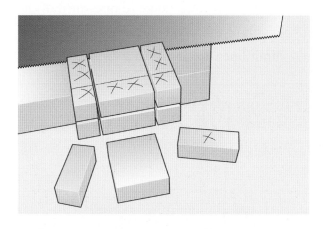

9. Remove the rest of the waste using a Tenon saw and the bench hook, as shown.

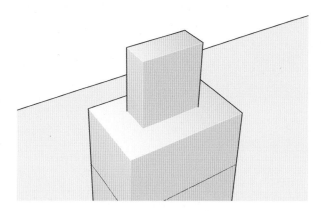

Part 2 – Female
Marking Out

1. Mark the face side, the edge and 10 mm waste on the end.

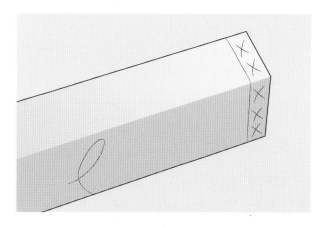

2. Mark the width of the male wood piece from the waste line.

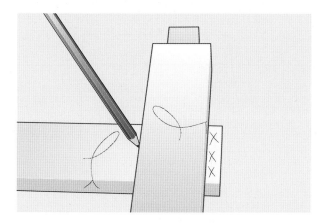

3. Hold the male pin to the female piece in line with the two lines drawn already and mark the size of the mortise from the male pin.

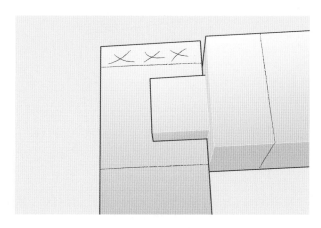

4. Carry the lines around with the Try square.

5. Using the same mortise gauge settings, mark the limits of the mortise.

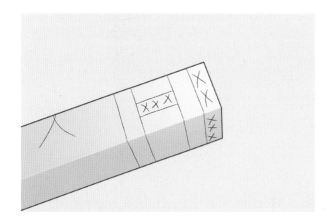

6. Scribe the top and bottom of the mortise to be removed.

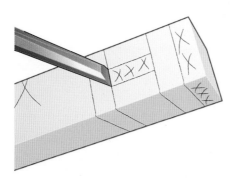

Processing

7. Chisel out the waste with a mortise chisel as described in Chapter 17, Hand Tools.

8. Check the depth of the mortise with a rule to ensure that it matches the width of the tenon.

9. Press the two parts together to form the joint.

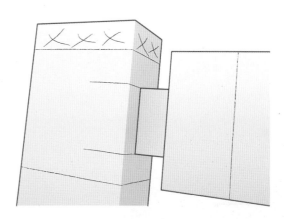

Note: Be sure to follow strict rules in relation to the face side and the edge. Use a mortise gauge against the face side on both pieces so that the joint ends up flush on both faces.

Through Dovetail

✸ Making a through dovetail joint

Part 1 – Male

Marking Out

1. Mark the face side and edge and 10 mm waste on the end of the male piece.

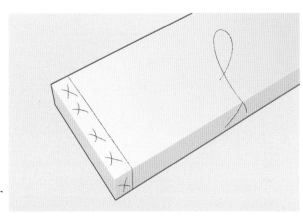

2. Mark the width of the female piece from the male waste line as shown. This is called the **baseline**.

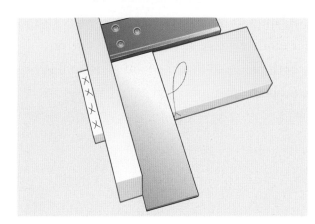

3. Divide the baseline into five equal spaces on both sides of the timber.

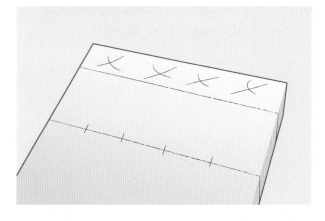

4. Measure out the required angle using either 1:6 or 1:8.

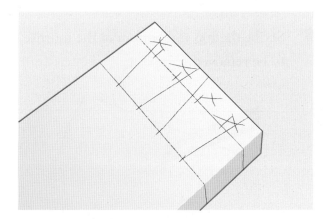

5. Repeat for the other side and transfer over the end grain.

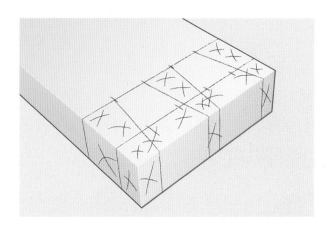

6. Scribe the waste areas to be removed.

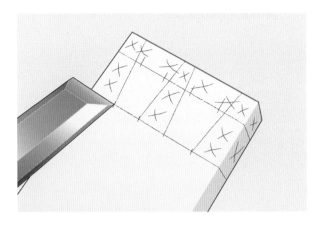

Processing

7. Place the wood in a vice with the lines to be cut in a vertical position as set out by the Try square, as shown.

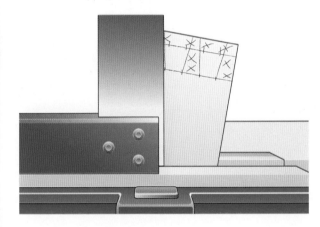

8. Saw down to the baseline with a Dovetail saw or a Tenon saw.

9. Remove the edge waste with a Tenon saw, remove the inside waste with a Coping saw, and finish with a mortise chisel.

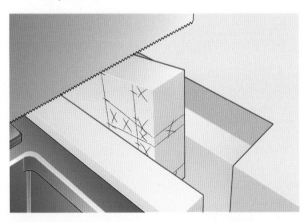

Part 2 – Female

Marking Out

10. Mark out face side and edge and 10 mm waste.

11. Align the male dovetail pins with the end grain of the female wood and trace the lines, as shown.

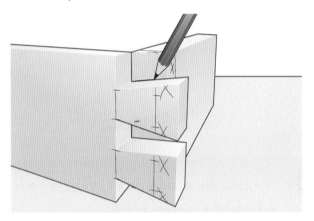

12. Carry the angle lines straight down the sides of the female piece, as shown.

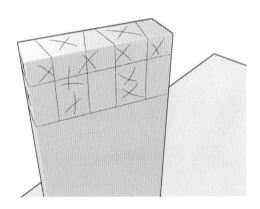

13. Mark and scribe the waste for the female piece.

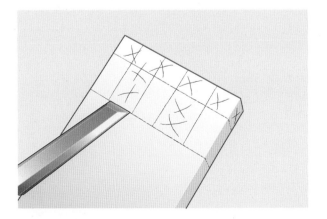

Processing

14. Saw down the waste side of the lines to the female base line.

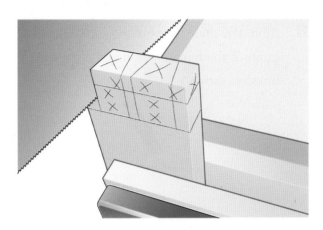

15. Remove the waste with a Coping saw and level with a mortise chisel.

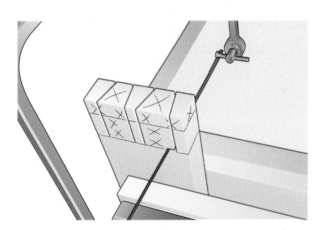

16. Fit to the male piece using a file or rasp where appropriate.

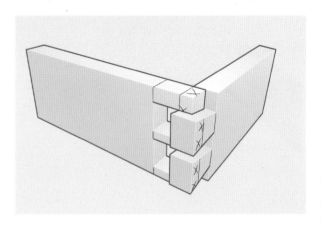

17. Finally saw off the waste from both pieces.

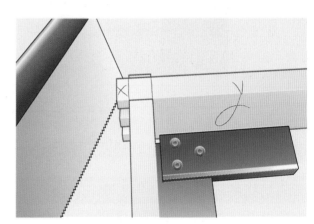

Dowel Joint

✹ Making a dowel joint

1. Mark the position of the dowels on one of the wood pieces.

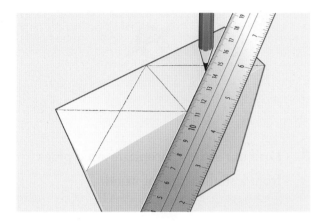

2. Drill out the correct size holes for the dowels.

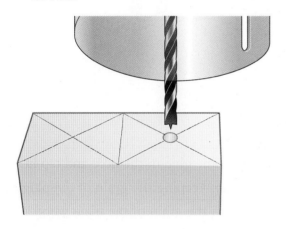

3. Use a simple dowelling jig (as shown) to locate the centre of the opposite dowel hole.

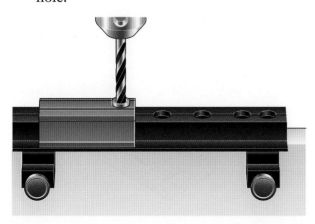

4. Drill the other dowel holes.

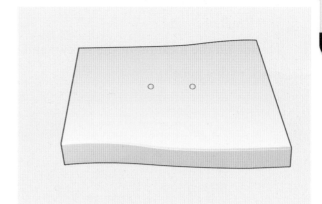

5. Place the glue in dowel holes in both pieces of wood and tap in the dowels.

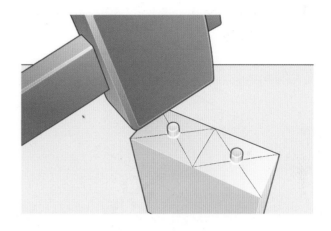

6. Clamp together.

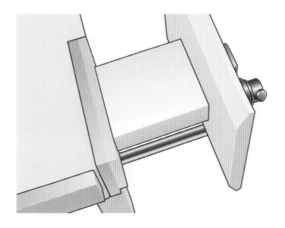

Screw Joint

❋ Making a screw joint

1. Decide on the location of the screws and mark with a pencil.

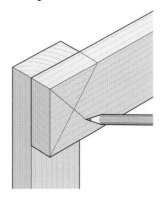

2. Drill pilot holes with a 2 mm or 3 mm bit.

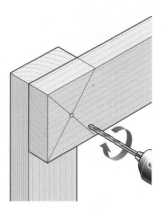

3. Drill counter-bore hole with a bit the same size as the head of the screw or a little bigger.

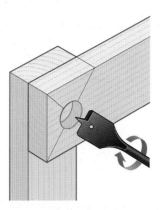

4. Screw the wood together with screwdriver.

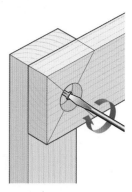

5. Drill out some appropriate sized plugs from a similar type of wood.

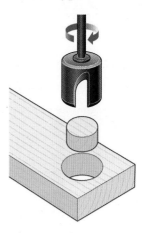

6. Place some glue in the hole and tap in the plug, keeping the grain of the plug in line with the grain of the main wood piece.

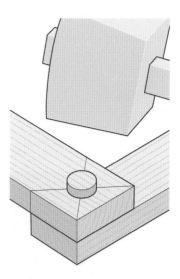

7. Pare off the protruding plug material with a chisel and sand finish.

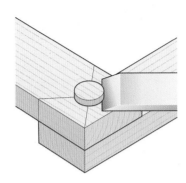

Joining Plastic and Metal to Wood

Plastic can be glued to wood with epoxy resin, but frequently the glue can be seen through the plastic and looks unsightly. An alternative is to drill holes and countersink them in the plastic (as shown) and to screw the plastic onto the wood.

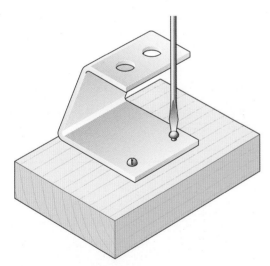

 Joining plastic to wood

Metal can be joined in the same manner as plastic either by glue or by screwing.

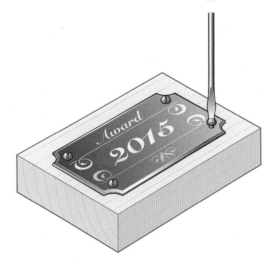

 Joining metal to wood

Hands-on Tasks

1 Take a look at the furniture in your school and identify the areas where pure wood joints have been utilised to hold the objects together.

2 If time allows in class, prepare test joints for your designs and test the joint under the different forces listed above.

3 Practise drilling pilot holes, screwing in screws and covering screws with plugs. (See Chapter 27, Fixtures and Fittings, for help with screws.)

4 Practise constructing all the joints in this chapter. Use scrap wood (44 mm × 18 mm or 44 mm × 30 mm) to reduce your carbon footprint.

Homework Sheet on Woodwork Joints

1 Name the joints in the diagrams below.

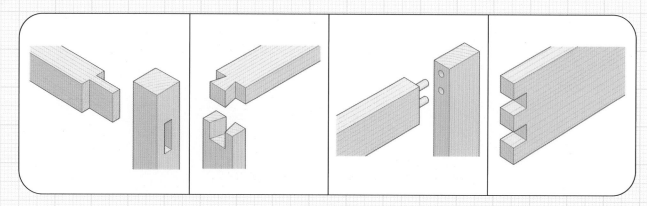

2 Draw a joint suitable for use in the areas circled below.

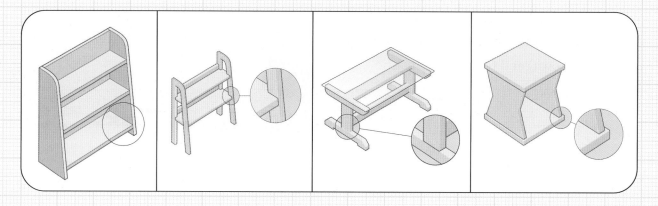

3 Complete the missing lines in the joint drawings below.

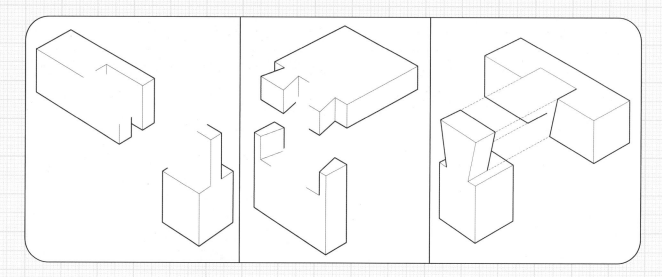

INTERNET LINKS AND TASKS

Making Joints

http://www.dixieline.com/woodjoint/woodjoints.htm

Video on Wood Joints

http://www.ehow.com/video_4993813_different-wood-joints.html

Making Dovetail Joints

http://www.am-wood.com/joints/dove2.html

SEARCH

Sample Exam Questions on Woodwork Joints

Ordinary Level — 2010

Name the joint shown.

NAME _____

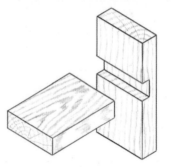

Ordinary Level — 2010

Complete the marking out of the waste on the **Finger Joint** shown.

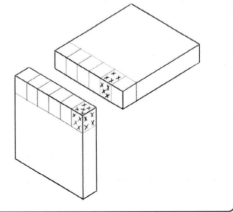

217

The diagram shows a piece of wood with a
face edge mark.
Show the **face side** mark in its proper
place on the sketch.

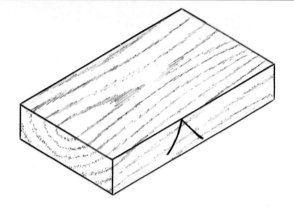

Name the joint shown.

NAME _____

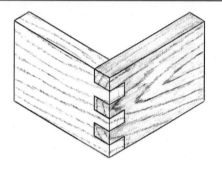

Complete the marking out of the **Mortice and Tenon** joint shown.

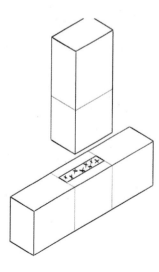

Ordinary Level 2009

The diagram shows a plant stand. The flowerpots sit into the circular holes which are 120mm in diameter.

(i) Describe, using notes and sketches, a suitable method of **jointing** the top **A** to the side **B**.

(ii) Using notes and sketches describe how the two large holes could be cut out and shaped to a smooth finish.

(iii) Name **one** of the tools used to shape the holes. Make a neat sketch of this tool.

Ordinary Level 2008

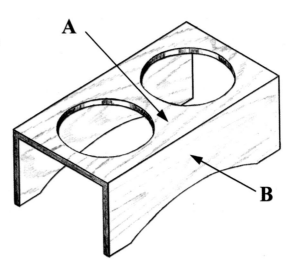

Name the joint shown.

NAME ______________________________

Ordinary Level 2008

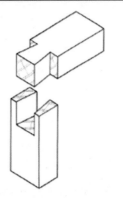

Complete the diagram of the bridle joint shown.

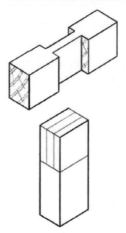

Ordinary Level | **2009**

Complete the diagram of the cross-halving joint shown.

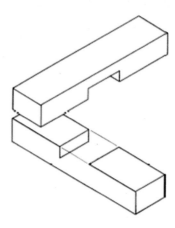

Higher Level | **2009**

The edge of a piece of timber is finished with a common moulding as shown.
Name the moulding.

NAME _____

Higher Level | **2009**

The diagram shows an unfinished 3D sketch.

(i)   Apply grain and shading to the sketch so that it resembles a piece of wood.

(ii) On the sketch, show the face side and face edge using the appropriate symbols.

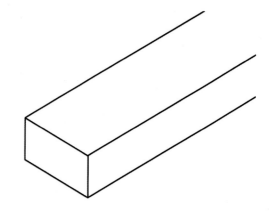

A bookshelf unit is shown below.

In the space provided sketch a suitable means of joining shelf **A** to side **B**.

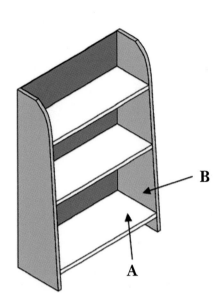

The diagram shows an incomplete exploded isometric sketch of a **bridle joint**.

Complete the sketch of the joint.

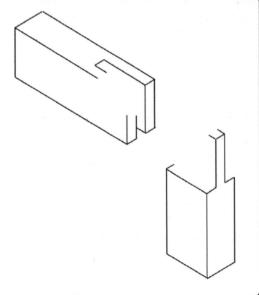

The elevation, plan and end view of a **tee-halving joint** are shown.

Make a 3-D sketch of the **tee-halving joint** on the given axes.

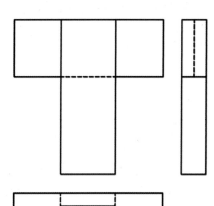

The diagram shows an incomplete exploded isometric sketch of a box dovetail joint.

Complete the sketch of the joint.

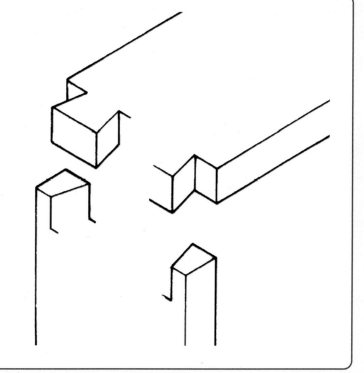

Introduction to Woodturning

Woodturning is the art of changing wooden **blanks** from common trees into spindles, bowls, cups and other interesting pieces.

❋ Wooden bowl

The earliest record of woodturning can be found in the hieroglyphics in Egyptian tombs around the third century BC. The Romans were skilled woodturners even with the crude equipment they possessed. Throughout the Middle Ages wooden tableware such as cups were in abundance. The famous inventor Leonardo da Vinci invented his own woodwork **turning** machine around the year 1500. Some of the first practical **lathes**, as they came to be known, appeared around 1850.

Early Pole Lathe

Using a **pole lathe** reduces the amount of electrical energy used in woodturning. This was a simple machine using foot power to turn the wood into the cutting edge of the chisel.

❋ Wooden baluster

❋ Early pole lathe

The Modern Lathe

This was developed during the Industrial Revolution at the end of the 1800s. This use of greater power allowed faster speeds and as a result more work was produced to a higher standard. Today's lathes can have computers attached to create identical designs and unusual designs. These are called **CNC lathes**.

❋ Modern CNC lathe

❋ Modern lathe

Key Elements to Understand for Junior Certificate Course

❋ using the lathe
❋ chisels
❋ wood selection
❋ techniques
❋ templates and designs
❋ finishing

1. Using the Modern Woodwork Lathe

The diagram below is an example of a woodwork lathe in the modern MTW room. This example is freestanding but it may also

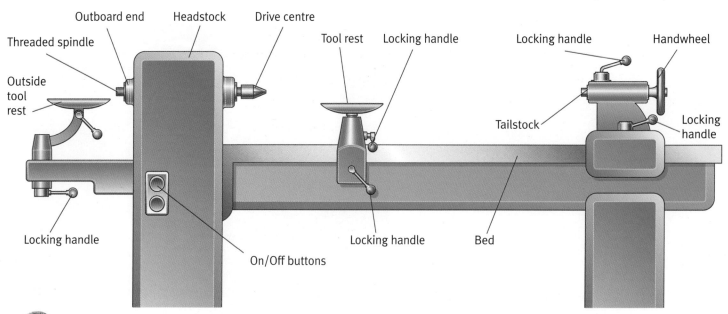

❋ Parts of the modern lathe

be placed on a side bench and bolted to the
table. Ideally the lathe should be bolted to the
floor to reduce vibration. The lathes comprise
many different parts and the
knowledge of each part will enhance
the enjoyment and skill of the
operator.

An deil

The main components of the lathe are
described in the following text.

Headstock — *Ceann Stoc*

This contains the motor, gearing, and drive
centres or face plates. The motor is connected
to the pulley gears and many speeds can be
obtained simply by changing the various belts.
The diagram shows both the maximum and
minimum speeds achieved by alternating the
belts on the motor and spindle shafts. The
ON/OFF switch is also located at the
headstock.

❋ Headstock

Tool Rest *tá cai* *Gabhach*

This is for resting gouges when in use. This
must be locked in place before use by
activating the lever underneath.

❋ Tool rest/banjo

Bed — *tábla*

Holds all the components in the correct
location. All parts are bolted to the bed. It is
normally made from steel which should be
greased regularly to ensure smooth operation.

❋ Lathe bed

Tailstock — *Cúl stoc*

Holds the various centres at the opposite end
of the lathe – it must also be locked before
use. It contains a locking wheel which is used
to tighten the wood on the lathe. This is then
also locked in place.

❋ Tailstock

Stand

This raises the lathe to the correct operational height. It should be bolted to the floor.

Auxiliary Components

The main rotating component is the **drive centre**. This is attached to the gears in the headstock and must be greased after each use. It grips the wood and its rotation (in an anticlockwise movement) turns the wood.

> **Safety**
> Do not allow loose clothing to catch in the rotating **drive centre**.

Pláta aghaidh

A <u>faceplate</u> may be attached to the headstock as an alternative for turning bowls and plates.

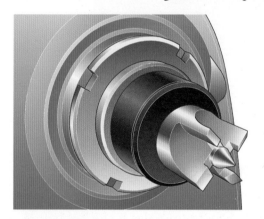

⬥ Drive centre

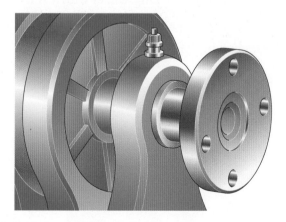

⬥ Faceplate

At the other end of the lathe in the tailstock is found the dead, live or hollow centres. These are used to allow the wood to turn freely. The hollow version allows holes to be drilled in the centre of the wood. Failure to lubricate the end of a dead centre will lead to burning of the wood.

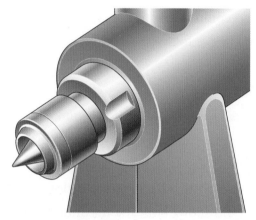

⬥ Dead centre

2. Chisels
Tools for Woodturning

A gouge is used to remove wood, thus creating the desired shape. The parts of the gouge are the **handle**, **ferrule** and **blade**.

⬥ Different woodturning chisels

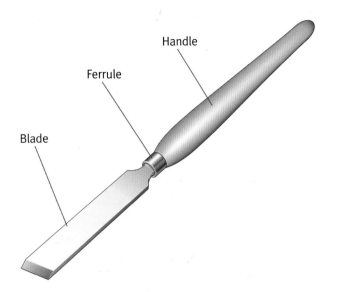

Handle

Ferrule

Blade

❋ Parts of a woodturning chisel

A sample set of gouges (chisels) used for woodturning is shown in the photos above. Each one has a different function and produces a different design on the wood. Each chisel has a different shape or profile. Gouges are made from **high speed steel** (HSS) and include the **roughing gouge** (for rounding square wood), the **skew chisel** (for smooth finishing), the **spindle gouge** (for grooving and contouring), the **parting** tools (for beading and parting off), the **scrapers** (for cleaning inside bowls) and the **bowl gouges** (for turning bowls and vessels).

Safety
Be careful not to cut your finger at the sharp end of the gouge. ⚠

3. Materials for Turning

Wood pieces for turning are known as **blanks**. Pine can be used for practising but due to the large grain sizes it is difficult to get a good finish. Other suitable materials include Purpleheart, Oak, Ash, Beech, Maple, Sycamore, Walnut and Lime.

❋ Wood sample blanks

4. Techniques in Turning

Safety
Follow the following rules: ⚠
* Wear a face visor.
* Remove all jewellery.
* Tie up long hair.
* Wear a suitable safety apron.
* Wear a dust mask during sanding and finishing.
* Ensure the wood is securely held in the lathe.
* Check the clearance of the wood in relation to the tool rest before turning on the lathe.
* Use the correct technique for each chisel or gouge.

Spindle Turning – Centre to Centre

Spindle turning, as its name suggests, refers to rounding wood in thin sections relative to its length. Chair legs, lamps, stair balusters and rounders bats are some of the items one can make this way. Following the sequence of charts below one can set out the wood in preparation for the turning.

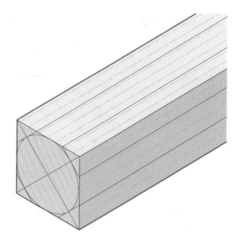

● Steps in preparing wood for lathe

1. An **X** is marked on the ends of the wood.

4. Using a plane, the wood is pared down to reduce the workload on the gouges at the lathe.

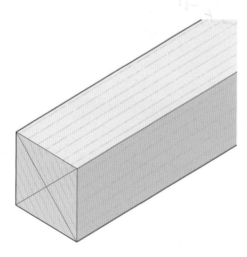

2. The maximum size circle is then drawn from this **X** to the edge of the timber.

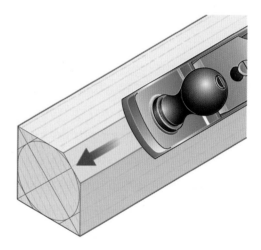

5. The drive centre is then hammered into the wood and locked into position with the tailstock.

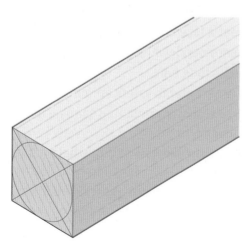

3. An octagon is then drawn and extended down the timber sides using a marking gauge or thumb gauge.

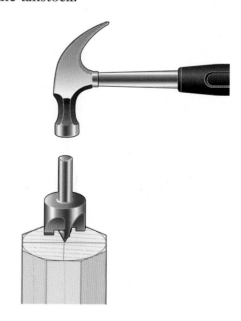

6. The toolrest is positioned at the wood. The wood is hand spun to check that the turning wood will not catch the banjo of the tool rest.

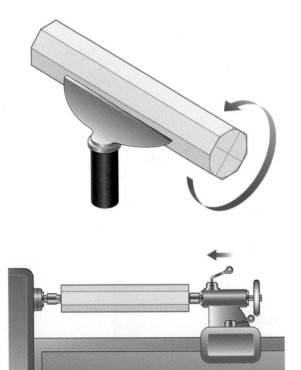

7. The roughing gouge is used to round down the wood and callipers (or outside callipers) used to check that the desired diameter has been achieved.

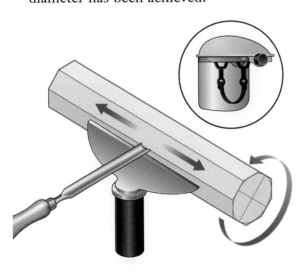

8. From here the wood can be levelled out using the scrapers. Remember with the gouges to keep the handle lower than the wood (as in the diagram). Also, keep the blade angled to the wood for a more accurate cut.

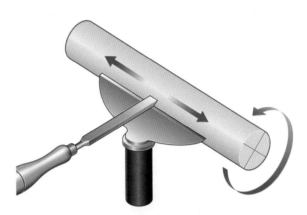

9. Callipers (as shown in the diagrams and photos) ensure that the correct diameters are achieved in the turning.

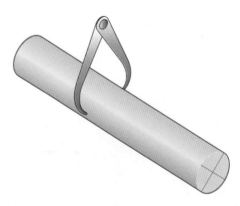

10. Beads or grooves can then be formed using the other gouges. Remember to work the gouges downhill (as in diagram) and never uphill. A description of how to create beading is shown below.

Beads   **Grooves**

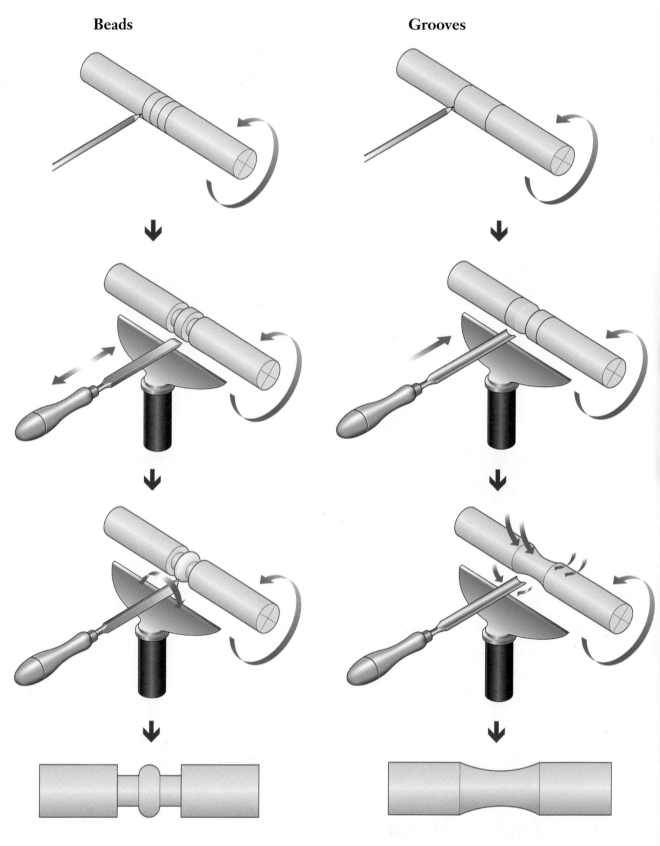

🌼 Turning beads and grooves

For further advice on spindle turning, look at www.diynetwork.com

Face Plate Turning

This can be used to create bowls and cups etc. Only one centre is used, as in the diagrams below. The wood blank is prepared in a similar manner to spindle turning but is attached to a faceplate using screws. The tool rest is moved into location at the front of the blank and scrapers are used to remove the inside material. Gouges can be used to shape the external face of the bowl. For extra thin bowls and cups, a light can be placed inside the bowl to help in judging the thickness of the walls – this is for more advanced woodturners. Chucks can also be used to hold the wood blank as in the photo below. The jaws firmly hold the wood blank in place.

Hole Boring

When making a lamp it is possible to create a void in the centre of the wood using the long-hole boring kit supplied with the modern lathe. The boring shaft enters the wood from the tailstock end (as in diagram below) and the rotating motion drills out the centre. It is normal to go half way in and then to turn the wood around to work the other end.

Keep the parings and waste from this hole-boring process and use them later on in the **sanding process**.

❋ Long hole boring kit

❋ Person facer turning

❋ Woodturning jaws

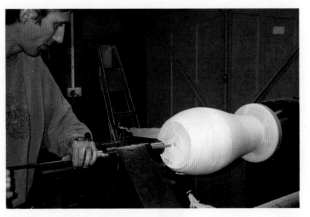

❋ Long hole boring operations

5. Templates, Profiles and Patterns

The shape for any turned piece of wood can be designed beforehand and used to get the correct shape at the lathe. One method is to cut out a profile in a piece of plywood and to hold it up to the piece of wood on the lathe intermittently.

> Keep all templates safe for future use and to reduce wasted material.

This allows one to retain a copy of an acceptable design in cheaper wood before applying it to the more expensive wood used

● Copier lathe

on the lathe. A more advanced lathe, the copier lathe, allows the woodturner to precisely copy a master design profile. Many identical copies can be obtained from the master profile. To create different colour patterns in a turned piece such as a lamp, different species of timber may be laminated (glued) together as in the diagram below, and then the spindle or the face turned to give interesting patterns. The glued piece must be

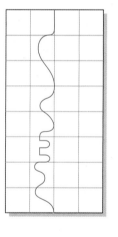

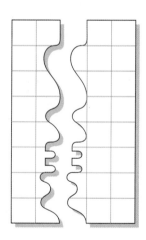

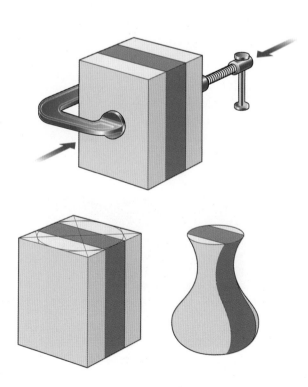

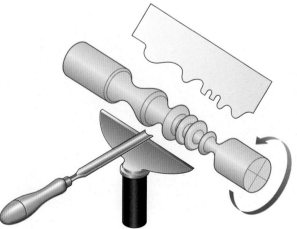

● Profile for turning

● Turning laminates

allowed to cure (dry) for at least a day to ensure that the new blank is very strong and can survive the turning process.

6. Sanding and Finishing on the Lathe

Sanding of the work happens whilst the wood is still on the lathe and, for many, this is the most enjoyable part of the process. Just like sanding normal wood pieces, start with a coarse paper, then medium, then wet and dry paper – finally some 000 wool to finish. Some turners like to use old shavings to get a final smooth finish but this may cause burns to the hand if it comes in contact with the revolving surface. Bending the paper to the shape of each feature in the turned piece gives a better

finish, such as in the sanding of the coving shown below.

❋ Sanding covings

The finish is also applied whilst the piece is on the lathe. Suitable finishes which may be applied with a brush or linen cloth include Danish oil, satin varnish, stains, lacquer and beeswax.

Safety
A dust mask and a visor should both be worn, even at this stage.

Safety
A face mask must be worn throughout the application of any finish.

❋ Finishes suitable for turning

Hands-on Tasks

1 Research Internet sites to find more interesting facts about the history of woodturning.

2 Make a neat rendered sketch of the woodwork lathe in your classroom.

3 Locate images of auxiliary components on the Internet and glue them into your copy.

4 Make a small poster showing the end points of each chisel for the lathe in your classroom.

5 Make A4 safety information signs to be located near the lathe in your classroom.

6 Mark a 44 mm × 44 mm × 200 mm pine timber length for use on the spindle lathe and turn the piece as described in the chapter.

7 Mark and cut out a template 200 mm × 22 mm from 3 mm ply using the Scroll saw on your spindle. Create your design using the lathe in the classroom.

8 Sand and apply the finish to your turned spindle.

Homework Sheet on Woodturning

Label the different parts of the lathe.

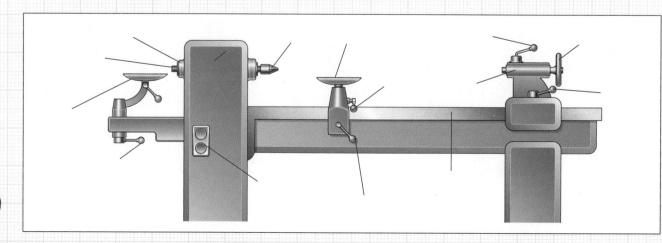

② Name the gouges in the profiles below.

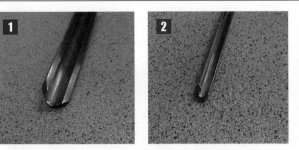   

③ Using the Internet, print three pictures of spindled turnings, and three pictures of faceplate turnings, then attach the pictures here.

④ Describe how you would prepare the blank piece of wood for turning into a candle, on the lathe.

⑤ Create a safety poster to be placed beside the lathe in your classroom. Include five safety tips on the poster.

⑥ Design a profile for the leg of a chair on the following template.

Sample Projects for Students to Try

Practice piece basics

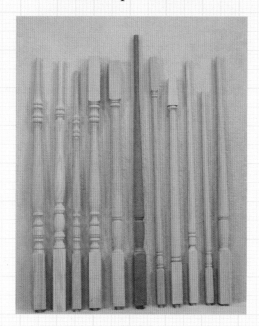

Candleholder

Baseball bats

Lamp

Bowl

INTERNET LINKS AND TASKS

Visit the following or similar websites for more facts in relation to woodturning.

The History and the Art of Woodturning

http://www.britishwoodturners.co.uk/

Samples of Woodturning

http://www.woodturninggallery.net/

Irish Woodturning Company

http://www.spunwood.ie/

SEARCH

Sample Exam Questions on Woodturning

Ordinary Level — 2010

From the list given, name the lathe parts shown at **A** and **B**.

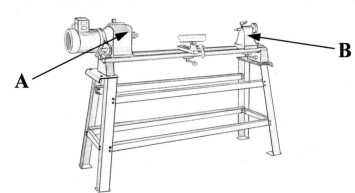

Toolrest
Headstock
Tailstock
Bed
Faceplate

A ______________________________

B ______________________________

Ordinary Level 2010

The diagram shows a wooden handle which has been turned on a lathe.
The handle is to be used for a garden trowel.

(i) Name **one** turning **tool** that would be used to make this piece.
Make a neat sketch of this turning tool.

(ii) You wish to make several handles similar to the one shown in the diagram.
With the aid of notes and sketches, describe **one** method that could be used to make sure that all the handles are the same size and shape as the first one.

(iii) List **three** specific safety precautions that should be followed when using a lathe.

Ordinary Level 2009

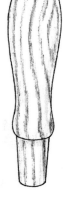

From the list given, name the lathe turning tools shown at **A** and **B**.

A

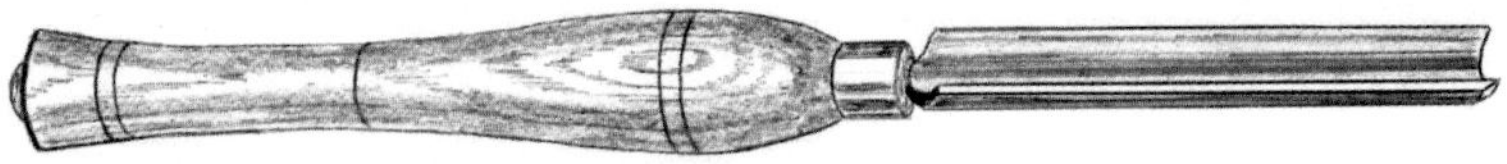

B

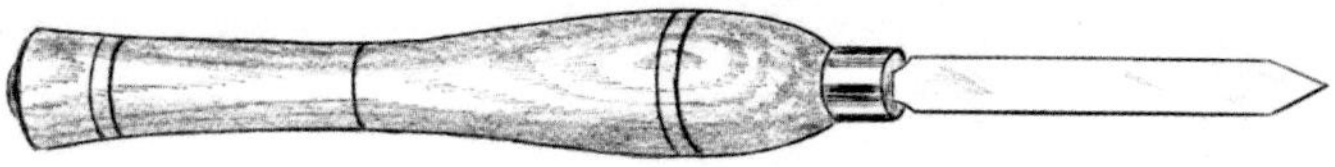

Parting tool
Square-end scraper
Skew chisel
Roughing gouge
Round scraper

A ______________________

B ______________________

Ordinary Level 2009

The diagram shows a snooker cue which has been turned on a lathe.
The cue is made in two halves with a screw-thread joint.

(i) Explain why it is easier to make the cue in two halves rather than in one full length.

(ii) Suggest a suitable applied finish for the cue.
Give **two** reasons for your choice.
Explain, in detail, how this finish would be applied.

(iii) List **three** specific safety precautions that should be followed when using a lathe.

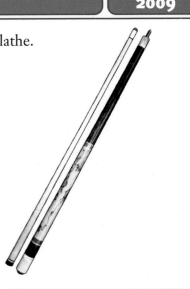

Shown are two pieces of equipment associated with woodturning.

(i)   Name the two pieces of equipment.

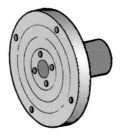

_____   _____

(ii) State **ONE** safety precaution that should be observed when using the woodturning lathe.

PRECAUTION _____

The diagram shows a woodturning lathe.

(i)   Name the parts of the lathe labelled **A**, **B** and **C** and briefly describe the function of **each** part.

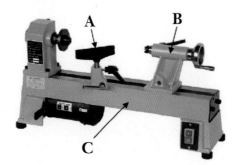

A   _____

B   _____

C   _____

(ii) The diagram shows a table lamp turned from wood. Describe, in detail, and with the aid of notes and **neat freehand sketches**, how a hole could be formed in the body of the lamp to accommodate the electric cable.

(iii) The lamp has a maximum diameter of 150 mm. Which of the following speeds would be the most appropriate for turning the lamp, **100 rpm, 400 rpm** or **1,000 rpm**?

(iv) State **three** specific safety precautions that should be observed when turning wood on a lathe.

The diagram shows the leg of a stool which has been turned on a lathe.

(i) With the aid of notes and **neat freehand sketches**, describe **one** method that could be used to make another leg identical to the one shown.

(ii) Select **two** specific woods which are suitable for turning and give **two** reasons for your selection.

(iii) With the aid of notes describe how a square piece of wood should be **(a) prepared**, and **(b) mounted** for turning on a lathe.

When turning a large bowl of wood on the lathe, should the lathe speed be set at **fast** or **slow**?

ANSWER _____

The diagram shows a baseball bat which has been turned on a lathe. The bat is to be made from the piece of wood shown at **A**.

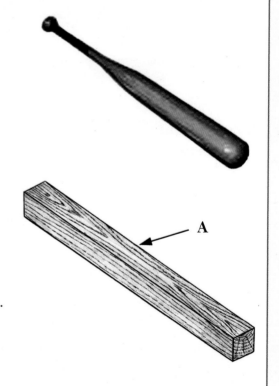

(i) Describe, using notes and sketches, **three** steps that should be taken to prepare the wood for mounting on the lathe.

(ii) Name one turning tool that would be used to turn this piece. Make a neat diagram of this tool.

(iii) List **two** safety rules that should be observed when using the lathe.

Introduction to Embellishments and Ornamentation

It will frequently be desirable to add some character to any final woodwork design to enhance its function and aesthetic qualities. Any design in wood can be embellished using the techniques listed below. While it is not necessary to use all the techniques, practising one or two before designing larger projects, will assist you in creating a masterpiece.

Wood carving goes back to when humans began making tools for hunting, to shelter areas such as caves, and to the tombs of ancient kings and queens. Carvings of spiritual leaders are essential to many religions of the ancient and modern world, such as in the picture opposite.

Many of the first carvings were in the form of **hieroglyphics**, carved initially in the Stone Age inside caves and later by woodcarvings. The woodcarvings have not survived the test of time as the stone carvings have – it is rare to find woodcarvings from before 1100 AD. The dry climate of Egypt has allowed many

🌑 Wood carvings

🌑 Totem pole

carvings to survive in that region, and examples of 6,000-year-old woodcarvings can be viewed in museums.

Woodcarving reached its peak between the twelfth and the fifteenth centuries where many religious carvings were created and are still intact today. In the Renaissance period most carvings were applied to house furniture and to the exterior of homes. In more recent times, Australian Aboriginal and Native American carving was very common and many examples can be seen on **didgeridoos** and **totem poles**.

Key Elements to Understand for Junior Certificate Course

* carving and carving tools
* chip carving
* relief carving
* wood sculpture

Carving and Carving Tools

Carving wood involves the removal of material from the main wood piece, to create a pattern, shape or likeness in the wood. This is mostly achieved by the use of carving gouges used by hand or with the help of a mallet.

Carving Equipment

In the materials technology room, knives and gouges are the main tools used to remove material to form the finished article. Gouges are the chisels, and they have different shaped points (ends) to achieve different results. Only by practice can one fully see the use of each gouge.

Knives: Used to pare wood into simple shapes such as a 3-D finish.

Firmer Gouge: Used for rough work such as waves on water.

Paring Gouge: Used for grooving material as in relief carving pictures.

Fish Tail Chisel: Used for carving grooves in hard-to-reach places such as 3-D carvings.

V Gouge: Used for carving small shapes such as bird feathers and lettering.

Veiner Gouge No. 11 Sweep: Used for writing on wood, e.g. such as your name or the title of the piece.

Carver's Mallet: Round in shape to reduce the depth of cuts and to give more control of the gouges.

Surforms: Metal tools used for rough paring of wood. They may be flat or rounded for different effects.

Files: Rough files used to create texture on sculptured pieces.

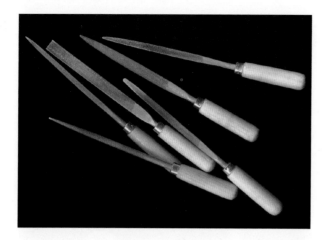

Holdfast: Used to secure the wood to the bench when chiselling.

Carver's Vice: Used in 3-D carving.

Engraver: Electric tool used to carve large pieces or to engrave small detail.

Sharpening of Gouge Chisels

Before taking any gouge to a piece of material, it is vital to have it sharpened correctly. The chisel should reach you in good condition from your teacher. If there are any nicks at the tip of the blade, have it ground by your teacher and then you can hone it using techniques described in the Chapter 17, Hand Tools.

For the gouges, a slipstone may be used (as in the diagram) to achieve a very sharp edge, following initial sharpening on an oilstone. Be careful to remove any burring, as it will affect your work. Removal of the burr can be done with a piece of leather. Continue to check your gouge to maintain its sharpness and this will lead to safer and better carving.

For the slipstone simply rub the chisel back and forth until happy with the sharpness.

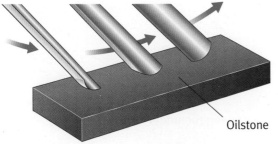

Oilstone

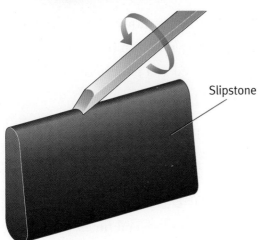

Slipstone

❋ Sharpening gouges for carving

Carving Techniques
Whittling

A simplified form of carving where a rough piece of wood is carved using a penknife to form shapes.

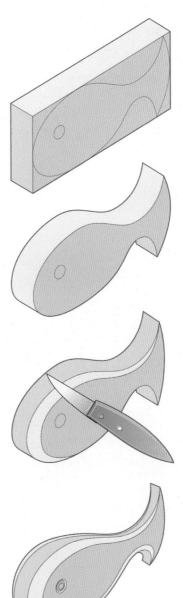

❋ Whittling technique

Safety
In general, one always carves away from the body for safety reasons.

Incised Carving

This is a simple form of **relief carving** whereby the shape drawn on the wood is notched around the edges as shown. It gives the appearance of the drawing standing out slightly from the background. This is useful for simple designs such as lettering and simple pictures and is mostly achieved with the use of a V Chisel or Gouge.

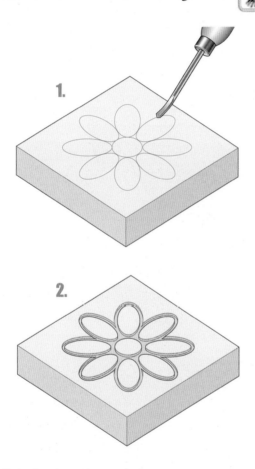

● Incised carving technique

Chip Carving

Chip carving is one of the easiest forms of carving and involves the removal of mostly geometric shapes such as diamonds, triangles and circular patterns. A soft touch with one's hands is required to achieve an even design.

The simplest form is a triangle lowered to one side, see diagram above. This is achieved with

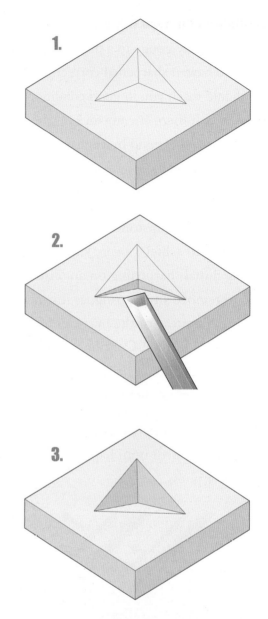

● Chip carving technique

a flat chisel used as shown. This results in simple patterns as shown below. For example, this may be used as a pattern on the border of a picture frame.

A more complicated design requires the woodworker to drop the centre of an equilateral triangle (as shown) using the V gouge and flay chisel to get the required effect. When used several times, interesting patterns can be achieved (as shown). This more elaborate carving method can be used for bordering on mirror backgrounds.

Relief Carving

One of the most popular carving techniques. The woodworker lays out a picture or design on the material, then the material around the

design is removed to allow the design to appear raised.

The method involves using carbon paper to transfer the design to the wood. After this, any one of the curved gouges (e.g. V Gouge) can be used to pare the wood away from the design to the outside, as shown. It is always easier to work with the grain of the wood or at an angle to it, but not across, depending on the wood used. Grounding is important to ensure that the final carving is clearly what it was intended to be. This method can be used to create landscape or portraits of any topic. Again, experimentation and practise with the various gouges and tools will help one find the desired effect.

Carving in the Round (3-D)

A most enjoyable form of carving requiring as much preparation as skill to achieve a good result. Any real life form such as a head, hand or animal can be created with skill and imagination.

The image of the object from the front and from the side must be at the same scale and transferred to the wood. Blank as shown. The bandsaw is used to cut right around the front view (as shown). Following this, the waste is reattached to the blank with masking tape and recut on the bandsaw. The result is a rough outline of the finished carving. The rough sculpture is held in a carver's vice which can be manipulated to make the carving easier. From here the carver uses skill and many different gouges to achieve the final 3-D sculpture. This technique is mostly used to create trophies (awards) and statues.

1.

2.

3.

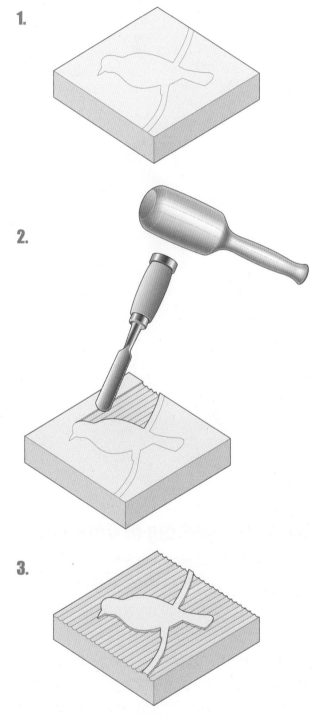

❋ Relief carving technique

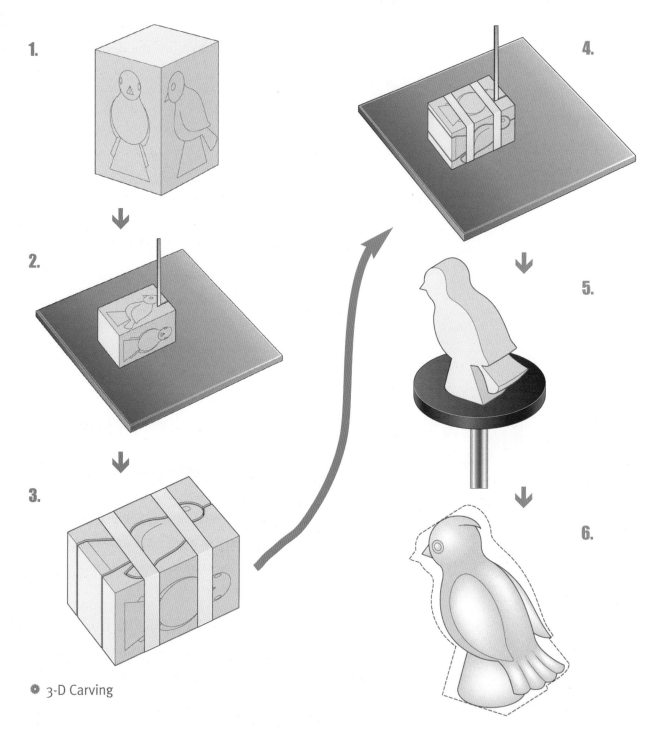

1.

2.

3.

4.

5.

6.

⚙ 3-D Carving

Materials Suitable for Carving

Lime is a hardwood and is very easy to carve.
Oak, **Chestnut**, **Walnut**, **Mahogany** and
Teak are also very easy to carve with. For
very fine work, **Apple**, **Pear** and **Plum** wood
is very easy to use. Carvings in **pine** are fine
as long as very sharp tools are used and if the
finished product is to be painted.

Applied Finishing of Carvings

Carvings left unfinished can look very good
but they are susceptible to the normal damage
expected with untreated timber. Whether a
high-gloss varnish is applied or a low-sheen
finish is chosen, the choice is up to the carver.
In general, low-sheen finishes such as
beeswax, Danish oil, satin varnish and
sanding sealer give the best effect.

Hands-on Tasks

1   Research the Internet to discover more about the history of **wood carving** in Ireland.

2   Make neat 3-D sketches, in colour, of the various gouge points and their resulting effect on the wood after carving.

3   Practise honing gouges using the slipstone and ask your teacher's opinion on the quality of your work.

4   Using a small piece of wood, try carving a small fish or other animal using a penknife.

5   Using a 300 mm × 300 mm piece of **Lime** or **MDF** carve any image using **incised** carving techniques.

6   Using a 300 mm × 300 mm piece of **Lime** or **MDF** carve any image using **chip** carving techniques.

7   Using a 300 mm × 300 mm piece of **Lime** or **MDF** carve any image using **relief** carving techniques.

8   Using a 200 mm × 200 mm × 400 mm blank of **Lime** or **MDF**, try carving either a **hand**, a **head** or an **Owl** using sculpture techniques.

9   Apply any three applied finishes to your various carvings (above) and evaluate each for appearance after drying out is complete. Make notes on your findings.

Homework Sheet on Carving

1   Write a short history of woodcarving including two sketches of carving designs from different parts of the world.

2   In your opinion, would it be better to carve the design below with incised or relief carving format.

3 Suggest a suitable applied finish for the carving below which will be glued to the side of a post box on the entrance wall of a house. Give a reason for your answer.

4 Describe, using sketches, how one could transfer the design below onto a piece of Lime for a relief carving.

5 On a piece of A4 paper (copier paper), draw a design for a relief carving to be applied to a piece of Chestnut, for an award to be presented to a county football player of your choice.

Sample Projects for Students to Try

Fish – Using whittling technique

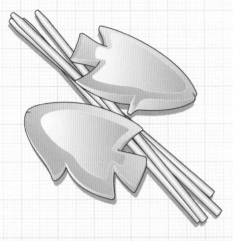

Clock – Using relief carving

Flower – Using incised carving technique

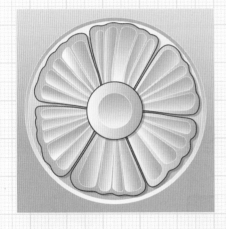

Rabbit – Using 3-D sculpture carving

Jewellery box – Using chip carving

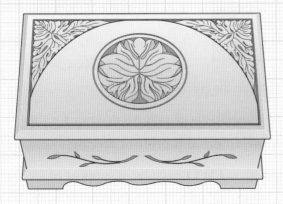

INTERNET LINKS AND TASKS

Visit the following (or similar) websites for more facts in relation to the history of carving and carving designs.

How to carve

www.canucarve.com/howto.php

Patterns for wood carving

www.carvingpatterns.com

Wood carving in Ireland

www.woodcarvingireland.ie

Examples of wood carving

www.thesculpturestudio.com

SEARCH

Sample Exam Question on Carving

Higher Level | **2010**

The diagrams show three carving methods

A

B

C

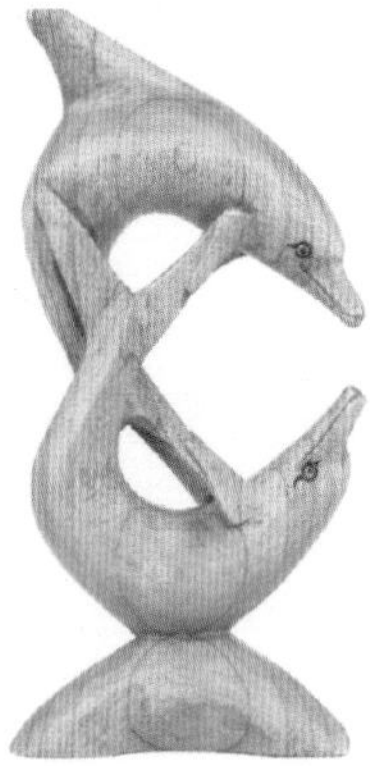

(i) Name the **THREE** methods of carving shown in the diagrams.

(ii) With the aid of notes and *neat freehand sketches* describe how you would transfer the design from a sheet of paper onto the wooden panel in piece **B** prior to carving.

(iii) Select an appropriate clear finish for piece **C** and give **TWO** reasons in support of your choice.

(iv) Describe, in detail, how you would apply your chosen finish.

Test Yourself

eTest.ie

Introduction to Veneering

Wood veneering dates back to the Egyptians around 3000 BC. Wood was scarce so they used veneers to cover less expensive woods. Examples of early veneering were present on artefacts found in King Tutankhamen's tomb in 1922. Veneering was at its strongest during the Renaissance, especially in Italy. This soon spread to the British Isles. Most veneers were hand cut until the Industrial Revolution, at which time a veneer-cutting machine (similar to today's splicers) was invented. In recent times, veneering is still extensively used in Italy and many shops in the towns still sell veneered pictures.

Key Elements to Understand for Junior Certificate Course
● obtaining veneers
● applying veneers
● inlayers (wood and other materials)
● marquetry (geometric and pictorial)
● fretwork and moulding

Veneering

Veneering is a method of taking thin slices of a more expensive wood and gluing them onto cheap manufactured boards. This achieves many objectives.

1. Larger boards can be created than could be obtained from the original tree.
2. Patterns can be formed with various veneer colours.
3. It saves the more expensive timbers.

Veneers are cut in special factories and then shipped around the world. The logs with the straightest bores (trunks) are selected because they leave the least waste. The logs are immersed in warm water to soften the fibre in the wood (just like steaming wood for lamination). The logs are lifted onto a roller

● Veneered table

and rotated against a lateral moving blade, as shown. This blade is resharpened after each log has been shaved down.

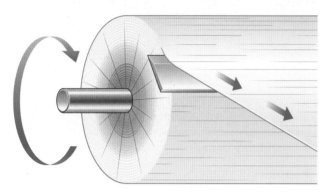

🔅 Making veneers from logs

The patterns obtained from the tree depend on the quality of the tree, location of removed branches and any other defects on the timber. Some defects such as burring can give attractive patterns, as shown.

🔅 Burred veneer

Veneers must be applied on both sides of larger timber backgrounds (groundwork) because the board can bend as the veneers dry out. To counteract this, a second cheaper veneer is applied to the back.

Veneers can be applied in the MTW room using a veneer press or similar mechanism. PVA glue is applied to the groundwork (backing timber) and the veneers pressed on by hand and rolled out using a veneer hammer (or wallpaper roller), as shown. A more expensive version of veneer is a pre-glued veneer and this can be applied without any pressing.

Cutting veneers is a great skill in itself. Cutting along the grain is easy and can be done with a scalpel and ruler. Cutting across the grain requires the veneer to be held down firmly under a piece of MDF and a heavy steel rule used against the cut line. Up to eight strokes of the knife will be required to cut the veneer.

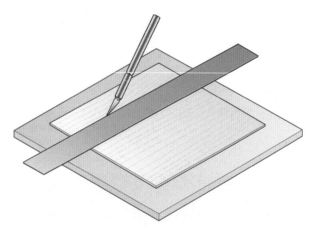

🔅 Cutting veneers along the grain

Safety
Never take any risks while cutting veneers. Gentle action of the blade will get there in the end.
Keep hands away from the cutting edge of the scalpel.

Patterns with Veneers

You can use the grain pattern of the veneers to embellish your designs. For doors of a cabinet, the veneers should be aligned (as shown below) to give a more aesthetic appearance.

❋ Selection of borders for inlay

Inlaying is a process involving the removal of the groundwork to accommodate the insertion of a material to create a border or effect. The inlay can be made from veneer, solid wood, glass, ceramics or metals. All are glued in with epoxy resins for a strong bond.

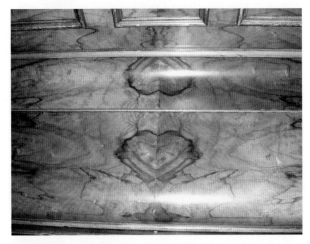

❋ Split veneering on a piano lid

Other patterns can be created through experimentation (as shown across) and you can also experiment with the colour of the veneers. Try to get a neat symmetrical pattern.

Inlays and Borders

To enhance the design with veneers, a border can be created in a couple of ways. For a simple border, a one-inch piece of veneer is glued onto the edge of the groundwork. The angles on the corners are marked and cut with the use of a sliding bevel set to forty-five degrees.

This border can be oriented in a different pattern by aligning the grain in different directions.

❋ Inlay with border design

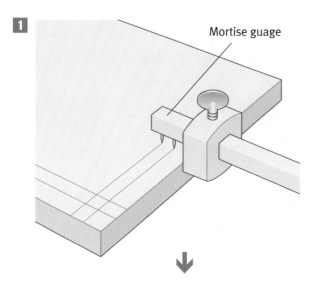

Mortise guage

⚙ Using a cabinet scraper to even surface

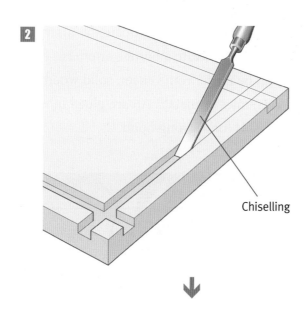

Chiselling

A mortise gauge is used (as shown) to scribe the required track. Using a chisel, turned on its back, the material is removed slowly to the required depth. The depth can be checked by drawing a line on the reverse of the chisel at the correct depth and placing this in the trench to check the depth, as shown. The strip of inlay material is then glued into place, pressed for a few hours, levelled with a Cabinet scraper and sanded to a smooth finish.

More decorative inlays may be purchased online or in specialist shops. The outline of these inlays is drawn on the wood and the material removed, as above. The inlay must be pressed for a number of hours after gluing to ensure a good bond.

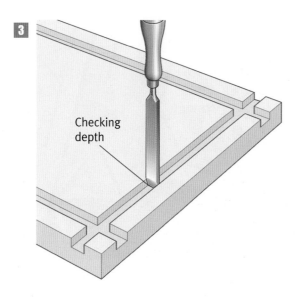

Checking depth

⚙ How to inlay a border

Marquetry
Pictorial

Marquetry is the art of creating a picture using two or more colours of veneer. This is a specialised art form in many countries and it is easy to achieve a good result in the MTW room. Almost any picture can be created, but for a beginner it is best to keep the pattern simple by using only three veneer colours.

Method

1. Select the picture to use in the marquetry exercise and make a photocopy.

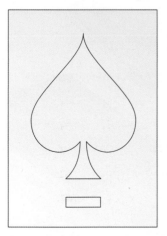

2. Cut the wood to the same size as the picture.

3. Cut three different veneers to the same size as the wood background.

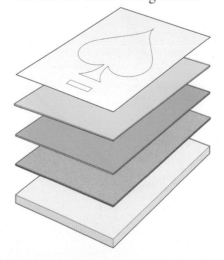

4. Cut out the carbon paper to the same size as the veneers.

5. Place the picture on top of the carbon paper, then place these on top of the first veneer. Tape the three together at the top, as shown.

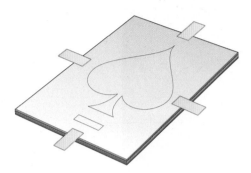

6. Trace the picture outlines onto veneer number one.

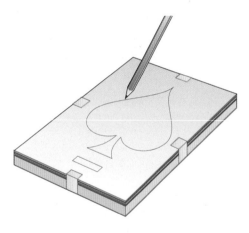

7. Repeat for the other two sheets of veneer.

8. Cut out the lines on the three veneers very carefully to create three different colour veneers for each segment of the picture.

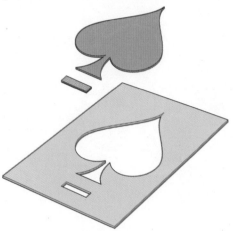

9. Select veneers from the three colours to create one picture.

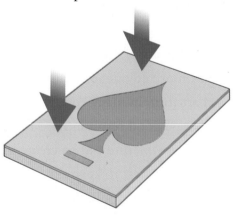

10. Glue and press into place or preferably use adhesive-backed veneers for an instant result.

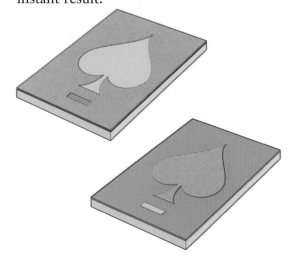

11. Two more copies of the image can be created using the remaining veneer pieces.

12. If you cannot get the veneers to match perfectly, use a wood burner to mark in between the veneers. Some do this anyway because the result can be excellent.

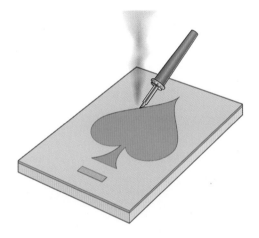

Geometric

Geometric marquetry is known as **parquetry**. This is a method of applying veneers to form linear and technical patterns. Examples of this can be seen in expensive furniture and expensive floors.

* The most common use of this skill is in the creation of chessboards for table tops.
* The secret of accurate parquetry is to draw out the pattern using **technical graphics** techniques.

To Create a Chessboard

1. Cut strips of equal width veneer in two colours (five of one shade and four of the other).

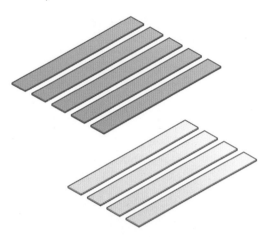

2. Secure all strips together using rows of masking tape on the reverse side to form a page.

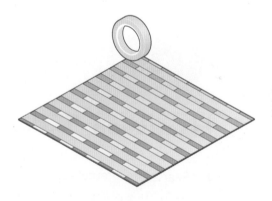

3. Use a steel bar and knife to cut the page into strips the same width as in point 1 above.

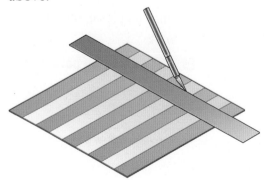

4. Align the strips to form the chessboard pattern, then stick it onto the background material.

5. Finish the edge of the board with moulding for a decorative finish.

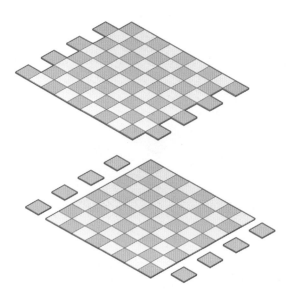

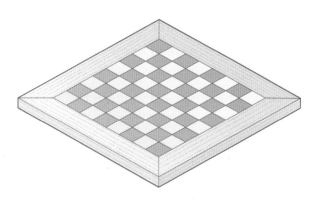

Hands-on Tasks

1 Search the Internet for images of Italian veneered products and print off results to create a collage for the classroom.

2 Make a poster showing the manufacture of **veneers** from logs.

3 Find pictures of **burred veneer** furniture and make a collage of the results.

4 Practise cross-cutting offcuts of veneer in preparation for more detailed work.

5 Find samples of **marquetry** from the Internet and save these for use in future work.

6 Find samples of **parquetry** from the Internet and save these for use in future work.

Homework Sheet on Veneering

1 How far back can the history of veneering be traced?

2 What are the advantages of using veneers?

3 Name an appropriate glue for sticking veneers to groundworks.

4 Make a sketch to show how veneers should be matched for doors.

5 Make a sketch showing two different borders which can be made from inlaying.

6 What is **marquetry**?

7 What is **parquetry**?

INTERNET LINKS AND TASKS

Visit the following (or similar) websites for facts in relation to veneering.

Applying glue to veneers

http://www.thewoodbox.com/data/veneers/woodveneerglueb.htm

Tips on veneering

http://www.joewoodworker.com/veneering/why-use-veneer.htm

 SEARCH

Sample Exam Questions on Veneering

Ordinary Level — 2006

The diagram shows a picture made using veneers applied to an MDF base board.

(i) Using notes and diagrams describe, in detail, how veneers are cut from logs.

(ii) The picture is to be placed on a desk. Using notes and sketches design a suitable support.

(iii) Explain how using veneers saves on the use of rare and expensive timbers.

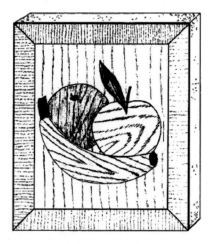

Ordinary Level — 2003

The diagram shows a low table with a veneered top which includes a chess/draughts board.

(i) Using notes and neat freehand sketches describe how veneers are cut from logs.

(ii) Recommend a suitable adhesive for veneering. Give **two** reasons for your choice.

(iii) Name a suitable material for:
  (a) the table top
  (b) the dark squares on the chessboard
  (c) the light squares on the chessboard.

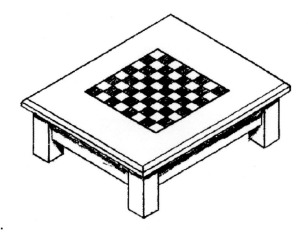

Ordinary Level — 2001

Name the thin sheets of wood on this decorative panel.

NAME _____

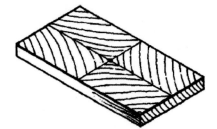

Higher Level 2009

The diagram shows a veneered jewellery box.

(i) With the aid of notes and ***neat freehand sketches***, describe how to mark out **and** cut the veneers for the top.

(ii) Describe, in detail, how the finished veneers would be applied to the top of the jewellery box.

(iii) Name three types of adhesive that could be used to apply the veneers.

(iv) Explain, with the aid of notes and a ***neat freehand sketch***, what is meant by **rotary cutting** in the manufacture of veneers.

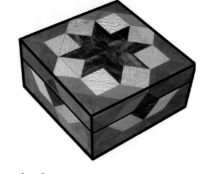

Higher Level 2008

The diagram shows a selection of wood veneers for use on a marquetry panel.

(i) Suggest the most suitable adhesive for gluing the veneers to the panel.

ADHESIVE ______________________________

(ii) Give a reason for your choice.

REASON ______________________________

____

Higher Level 2007

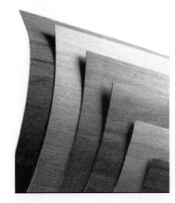

(i) The diagram shows a log being peeled to produce a continuous thin layer of wood. What is the layer called?

NAME ______________________________

(ii) What can this layer be used for?

ANSWER ______________________________

____

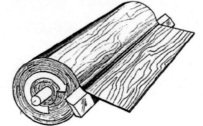

CHAPTER 23

Laminating and Bending Wood

Introduction to Laminating and Bending Wood

It may be necessary from time to time to make larger wood projects. Large pieces of timber are difficult to acquire and manage and are often very expensive. It is possible to glue smaller sections of wood together in the MTW room to solve this problem. The process of gluing small boards together is known as **lamination**.

Some woodwork applications require the wood to take on a curved shape, e.g. a wooden decorative wheelbarrow or roof joists. This can be achieved either by simple or elaborate means. Bending wood gives the designer many more options with regard to the shape and form of the final artefact.

❀ Curved arms on wheelbarrow

❀ Laminated roof beam

Key Elements to Understand for Junior Certificate Course

- ❀ reasons for lamination and bending
- ❀ laminating techniques
- ❀ making and using jigs
- ❀ choice of materials
- ❀ choice of glues
- ❀ bending techniques
- ❀ finishing bent and laminated elements

Laminating in the MTW Room

The easiest way to laminate and shape wood in the MTW room is to use thin (3 mm) strips of the timber you wish to use. These strips will have to be cut to thickness by your teacher on the circular saw. Hardwoods may require a 2 mm thickness to prevent snapping during the laminating process.

✷ Cutting laminates on saw

Making Formers

Formers are wooden shapes against which the laminate strips are pressed while the glue between the laminate strips is curing.

1. The shape of the former is determined in the design stage of the project. Formers are normally made from a sheet material such as MDF, and can be reused time and time again.

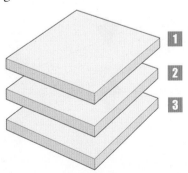

2. The sheets are bolted or glued together and the curve profile is drawn on the surface.

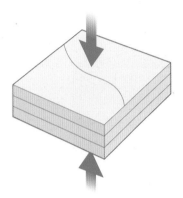

3. The bandsaw is used to cut the profile which is then sanded on the bobbin sander or finished using scrapers and spokeshaves.

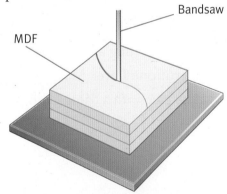

Bandsaw

MDF

4. The laminates are then placed between the male and female formers. Clamps are then applied.

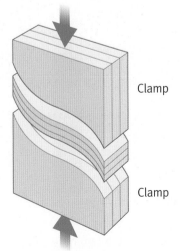

Clamp

Clamp

5. Ensure that no glue comes between the formers and the laminates as they will be difficult to separate.

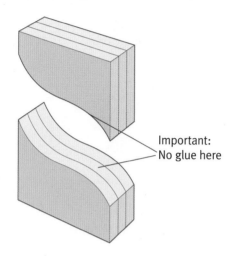

Important:
No glue here

Glues Suitable for Lamination

The standard PVA white glue in your MTW will suit most laminating applications required for Junior Certificate Level. Make sure to remove excess glue with a damp cloth prior to

❋ Apply glue to a laminate using glue roller

clamping. The glue may be applied by paintbrush or spread out with a wallpaper roller, as shown. For stronger hardwoods, animal glues will give a better result (see Chapter 26, Adhesives and Clamping Wood).

Process 1 – Forming

1. Make the former (as shown) to the desired contours.

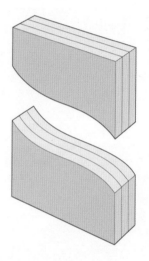

2. Use a small paintbrush to coat the under surfaces of the laminates, as shown.

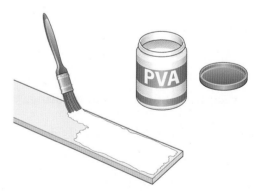

3. Press all the laminates together by hand.

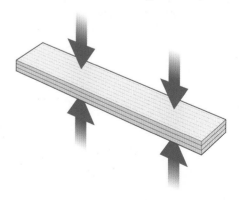

4. Place the strips over the former and clamp them together ensuring that the edges are flush.

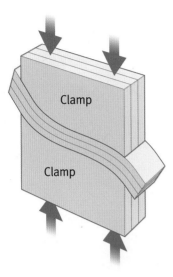

5. Leave for twenty-four hours and then remove the clamp.

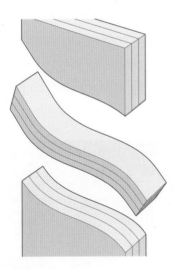

6. There will be some springing back of the wood – this is normal.

7. Save the former for future use.

Process 2 – Vacuum Lamination

Your school may have vacuum bags which makes the clamping process easier.

1. Make the former to the desired contours.
2. Use a small paintbrush to coat the undersurfaces of the laminates, as shown.
3. Press all the laminates together by hand.
4. Place strips over the former and clamp them together ensuring that the edges are flush.
5. Place in former vacuum bag and seal.
6. Turn on the vacuum and the laminates take the shape of the former.
7. Remove the vacuum hose and leave the bag in a sealed position.
8. Leave for twenty-four hours, then open the vacuum bag.

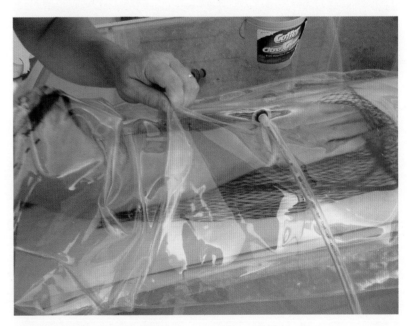

❀ Vacuum laminating bag

Bending Wood in the MTW Room

Steam Bending

Most MTW rooms will not have elaborate steam wood-bending apparatus as shown in the diagram below.

❈ Steam bending apparatus

1. The wood to be bent is placed in the steaming chamber for a number of hours depending on the species and the thickness of the wood.
2. The steam and heat moistens the wood which softens the cells allowing them to become pliable when removed.
3. The wood is quickly placed on the former and clamped in place.
4. When the wood dries and cools it will retain the desired shape.

Kerfing

Kerfing is a process which is carried out mostly by the use of the radial arm saw. Kerfs are the channels left in the wood after the saw

cut. When there is more wood material removed than is left behind, the wood will bend as shown below.

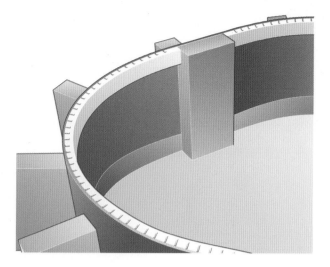

❈ Kerfing on a guitar body

This process wastes a lot of wood and the appearance of the bent wood can be poor. The edges can be veneered to cover over the kerf side marks, as shown. Kerfed wood often requires fixing at both ends to prevent springing.

❈ Veneer for guitar kerf work

Hands-on Tasks

1 Search the Internet for other examples of structures using laminated beams.

2 Ask your teacher to prepare 3 mm laminates for use in later bending tasks.

3 Design various shapes for use as **formers** on A3 paper and place on the classroom notice board for others to use in their projects.

4 Practise **kerfing** technique on long strips of waste wood from the MTW room.

Homework Sheet on Laminating and Bending Wood

1 What is a laminate?

2 Suggest a tool or device suitable for holding the two sides of a former together during laminating.

3 Name a suitable glue for use in laminating.

4 Outline the process required to make a former for the laminating process.

5 How does a steam-bending apparatus work?

6 Make a sketch of the process of **kerfing** wood for bending.

INTERNET LINKS AND TASKS

Visit the following, or similar, websites for facts in relation to laminating and bending.

Bending techniques

http://www.ultimatehandyman.co.uk/WOODWORKINGBENDING_WOOD.htm

Bending techniques

http://www.allwoodwork.com/article/woodwork/methods_of_bending_wood.htm

Bending techniques

http://www.articlesbase.com/home-improvement-articles/
how-to-bend-wood-119731.html

SEARCH

Sample Exam Question on Laminating and Bending Wood

Higher Level		2004

The diagram shows three boards that are to be edge-jointed to form a wider panel. The end grain is shown on one of the boards. On the diagram indicate the end-grain pattern of the other boards which would minimise distortion of the panel.

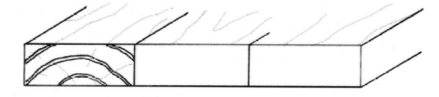

Pyrography

Introduction to Pyrography

Pyrography is the art of using heat to burn designs and patterns into wood and literally means 'writing with fire'. Pictures can be built up by burning with a hot nib and then colouring between the lines to bring the work to life.

The process dates back to ancient Egyptian times and ancient African tribes. Tinting and shading of the designs is relatively new having been practised in the nineteenth century by Alfred Smart in Australia. The process was simplified in the twentieth century with the invention of the hot wire etching tool which is still in use today.

Pyrography is the traditional skill of countries such as Hungary, Romania and Argentina. Pyrography can be applied to other materials such as leather and shell.

Key Elements to Understand for Junior Certificate Course
❋ equipment to use
❋ suitable woods to use
❋ burning technique
❋ colouring and glazing

Equipment to Use

There are two types of burning tool easily available to the MTW student – the simple wire burner (as shown), or the solid point burner with interchangeable heads.

❋ Dog created through pyrography

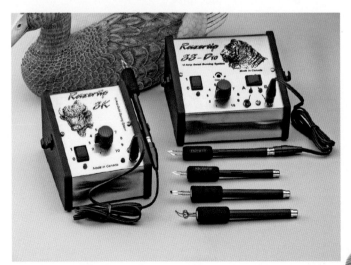

❋ Pyrograph tool

The wire-tip type is easy to use but the wire point requires regular reshaping and replacing. Turning the heat to the highest level on the burner causes the wire to wear out quickly.

The solid-point type is also easy to hold, but replacing the tips takes time as the nib must be allowed to cool before changing. There are three common tips in use today, as shown below.

Safety
Great care must be taken with both types of tool as the nibs reach temperatures in excess of 500°C. Never allow the nib to rest on a surface which could catch fire from the hot nib.

Carbon paper is very useful to transfer designs to the wood for burning.

❁ Flow point nib

❁ Carbon paper

❁ Mini flow point nib

Suitable Woods to Use

Any light-coloured wood will give the best effect and hardwoods will produce finer details. Always practise on cheaper pine wood scrap first to improve your final work.

Woods such as cedar, aspen, poplar and white Oak all give excellent results.

❁ Shading nib

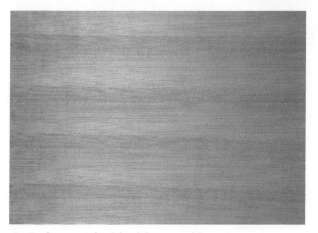

❁ Cedar wood – ideal for wood burning

Burning Technique

Practise using the pyrography tools on scrap wood first. Ensure that the wood is sanded prior to any burning because sanding is not recommended afterwards. On the good wood, trace the design to be copied (use designs from Internet) using **carbon paper**. The carbon paper is held in place with masking tape and removed before burning.

Heat the tool up to the desired temperature ensuring that the nibs have been cleaned with a wipe of light sandpaper to remove previous waste on the tip.

Then, as if using a pen, slowly burn in the design. The longer you stay in one spot the darker it will become. Some flames may rise, just blow these out. Pulling the nib toward you will give better results

Colouring and Glazing

On images, the area inside the lines can be coloured for better effects. This can be done in two ways. Use colouring pencils which have been dipped in water to colour as desired, or paint the spaces as shown and varnish over both when fully dried. A more advanced method involving the mixing of acrylic paint and special glazing chemicals can be attempted after perfecting the simple techniques above.

❀ Applying glazing to finished design

❀ Sample pattern to try

Hints and Tips

* Always start with a clean nib and sand off the residue every half hour.
* Use your breath to cool the nib during burning to lessen the darkening effect.
* Photocopy many copies of the same pattern to use in future projects.
* Never press the nib into the wood at the start of the line – keep it in motion.
* Use the nibs to give texture to your designs or to apply shading.

Always use water-based varnishes on the finished work as it will not dull the patterns.

Erasing pyrography work is not possible so be patient and careful at all times.

🌸 Shading using nib

Hands-on Tasks

1 Research the Internet to find examples of pyrography in five countries.

2 Design and make a wall chart to highlight five safety concerns for pyrography.

3 Test out the effect of burning on three different types of wood in the classroom.

4 Obtain Celtic designs from the Internet and transfer to the wood using carbon paper. Burn in the design with burning tools on a wood of your choice.

5 Upon completion of any design in pyrography, suggest three hints and tips you would give to someone starting out in pyrography.

Homework Sheet on Pyrography

1 Write a short history on the art of pyrography.

2 Name and sketch two different types of wood-burning tool.

3 Describe how you prepare wood and the burning tool for pyrography.

INTERNET LINKS AND TASKS

Pyrography equipment

http://www.patrickfaleur.com/pyrography/wpage4.htm

Pyrography patterns

http://www.woodworkersworkshop.com/resources/index.php?cat=524

SEARCH

Sample Exam Questions on Pyrography

No relevant whole questions in previous years.

Introduction to Sanding

It is important from an aesthetics and safety point of view that the projects you make are smooth to touch with no unwanted sharp edges or rough surfaces. A smooth well-finished project will enhance the enjoyment derived from woodworking. Naturally, there may be occasions where one wishes to have a rough surface as part of the design (such as in carving natural objects) but otherwise the material must be sanded to a high-quality finish. Sanding of various edges can also soften the appearance of a design, greatly adding to the overall effect of the piece. Very often, sanding can take more time than the making of the project, but the resulting finish is well worth the effort. The final result is a

blend of the skill of the woodworker and the choice of sanding papers etc. to achieve the final result.

Most people will want to sand with the electrical sanders, but quite often they remove too much material. Excellent results can be achieved by hand, and very often this is the best way to achieve the smoothest finish.

Key Elements to Understand for Junior Certificate Course

* sanding materials
* sanding techniques
* achieving high-quality finishes

Sanding Materials
Scrapers/Planes

Sanding is only effective if the surface of the wood is already level. This can be achieved by scraping or planing. The Cabinet scraper requires a lot of physical strength to work correctly. The blade must be held between the fingers (as shown on the next page) and drawn toward the body. This tool will smooth out small irregularities on the surface without removing too much wood. Alternatively, a Smoothing plane can be used to square up the wood, as shown. The Try square is used to

* Sanded wood looks clean

🌼 Using a Cabinet scraper

check for square edges. This method may
remove more material than is
necessary so must be used carefully.

Sandpapers

There are a number of sandpapers available to
buy and each comes in various grades of
roughness. Sandpaper is constructed by gluing
various fine stones and/or glass onto paper or
cloth. Sandpaper comes on rolls or in packs of
A4 size sheets – the required amount is cut off
with scissors. The choice of sandpaper will
depend on the sort of wood being
sanded and the level of smoothness
required.

Do not throw out used sandpaper
as others looking for a smooth
finish can use it. Store it in a
dedicated waste sandpaper area
(or box) in the room.

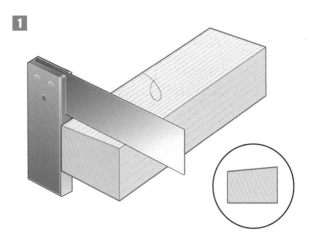

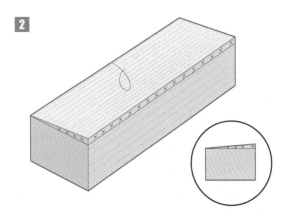

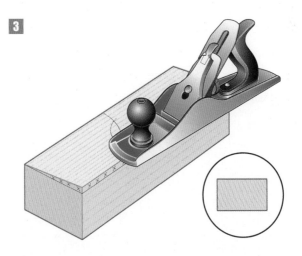
🌼 Squaring wood with a Try square and plane

Chart of Sandpaper Grades

ABRASIVE GRADING SYSTEMS			
CAMI (ANSI)	FEPA	MICRON	GRADE
1500		3	RELCO FINE
		5	
		6	
1200			
		9	
800			ULTRA FINE
		15	
600	P1200		
500	P1000		
		20	
400	P800		SUPER FINE
360	P600		
		30	
	P500		
	P400	39	EXTRA FINE
		28	
	P320		
		45	
		50	
240	P280	60	VERY FINE
		50	
		60	
220	P220		
180	P180		
150	P150		
120	P125		FINE
100	P105		
80	P90		MEDIUM
60	P80		
50	P50		COARSE
40	P40		
35	P25		EXTRA COARSE

Glass Paper

Normally yellow in colour, tiny glass fragments are glued to paper in A4 Sheets. It is not very durable and is suitable mainly for softwood timbers. This type of sandpaper usually tears after only a few minutes sanding.

✹ Glass paper

Silicon Carbide Paper

Commonly called **wet and dry** paper and black in colour. This is a very fine sandpaper which gives excellent results. It is expensive to buy but will last for a reasonable length of time when sanding. This is an excellent paper for sanding soft metals and hardwoods.

✹ Silicon carbide paper

Aluminium Oxide

This is the most common paper used on orbital sanders and other electric sanders due to its durability. It comes in different colours but red is the most common for electric sanders.

✹ Aluminium oxide paper

Garnet Paper

This is similar to glass paper but is a lot tougher as it is made from harder glass crystals. This is general-purpose woodworkers' sandpaper, and is excellent on hard and soft woods.

✹ Garnet paper

Wools

Wire wool (Grades 000 and 0000) are used to achieve a very fine finish. A piece is made into a wad shape, and rubbed in the direction of the grain or in a circular motion. The wood must be very smooth as the wool fibres tend to grab protruding grain and cause a blackening of the surface. Wool is very useful in between varnish coats as the grain is already covered.

✹ Wire wool

Sanding Techniques

Straight Sanding

1. Remove dents in the wood by ironing over with a damp cloth or by filling dents with a plastic wood filler. Remove any leftover filler.

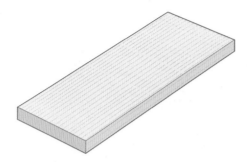

2. Select the type and grade of sandpaper, e.g. 120 grit glass paper.

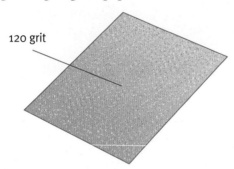

120 grit

3. Cut sandpaper to the required size to fit the sanding block of the waste piece of wood.

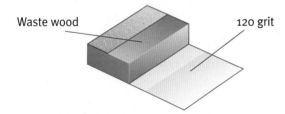

Waste wood   120 grit

4. Sand back and forth in the direction of the grain or in the direction of the lines on the wood.

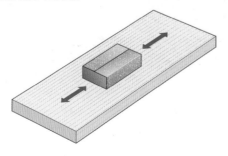

5. Do not sand perpendicular to the grain as the wood will scratch.

6. When all lines and marks have been removed, switch to the next grade, e.g. 240 grit and sand as before.

240 grit

7. When the paper is exhausted and a very smooth finish has been obtained, finish the sanding with 400 grit **silicon carbide**.

8. Using a damp cloth, wet the surfaces and leave to dry. This will raise any grains which have not been sheared by previous sanding.

9. Re-sand using the 400 grit paper.

10. The wood is now ready for the applied finish, e.g. the varnish stage.

400 grit

End Grain Sanding

This is one of the more difficult areas to sand as it equates to rubbing your hand on the end of a bunch of straws. The circular cell ends mean that the area must be sanded in a circular motion to achieve a good finish. It is easy to know the stopping point as the end

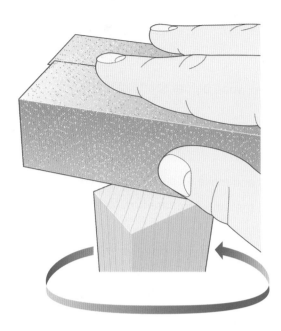

❂ Sanding end grain

grain loses all its scratch marks and looks as clean as the wood sanded on the sides of the wood.

Profile Sanding

If the wood to be sanded has curved edges or surfaces, the rule is to match the shape of the sandpaper to the surface to achieve the best results.

* pencil round
* internal curve
* mouldings
* carvings

Electric Sanders

The safe use of **orbital** and **electric sanders** is covered in greater detail in previous chapters, but it is necessary to state that the woodworker needs to be aware that electric sanders can remove more wood than is necessary. It is best to sand in the direction of the grain, as with hand sanding.

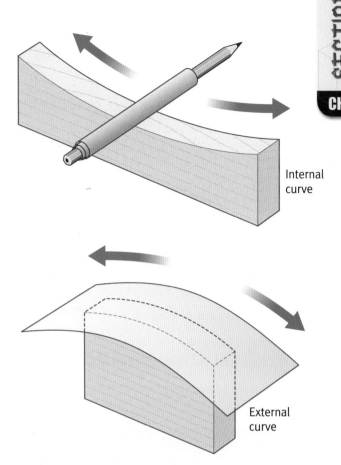

Internal curve

External curve

❂ Profile sanding

❂ Orbital sanding

281

Hands-on Tasks

1 Browse the Internet to discover how carpenters sanded wood before sandpaper was invented in its current format.

2 Practise the techniques for using scrapers as outlined on a scrap piece of timber in the MTW room.

3 Obtain 15 cm × 15 cm samples of different sandpapers and make a chart for the MTW room.

4 Select two different types of the same grade of sandpaper and compare how long they last when sanding the same type of wood.

5 Using sample wood pieces of the same material, sand one without using the damping technique described, and the other with the damping technique. Compare the smoothness of each on completion of the task.

6 Sand two pieces of wood with an orbital sander and by hand sanding, using the same type and grit rating of paper. Compare the result over a three-minute period.

Homework Sheet on Sanding

1 List two advantages of sanding wood.

2 Outline the correct procedure for using a Cabinet scraper by using diagrams and notes.

3 Outline the process for checking the edge of a wood piece to check if it is square.

4 List two factors which would influence your choice of sandpaper for a given sanding task.

5 What is the difference between **glass paper** and **garnet paper**?

6 Name a sandpaper for use on metals and hardwoods to achieve a very smooth finish.

7 Name two grades of wire wool which may be obtained?

8 Describe, using diagrams, how one could remove dents in wood.

9 Why can one achieve a better finish by lightly wetting the sanded wood and then re-sanding after it has dried again?

10 What is the difference in the sanding motion between sanding straight and end-grain sanding?

INTERNET LINKS AND TASKS

Sanding technique

http://www.house-painting-info.com/sanding-wood.html

Sandpapers

http://diydata.com/tool/abrasives/sandpaper.php

Test Yourself
eTest.ie

SEARCH

Adhesives and Clamping Wood

Introduction to Adhesives and Clamping Wood

Woodwork joints have a certain amount of strength on their own – especially when pulled in the direction for which they were designed. Other lateral forces can easily break or separate them so some form of mechanical adhesion is required. Due to shrinkage, joints can fall apart a few days after construction. Bonding the surfaces of the joints together prevents this from happening.

The most used type of glue today is PVA (Polyvinyl acetate) and this is used extensively in the MTW room today (white, milk-like glue). While you will have easy access to this type, there are many other types of glue, which may suit your design better.

You may have wondered why the glue never sets in the tube! Due to its composition, glue finds it difficult to bond to itself. This is important because it means that if you use too much glue the joint will fall apart. Always use glue sparingly.

In addition to knowing how to select the best glue for the task, correct clamping is also vital to ensure the glue sets properly and the artefact is clamped at the correct angles.

🌸 Selection of glues for the MTW room

Key Elements to Understand for Junior Certificate Course

* The chemical elements of common adhesives.
* The care of skin, eyes and protection from inhalation.
* The character and application of commonly used adhesives.

Safety

Health and Safety with Glue

* Never use glue without the teacher's permission.
* Always read the label and understand the glue that you are using.
* Never inhale the fumes of the glue.
* Leave a window open in the room where you are using the glue.
* Clean up all spillages.
* Wash off any glue from your hand immediately.
* Seek medical advice if skin gets bonded together.

Protein Adhesives
Casein

This is glue made from the protein in cow's milk. It is a superior glue in terms of its ability to maintain its bond properties over long periods of time. It is one of the last remaining natural and renewable glues in the world. It is excellent for use in hot and cold applications. On the downside, it is not resistant to moisture and fungal attack and therefore only suitable for indoor use. It is an excellent glue for use in furniture joints and laminated boards.

✹ Casein glue

Animal

This was the most common glue in use before the advent of PVA synthetic glue. It is made from the bones, skin and muscle of dead animals. It is used in a heated state and applied with a brush. It can be removed from the wood by reheating with a hair dryer. Once opened, its pot life depends on whether you can keep it heated by using a melting pot. It can bond wood to glass very effectively and therefore can be used to attach mirrors to wooden backgrounds.

✹ Animal glue

Synthetic Adhesives
Urea Formaldehyde Resin

This is a combination of urea and formaldehyde mixed in the presence of **ammonia**. It is technically a non-transparent thermosetting plastic. It is applied with a roller and is widely used in plywood, MDF and other large surface manufactured boards. It has excellent waterproofing ability, resistance to mould and a high tensile strength. It can also be obtained as a one-part formula and used in laminating and bending projects in your class.

* Urea formaldehyde glue

most materials to each other and it works well in the MTW to bond different materials in your design.

PVA (Polyvinyl Acetate)

This is most commonly used glue in the MTW room due to its safety and easy to use characteristics. It is the milky white glue used to bond joints and projects together. **Polyvinyl acetate** is mixed with water to create the glue. It is also known in the trade as **white glue**. Due to its ability to bond to other porous materials like fabric, it is advised not to allow it to come in contact with your clothing. PVA is poor under moist conditions and is mostly suitable for indoor use. It is not harmful to touch and does not produce toxic fumes. Another use for PVA glue is to dilute it heavily with water to use it as a sealer – especially over stained wood.

Epoxy Resin

This is a two-part glue which cures when one agent bonds to another hardening agent. Epoxy is widely known as a structural agent due to its high strength. One common use is to hold the head of golf clubs in place at the end of a shaft. Epoxies can be used to bond

* Epoxy resin glue

* PVA glue

Impact Adhesives
Contact Glues

These are adhesives which are applied to both opposing surfaces to be joined, left to cure for a few minutes and then pressed firmly against each other. The bond forms very quickly once the surfaces are pressed together. They can be used to bond both porous and non-porous materials. Natural rubber can be used as an impact adhesive. They are used to attach Formica® material to chipboard to make counter tops and also to join the sole of your shoes to the upper. Most give off strong fumes so use in a well ventilated room.

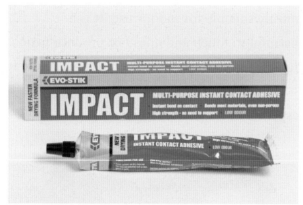
❋ Contact glue

Cyanoacrylate (Super Glue)

Commonly known as **super glue**. Excellent for bonding many surface materials and skin in seconds. Great care should be taken not to come into contact with super glues. This type of glue has a low shear strength and can be used to mount sacrificial pieces of timber to your wood (e.g. when planing to the edge) and then can be removed with a gentle tap of a mallet. **Cyano** for short, it is used to bond plastic aircraft kits together. It is not particularly useful for bonding wood and glass unless a specialised version is purchased at a high cost. Other uses include mixing it with **baking soda** to form a gap filler – but this gives off fumes.

Thermo Glues

These are glues, which require heating prior to application. In the MTW room this normally takes the form of a hot-melt glue gun. The glue gun must be kept on a stand to prevent the glue from attaching to other surfaces. Severe burns can also occur due to the high temperatures involved. These glues work best when joining porous materials and should not be used to attach mirrors to wood because the mirror will fall off when the glue hardens. Hot-melt glues can also be used to fill gaps.

❋ Super glue

❋ Hot-melt glue gun

Wood Glue Terminology

Shelf Life

This measures the length of time that the glue will stay fresh in its tub. This will be stated on the label of the glue and should be heeded. Placing the lid back on the tub after use will greatly improve the shelf life.

Pot Life

This is a crucial time where the glue has been removed from its storage tub and is in use. Many types of glue will 'go-off' quickly. PVA will start to thicken in just five minutes so that is how long you have to assemble and clamp the joint.

Closed Assembly Time

This is the amount of time you have to clamp the wood and square it up before the glue begins to set. This can vary but PVA gives you about five minutes – super glues only give you seconds.

Applying and Spreading the Glue

Two factors come into play when applying glue. Spreading it evenly and then reducing waste and spillages. Care in the application will fix both these issues. By far the easiest and technically most correct way to apply the glue is with a brush. This means that the glue is spread evenly and dripping is reduced.

Care must be taken to ensure that the glue is spread evenly to ensure an even bond and grip.

Clamping Wood

Clamping depends on what type of clamps you have available and the size of the object to be clamped. Most MTW rooms will have the following:

* **Bench Vice** – for small clamping operations

* **Spring Bar Clamps** – for intricate and small clamping operations

* **Quick Squeeze Clamps** – for medium-size clamping operations

* **G Clamps** – for small clamping operations and clamping long lengths in stages

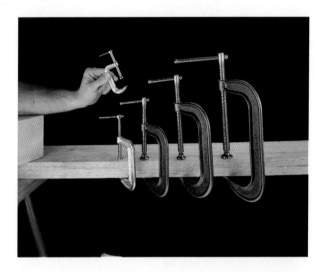

* **Sash Clamps** – for clamping wide laminates and projects

* **Frame Clamps and Mitre Clamps** – for clamping picture frames

In all the cases below, ensure that excess glue which squeezes out during the clamping

operation, is wiped away with a damp cloth as it will show up during the applied finish process.

Clamping Small Joints

Practice joints and small projects can be clamped in the MTW vice ensuring that scrap wood is placed over the entire area of the joint. Check that the joint is square before applying full pressure. PVA glue should be left overnight. Also, do not allow any glue to come between the vice and the wood. Some glue may get between the joint and the scrap but that can be removed easily with a gentle tapping.

Clamping Frames

Use mitre clamps on the corners, and ensure that the angles are square by using a Try square as shown. Check that the frame is

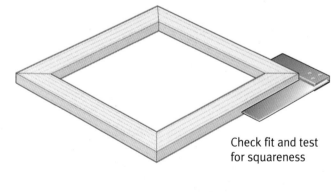

Check fit and test for squareness

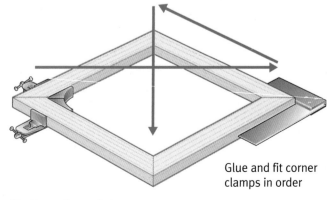

Glue and fit corner clamps in order

* Clamping a frame

square by measuring from one diagonal to the other, as shown. Ensure that the frame is not buckled but is flat on the surface below.

Clamping Leg Supports

The clamping process can be awkward for tables, so help from a classmate is essential. The key problem to avoid is that of allowing the bottom of the legs to fold inwards during the clamping process. Also, take care to use large flat pieces of scrap wood to protect the good timber.

Clamp the top of the legs with a sash clamp (as shown) ensuring that the legs are square to the top rail. Use a piece of material the same length as the distance between the faces of opposing joints to stop the legs folding inwards, as shown.

Clamping Laminates

To make laminate table tops (and similar items) use the following clamping method. Lay out as many sash clamps (as shown) with long pieces of scrap at each side. Lay boards on edge and apply glue to the internal edges, but not on the outside. Drop the boards down and square the ends with a straight edge. Lock all clamps loosely ensuring that the boards are flat to the clamp bar. Tighten gradually, constantly checking that the boards do not bow up – paying attention to the direction of the annual rings. (See Chapter 23, Lamination and Bending Wood, for more details.)

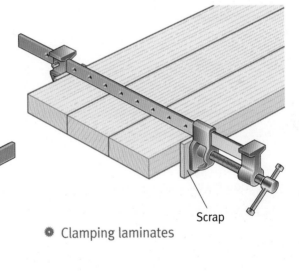

* Clamping laminates

* Clamping furniture legs

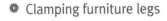

Hands-on Tasks

1 Make a list of all the glues available to you in your local DIY store and MTW room. Keep this list for future gluing requirements.

2 Test out three different glues on three different butt joints by gluing them, clamping them, leaving overnight and then trying to break them apart.

3 Leave small amounts of three different glues in small pots overnight and try to apply them to wood the following day. How easily do they spread and how strong do they hold?

4 Practise the use of **framing clamps** because they can be difficult to position.

5 **Glue** and **clamp** three boards together with the annual rings in the correct position as described previously. Repeat with the annual rings in the wrong alignment and monitor the boards as they settle over a few days. Which one warps the most?

Homework Sheet on Adhesives and Clamping Wood

1 Why should glue be used sparingly in joint bonding?

2 List three safety precautions to follow when using glues.

3 What is Casein glue made from?

4 What glue is used in the manufacture of plywood?

5 What do the letters **PVA** mean?

6 What is another name for **cyanoacrylate**?

7 How is hot-melt glue applied to a surface?

8 Explain the difference between **shelf life** and **pot life**.

9 What direction should the annual rings face in a laminate glued board?

INTERNET LINKS AND TASKS

How to use PVA glue

http://www.thistothat.com/glue/pva.shtml

How to make wooden picture frames

http://www.ehow.com/how_18709_make-wood-picture.html

SEARCH

Sample Exam Questions on Adhesives and Clamping Wood

| Higher Level | 2005 |

What do the letters **PVA** stand for in relation to adhesives?

P		**V**		**A**	

| Higher Level | 2003 |

The diagram shows a timber climbing frame, similar to those found in a children's playground.

(i) Suggest a suitable adhesive that might be used when constructing the frame.

   ANSWER _____

(ii) Describe **one** property of the adhesive that makes it appropriate for use in this situation.

   PROPERTY _____

Introduction to Fixtures and Fittings

Although it is possible to make woodwork projects entirely from joints (as in Chapter 19, Woodwork Joints) it is sometimes faster, cheaper and more environmentally sound to use mechanical fixtures and fittings.

There is a vast array of fixtures and fittings in any DIY shop. Narrowing them down to the ones which are useful for Junior Certificate projects can be difficult. Fittings can fall into a few main categories and it is then up to the designer and woodworker to investigate which ones suit their needs best.

Presented below are some of the more useful fittings for MTW – a number from each category are presented for you to choose from. Some of the fittings can be expensive or the wrong size for the task at hand, so it is vital to visit your local store to see them for yourself.

Key Elements to Understand for Junior Certificate Course

* knowledge of mechanical fasteners
* locks and hinges
* screws and nails
* pins and staples
* knockdown fittings

❋ Range of fittings for MTW

Joining Wood
Screws and How to Screw
Parts of a Screw

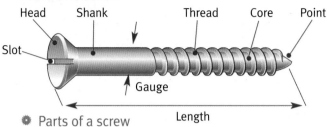

Head   Shank   Thread   Core   Point

Slot

Gauge

Length

❋ Parts of a screw

❋ Spax TM pozidrive screws

Types of Screw

There are many different screw types – all designed with different functions in mind. The main factor in your choice of screw is the length of the screw. This must be carefully decided, as the screw must not protrude from the other side of the joined pieces.

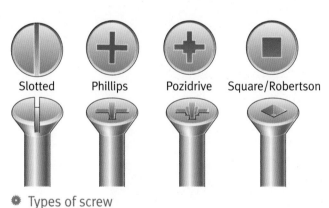

Slotted   Phillips   Pozidrive   Square/Robertson

❋ Types of screw

The size of the head comes next, large enough to resist breaking under screwing forces (torsion) and small enough so as not to look out of place in the design. The pattern of the head is important, as you must have a matching screwdriver to drive the screw.

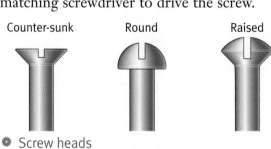

Counter-sunk   Round   Raised

❋ Screw heads

Screws are normally ordered by stating the length required and the size of the shank e.g. **25 × 4** is a 25 mm long screw with a 4 mm (gauge) width of shank.

Driving Screws

Screws can be driven by a hand-held screwdriver or by a **cordless** screwdriver.

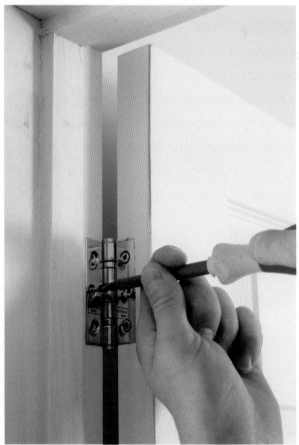

❋ Using a screwdriver

Frequently, too much pressure can be applied with the cordless screwdriver and the head of the screw gets damaged and is then difficult to remove. For small jobs a hand-held screwdriver is ideal.

Counterboring

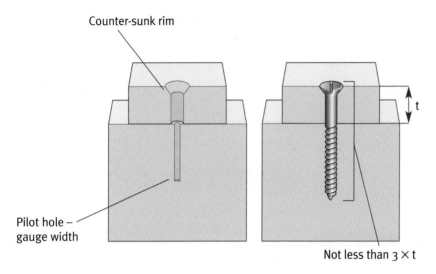

Counter-sunk rim

Pilot hole – gauge width

t

Not less than 3 × t

● Countersinking a screw head

Covering Screws

Screws can be unsightly in a quality project so there are a few ways of covering them up. The screw can be made more attractive with the use of **brass cups**, also **plastic colour caps** can be inserted onto the screw head to match the wood, or the screw can be counter-bored and plugged, as shown.

● Screw caps

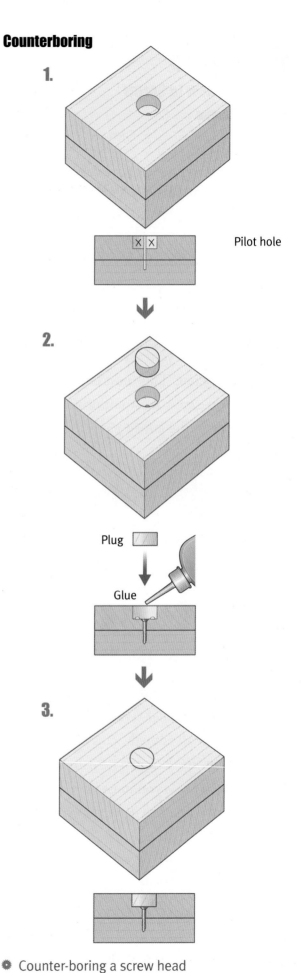

1.

Pilot hole

2.

Plug

Glue

3.

● Counter-boring a screw head

Nails and How to Nail

Nails are quick to use and have very good strength especially under shear forces. There are many to choose from so consideration must be given to the strength required to hold the wood together, and to the length of the nail, so that none of it is dangerously protruding from the wood.

Parts of a Nail

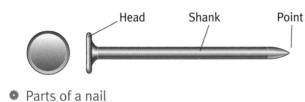

Head   Shank   Point

* Parts of a nail

Types of Nail
Round Wire Nail

A large circular section nail with a flat head used for heavy-duty nailing such as fencing and building timber-framed houses and roofs.

Panel Pin

A short and thin section nail for light-duty nailing such as securing back panels on furniture. Easy to bend if hit off-centre by a panel pin hammer.

Upholstery Tacks

A small decorative round-head nail used to secure fabric on seats. False runs of these nails can be used for decorative purposes.

Oval Nail

A strong nail that is used in heavy and light applications. The oval head is designed to be driven below the surface of the timber with a nail punch. It is a useful nail for use near the end grain of the wood – the oval section of the nail reduces the chances of the nail splitting.

Clout Nail

A small, galvanised nail with large flat head for outdoor use in applications such as holding down roofing felt and plywood decks. These nails will not rust due to the coating.

Inserting/Removing Nails
Insertion

Nails are inserted with a hammer or nail gun.

Dovetail nailing is very strong as more of the wood is in contact with the nail, as shown.

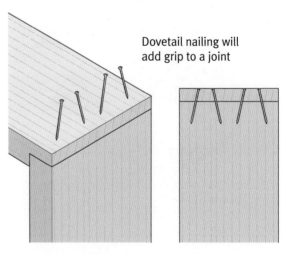

Dovetail nailing will add grip to a joint

* Dovetail nailing

Straight nailing at the end of planks requires the use of oval nails, used as shown.

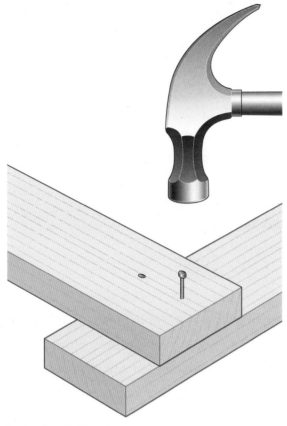

⬗ Oval nail direction

Removing a Nail

Nails can be removed with a claw hammer, as shown. Use a scrap piece of wood under the hammer head to protect the good wood.

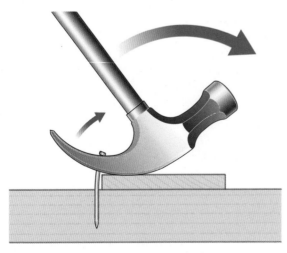

⬗ Removing a nail safely

Secret Nailing

For **tongued and grooved** board (flooring or back panels), secret nailing can be applied where the nail is inserted in a dovetail fashion. The next board's grooves covers up the last nail.

⬗ Secret nailing

Staples

Staples are U-shaped (round and square) nails used to hold down panels or wiring. They have excellent corrosion resistance due to their galvanised coating and therefore are excellent for outdoor use, e.g. fencing.

⬗ Staple holding fence wire

Square staples for use in staple guns come in cartridges and are loaded into a staple gun (stapler) for use.

Brackets and Other Knockdown Fittings

Knockdown fittings are generally used to hold panels of wood together and are designed to be reusable. They provide speed of fitting and many have replaced the art of joint-making as they are quick to install. The downside is that they can be expensive relative to their size and may look unsightly in a high-quality piece of furniture.

Types of Brackets and Other Knockdown Fittings

The positive aspect is that they can be reused in future projects after the current project is finished.

❀ Barrel and bolt connector

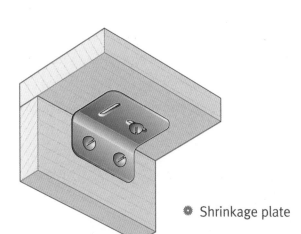
❀ Shrinkage plate

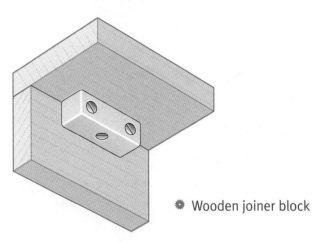
❀ Wooden joiner block

❀ Angle bracket

❀ Plastic block joiner

Wood screw

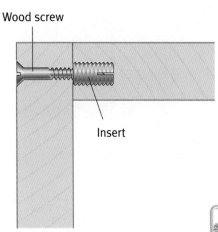
Insert

❀ Cabinet unit connector

CHAPTER 27

Doors

Doors require many different fittings for their correct operation. A door will require hinges, a handle and a locking mechanism.

Hinges and Fitting Hinges

There are many different types of hinge and they perform the same basic function of allowing the door to open and close. The choice of hinge depends on the function of the door, the size of the door and appearance of the finished door.

Types of Hinges
Butt Hinge

These are used for many applications such as cabinet doors and house doors. Available from very small 20 mm hinges up to 150 mm hinges. Can be obtained in steel or in a more attractive brass finish. It is held in place with countersunk screws so that the hinge can close right in on itself.

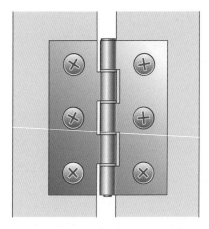

❋ Butt hinge

Piano Hinge

The long brass hinge is used on piano lids and folding doors. It can be bent easily when not in use.

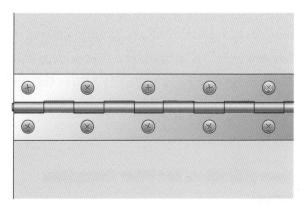

❋ Piano hinge

Parliament Hinge

This is a decorative brass hinge which is used because it allows the door to open well clear of the door frame. It is found in drinks cabinets to enable easy access to the cabinet.

❋ Parliament hinge

Flush Hinge

A small, weak hinge used for light doors. Easy to fit as it is fixed directly to the door and the frame with screws. It can be obtained in brass for a more attractive finish to the door.

Back Flap Hinge

This large hinge gives extra support to heavy doors and drop leaf tables, as shown.

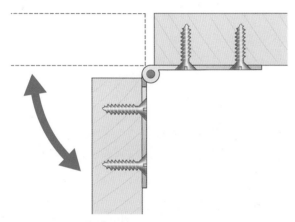

❋ Back flap hinge

❋ Drop leaf table

Blum Hinge

A large hinge which is used for wardrobe and kitchen doors. It is highly adjustable, allowing the door to be pulled away from the frame or closer to the opposite door in the wardrobe unit. Very strong when used in groups of two or three, as shown.

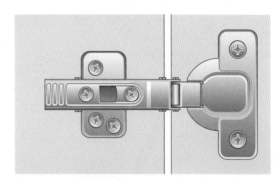

❋ Blum hinge

❋ Blum hinge on wardrobe door

Gate Hinge

A heavy-duty decorative hinge for hanging outdoor wooden gates and doors.

❋ Gate hinge

Fitting a Butt Hinge

1. Obtain suitable size hinge for the door. Mark the position of the hinge on the door frame.

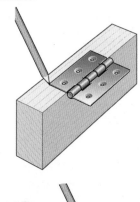

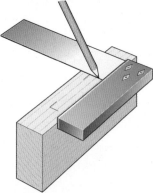

2. Set a marking gauge to the depth of the hinge.
Mark this depth on the edge of the door.

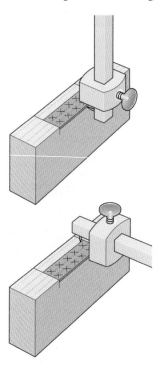

3. Scribe around the area to be removed.

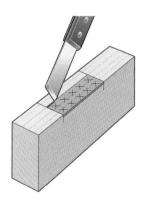

4. Chisel out the waste to receive the hinge.

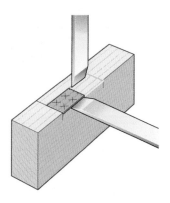

5. Screw the hinge onto the door.

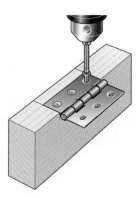

6. Repeat steps 1–7 for fitting the hinge to the cabinet frame.

Catches

Doors may sit in a closed position on their own, but often a more secure method is required. Any of the catches below can be fitted to secure the door in a closed position.

Types of Catches

❋ Magnetic catch

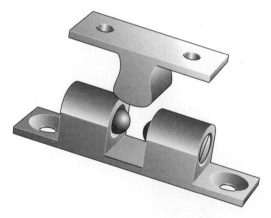
❋ Variable resistance ball door catch

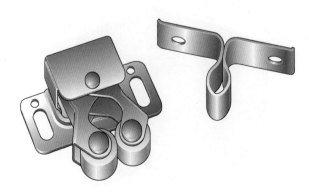
❋ Roller and ball catch

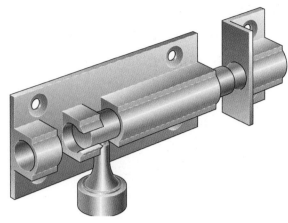
❋ Barrel bolt

Locks and Fitting Locks

Locks are used to secure a door and for the protection of valuable items. They can be obtained in many different sizes and types. The cupboard lock is the most widely used on MTW projects.

Types of Locks
Cupboard Lock

A small lock fitted directly onto the rear of the door. A hole is drilled for the lock key, see fitting below.

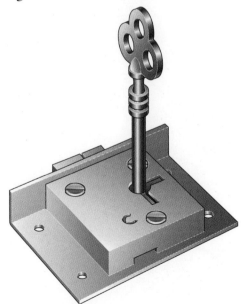
❋ Cupboard lock

1.

2.

3.

4.

5.

Fitting a cupboard lock

Mortise Lock

Also known as a **dead lock**. This is usually used for the front doors of houses and internal door locks. It is often use in conjunction with a rim lock on external doors.

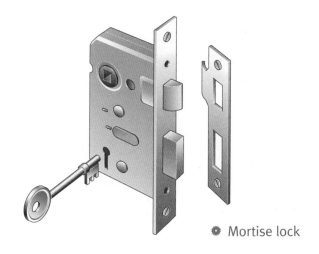

❋ Mortise lock

Enclosed Box Lock

A light lock used to lock boxes (e.g. a trinket box) or piano lids. The lock fits into the main wood of the item with the receiver fitted to the door or lid.

❋ Box lock

❋ Box lock on jewellery box

Handles
Types of Handle
Wooden

❈ Wooden handle

Metal

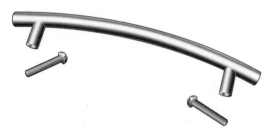

❈ Metal handle

Fitting Door Handles

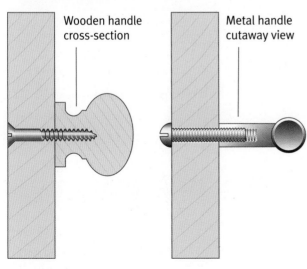

Wooden handle cross-section

Metal handle cutaway view

❈ Fitting handles to wood

Runners

❈ Drawer runner

Lighting
Light Fittings and Making Lamps

A lamp can be made to suit many applications and projects such as trophies or ornaments for the top of a table.

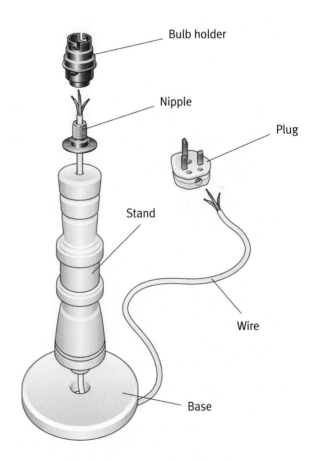

Bulb holder

Nipple

Plug

Stand

Wire

Base

Fitting the Lighting Fixture into a Turned Wooden Lamp

1. Drill a hole through the lamp with a long drill bit or on the lathe with the long-hole boring kit.

2. Pass the cable through the hole.

3. Fit the plug as in Chapter 15, Basic Electronics for MTW.

4. Fit the holder nipple to the top of the lamp.

5. Wire up the cord to the bulb holder.

6. Tighten the holder to the nipple and then fit the lampshade.

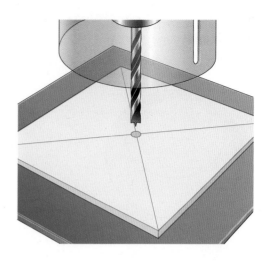

Clock Mechanism

Clock Mechanism and Fitting it into Wood

1. Locate and drill a 12 mm hole in the wood for the centre of the clock.

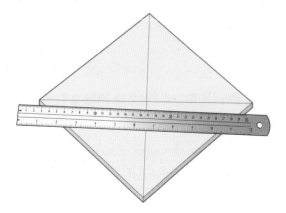

2. Mark the outline of the clock back on the rear of the wood.

3. Mortise out the back of the clock leaving 10 mm material to the front of the clock.

4. Insert the clock back and any rubber spacers required.

5. Screw on the front holding nut and tighten up with a screwdriver.

6. Push on the small hand and then the big hand.

7. Secure with a locking nut.

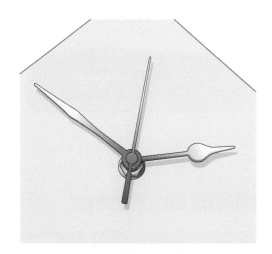

8. Insert the battery and set the time.

❉ Fitting a clock mechanism

Hands-on Tasks

1 Visit your local **hardware** shop to see the types of hardware fittings available to you.

2 Drive some screws into scrap wood with different torque settings on a cordless screwdriver. Remove screws for reuse when finished.

3 Practise making plugs on the pillar drill with your teacher's help.

4 Make a wall chart to show the correct way to drive in and remove nails.

5 Make sketches of different brackets available to you in the classroom or local DIY shop.

6 Practise fitting a butt hinge on some scrap wood until you achieve a perfect fit.

7 Make a clock using recycled timber and a clock mechanism from your teacher.

Homework Sheet on Fixtures and Fittings

1 Identify the various fittings below and state a use for each one.

2 Demonstrate, using diagrams, the correct method for counter-boring a screw head.

3 How can the good wood be protected from the hammer when a nail is being removed?

4 What are the advantages of using knockdown fittings over handmade joints in assembly work?

INTERNET LINKS AND TASKS

Visit the following (or similar) websites for more facts in relation to fixtures and fittings.

Wood screw insertion techniques

http://www.submityourarticle.com/articles/Mallory-Kramer-4792/screws-52035.php

Nailing

http://woodworking.about.com/od/mechanicalfasteners/p/nails.htm

Hinge type and selection

http://www.woodworking-news.com/woodworking/hardware/hinges.shtml

SEARCH

Sample Exam Questions on Fixtures and Fittings

Ordinary Level | 2010

From the list given, identify the nails shown.

A

B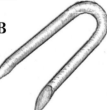

| Round Wire Nail |
| Staple |
| Clout Head Nail |
| Corrugated Fastener |
| Panel Pin |

NAIL A _____

NAIL B _____

Ordinary Level | **2010**

Name the fitting shown and give its correct use.

NAME _____

USE _____

Ordinary Level | **2010**

When joining wood using screws it is common to drill a large hole through the top piece and a smaller one in the second.

What is the correct name for the smaller hole?

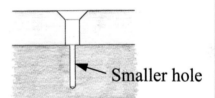

Smaller hole

ANSWER _____

Ordinary Level | **2009**

From the list given, identify the screw type shown.

| Round Head Screw |
| Raised Head Screw |
| Countersunk Head Screw |

NAME _____

Ordinary Level | **2009**

Name the fitting shown and give its correct use.

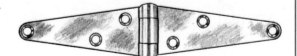

NAME _____

USE _____

Give **two** possible reasons why a nail might bend when being hammered into wood.

1. _____

2. _____

When pulling a nail, using a claw hammer, a piece of waste wood should be placed under the hammer head.

Give a reason for this.

ANSWER _____

_____

(i) The diagram shows a common type of hinge.
   Name this hinge type.

   TYPE _____

(ii) Where would this type of hinge normally be used?

   USE _____

Brass is an alloy of two metals. Name the **two** metals.

METAL 1 _____

METAL 2 _____

❋ Brass door fitting

(i) Name the hinge shown in the diagram.

NAME _____

(ii) Suggest an appropriate method of preventing this hinge from rusting when used externally.

ANSWER _____

Shown in the diagram is a common woodwork fitting.

(i) Name the fitting.

ANSWER _____

(ii) State one advantage of using this type of fitting.

ADVANTAGE _____

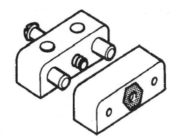

(i) Name the hinge shown in the diagram.

NAME _____

(ii) Where would this type of hinge normally be used?

ANSWER _____

Introduction to Finishing Wood

It is a personal choice how one finishes the surface of a wooden artefact. You may choose not to apply a finish or to apply a high-gloss finish involving many hours of work. In general, it is better to apply some finish to seal and protect the wood – in general, the quality of the appearance is often dependant on some form of applied finish. Finishing wood generally means sanding it and an applied

finish is any natural or chemical compound used to protect and shine the surface of the timber. Whilst sanding has been dealt with in a previous chapter, filling and repair of minor surface defects must also be considered before using any applied finish. Wood finishing can be carried out in three ways in the MTW room. Traditional finishes which are simple to use and apply, modern finishes which require care when handling and spray finishes which require strict safety procedures in their usage.

> Where possible you should select a finish which will do least damage to the environment.

Key Elements to Understand for Junior Certificate Course

* preparation for applied finishes
* stains and dyes
* waxes and oils
* lacquers
* varnishes
* paints

Preparation for Applied Finishes

Having sanded the wood (see Chapter 25, Sanding Wood) any indentations and blemishes must be remedied. For small dents,

* French polished table top

a damp cloth and a hot iron will lift the dents. Check the surface in case any grain fibres have been raised, allow to dry and re-sand with the finest paper or wool available.

For larger holes and rough knots, knot filler may be used to fill the holes. It works just like a self-levelling compound to smooth out the surface. Some prefer to use plastic wood filler but more often, this type of filler looks poor under varnish finishes and leaves a white residue around the affected area.

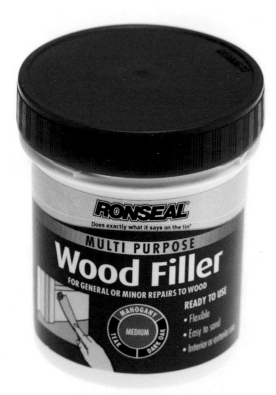

❋ Wood plastic filler

A simple way to fill any gaps, dents and spacing is to use a mix of very fine dust from the sander – this is mixed with **casein** glue to make a paste. Use sawdust from the wood to be repaired and sand after twenty-four hours when the glue has set.

For very fine holes, e.g. from panel pins driven below the surface, pump glue into the holes and sand over with a fine paper to get a good finish, as shown.

Filling a nail hole in wood

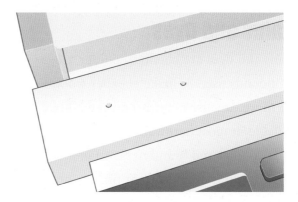

❋ Stage 1 – Drive nails below surface

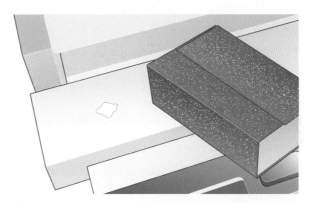

❋ Stage 2 – Fill holes with small amount of PVA glue

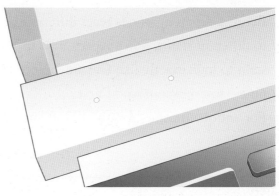

❋ Stage 3 – Sand to required finish

All rooms where the finish is to be applied should be free of airborne dust and insects.

Outside treatment is a secondary option as the chances of insects, rain and other contaminants ruining your work are high. A specialised finishing room should be established near the MTW room.

Eye protection must be worn

Stains and Dyes

Stains and dyes are chemical colour compounds used to make cheaper wood look like more expensive hardwoods etc. They are available in most hardware shops and come in many colours and brand names. Choosing the correct stain is an important process and the following points should be noted:

* Stains do not protect the wood and are only a base coat.
* Semi-transparent stains (light stains) are good if you want the grain of the wood to be seen in the final finish.
* Opaque stains should be used if you wish to hide the grain.
* Indoor stains will fade rapidly if used outdoors.
* Water-based stains take over twelve hours to dry.
* Because different woods react differently to different stains, don't expect an Oak stain to look exactly like Oak on a piece of pine – test on scrap wood first.
* For antique finishes always use wax-based stains.

Safety
Always wear eye protection and a good pair of cloth gloves – stains are hard to remove from the skin.

Applying Stains and Dyes

1. Make up a wad of good quality cloth and dip in stain or dye.

WOOD STAIN

2. Apply using even strokes and wipe off any excess until the surface colour is even.

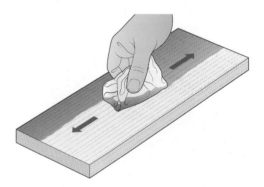

3. The more coats you apply, the darker the finish will appear.

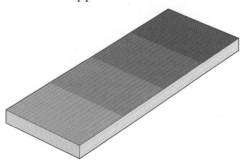

4. Seal the colour in with a clear varnish or wax, but only after the <u>dye is fully dried</u>.

Waxes and Oils

Wax and oil can be used on their own to give a natural look to the finished wood or used to seal in stains or dyes already applied. They protect the wood from moisture damage.

Beeswax

Beeswax gives a lustrous finish to any surface and is easy to apply. The more coats applied, the higher the shine from the finished

artefact. Wax is available in solid form or as a liquid. The liquid form, while easier to apply, takes many more coats to achieve a superb finish.

Both forms of wax are applied using a cloth. Rub the wax into the wood in circles and wipe off any residue. Thin coats are always best. Allow to dry for twenty-four hours, polish with a dry cloth and apply wax again. Repeat as often as required.

Linseed Oil

Also known as **flax seed oil**. It is very slow drying but gives a high-quality finish. It soaks into the wood – unlike many other chemical finishes – giving a deep protective layer. It is not as hard as varnish but can be repaired easily. It is applied with a cloth just like the other finishes. Its most common use is to oil cricket bats to keep them protected and supple.

✸ Linseed oil

Danish Oil (Tung Oil)

Danish oil gives one of the best satin finishes available and allow the natural beauty of the wood to emerge. It is used on cabinets, panelling and chopping boards. It is also one

✸ Beeswax

● Danish oil

of the most economical finishes to use as it covers a large area easily. Apply in thin coats five minutes apart so that it can soak deep into the wood. More layers lead to greater protection, but will not add to the shine produced. The strong smell in the early stages will disappear after a few days.

Boiled Oil

This is linseed oil heated to give a thicker oil. Although harder to apply, the drying time is greatly reduced. It is applied in the same manner as other oils.

● Boiled oil

Lacquers

Lacquer is a substance derived from the sap from certain trees. Modern lacquers have the ability to dissolve the layer underneath allowing each layer to fuse. This gives an even finish and a very tough, durable surface finish. Lacquer can be applied with a brush or from a sprayer, as shown. The wood must first be sealed with a base coat lacquer. Thin layers are best and the surface must be horizontal to achieve the best finish. An electronic spray gun will allow the size of each lacquer droplet to be adjusted from a thick mist to a fine mist.

The lacquer dries very fast and will show less brush stroke marks than varnishes.

Safety
Proper face and respiratory
protection must be used.

● Lacquer application

Varnishes

Varnishes are very hard, transparent wood finishes. They are made by blending resin, oil and thinner or solvent. They are normally very shiny in appearance but can be altered to produce satin and semi-gloss finishes. Varnish has no colour due to the lack of pigments but it can be obtained with light stains added. Varnish is excellent when applied over a stain or dye for wood protection. Varnish will dry quicker when exposed to sunlight or heat. Polyurethane varnish gives the hardest finish and is used on hardwood or softwood floor coverings. Yacht varnish can be used for outdoor applications such as boats and bird tables.

Applying Varnish

Varnish must be applied properly or the result can be disappointing. Application of thin coats will ease any problems but constant attention to dripping at the edges and grouping on other surfaces must be maintained. Varnish may be thinned down with white spirit for the first coat to allow it to soak into the wood. A light sanding (<u>denibbing</u>) between coats will give a better finish. Use long, light, even strokes with the brush or if that's difficult use the small foam rollers available in hardware shops to apply the varnish.

French Polishing

If you have the time and patience, a fabulous finish can be achieved by French polishing. It is the finish found on many old fine pieces of furniture and the finish is mirror-like. In reality, one is applying shellac (a solution of an insect resin in alcohol) to the surface of the wood rather than a polish. French polish is tough and easy to repair but requires a lot of time and work to perfect. There are many opinions on how to apply the **French polish** technique – whichever one you choose, be prepared for some rewarding effort. A simple method involves using **linseed oil** to prepare the wood, followed by multiple layers of **French polish** from a bottle, with a final polish by wiping the surface with methylated spirits. The result is adequate but not as good as a more technical and traditional approach.

Materials required to French polish
- shellac (flakes)
- alcohol
- pure olive oil
- very fine sandpaper
- cotton wool
- cotton t-shirts
- squeeze bottles and eye droppers

1. Wipe all the dust off the wood with white spirit.

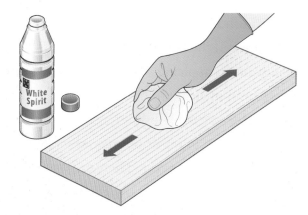

2. Re-sand and wipe again with alcohol on a cloth.

3. Wrap the cotton wool in the cotton cloth making a wad, as shown.

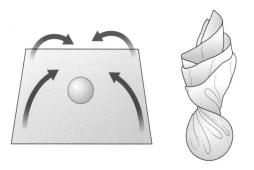

4. Soak the wad in shellac and apply olive oil to the outside of the wad to improve the now sticky surface. Don't worry, the oil will rise to the surface and will not form part of the final finish.

5. Using straight strokes, apply the shellac to the wood using olive oil to lubricate the pad.

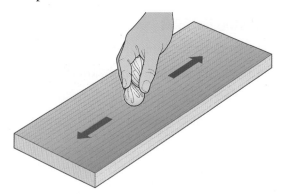

6. Allow to dry and repeat the shellac application. This is the base coat and seals the wood.

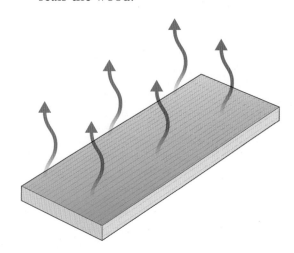

7. Next apply as many coats of shellac as you can in a circular motion.

8. Allow to dry and repeat a number of times allowing the shellac to dry overnight between coats. Store the wad in a plastic airtight container overnight to prevent it from drying out.

9. Between coats, a mix of shellac and alcohol can be applied in straight lines to improve the shine of the finish. This is known as **spiriting off**.

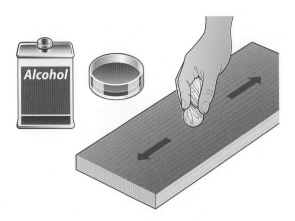

10. Examine the finish under bright lights and any blemishes can be sanded out and further coats applied to achieve that perfect finish.

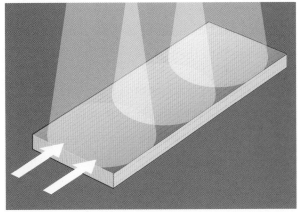

The secret to a professional finish is the final glazing coat. A coat of olive oil and a very small amount of shellac are applied in circular motions, paying particular attention to the edges of the surface.

Olive oil

Shellac

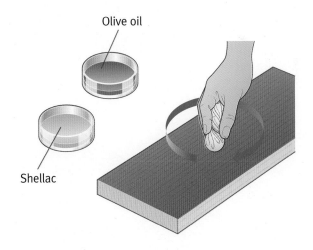

317

Paints

There are a number of ways to paint effectively in the MTW room. Painting results vary from student to student so choose the best method for your ability. All paints can give an added dimension to your designs and breath life into them.

The simplest way to paint is with cans of spray paint. Due to the lack of undercoats, the grain of the wood will be very obvious. Some people will like this effect – especially with pine.

Correct painting involves many coats and requires more skill to get a high-quality finish. Also, the natural grain of the wood will be lost to this process. The layers of paint are applied using a good quality brush, as shown.

Primer paint: This is used to seal timber and give a good bond to the wood for the coats to come.

Undercoat: The next layer, which is similar in colour to the final coat, is used to bond the final coat to the primer. Two or three coats should suffice here.

Topcoat: This is the paint that everyone sees on the final product. It will only look good if the other coats have been applied properly. The final coat must be applied in a dust-free environment and allow to dry thoroughly before touching. The finish can be high gloss, satin or matt.

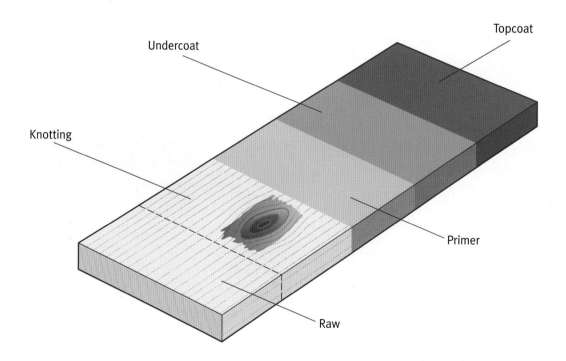

✹ Paint layers for proper protection

Hands-on Tasks

1 Practise removing dents from wood in case this is required for one of your design finishes.

2 Make a list of the different wood fillers available in your local DIY shop, for future reference.

3 Identify the room or location where you will apply finishes to your wood and make sure it is clear of dust and other contaminants.

4 Apply different colours of stain on one piece of timber to use them as a comparison on the same type of wood.

5 Apply different types of waxes and oils on one piece of timber to use them as a comparison on the same type of wood.

6 Practise varnishing old projects, checking all the time for drips and poor application.

7 Make a chart for the MTW room showing the correct way to apply paint.

Homework Sheet on Finishing Wood

1 Why is it necessary to apply a finish to a bare wood surface?

2 How can you remove dents in the surface of the wood prior to application of finish?

3 What types of contaminants could be present in a finishing room?

4 What is a stain or dye?

5 What is the correct procedure for applying a stain?

6 What types of wax and oil are available for finishing wood?

7 Linseed oil is also known by what other name?

8 What safety guidelines should be followed when applying lacquer?

9 What is meant by the term **denibbing**?

INTERNET LINKS AND TASKS

Applying stain technique

http://www.ehow.com/how_14417_apply-wood-stain.html

Applying varnish

http://www.ehow.com/how_14423_apply-varnish.html

Advanced French polishing

http://woodworking.about.com/od/finishing/p/FrenchPolishing.htm

SEARCH

Sample Exam Questions on Finishing Wood

Ordinary Level — 2009

What is used to clean a brush after applying oil-based varnish or gloss paint?

ANSWER _____

Higher Level — 2009

(i)   Describe the steps involved in **preparing** this artefact for an applied finish.

(ii) Select a suitable clear applied finish and give **TWO** reasons for your answer.

(iii) The box is assembled using recessed screws as shown on the right. Describe, using notes and *neat freehand sketches*, **ONE** method of concealing the screws in order to improve the overall appearance

UNIT 3: DESIGN

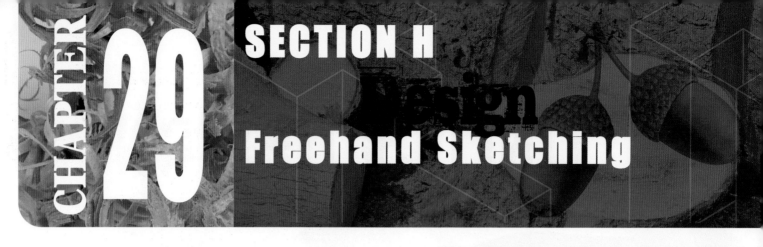

Introduction to Freehand Sketching

Sketching has been used for many years to convey ideas about designs. One of the most famous freehand sketchers was Leonardo da Vinci. Although he sketched and wrote backwards, his drawings were essential to him in creating his inventions. Today, designers still use sketching to convey (mostly initial) ideas before they are drawn on computers.

Sketching takes many years to perfect, and so your skills should be developed in conjunction with report writing and project design, so that the skill can evolve and improve.

As with any skill we must start with the basics. Begin with 2-D drawing and develop this over time into full colour, rendered, 3-D formats.

❋ Sketches by Leonardo da Vinci

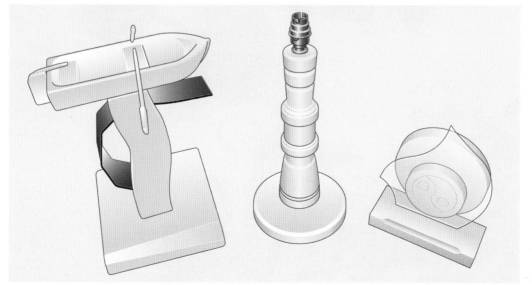

❋ Sketches of woodwork projects

A key element of being able to develop the skills is to have the right tools at hand. For our lesson on sketching you will need:

* 2H pencil
* 4B pencil
* 12 colour pencils
* eraser
* promarker
* highlighter.

We will take the sketching in six parts – work is needed on each part before moving on to the next. Only when you are happy with each section should you move on.

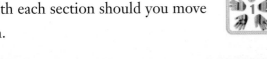

Key Elements to Understand for Junior Certificate Course

* Freehand 2-D sketching and outline.
* The 2-D reproduction of basic drawings.
* The 3-D sketching, shading and colouring.
* Procedural sketches, i.e. building up pictures.

Section 1 – 2-D Sketching in Pencil

1. Practise drawing the lines with a 4B pencil.

2. Hold pencil near the tip.

3. Keep the wrist locked and hold the pencil gently.

4. Use ghosting technique, where you lightly sketch the line first and then get heavier with each passing of the pencil.

5. Do not turn the page. Instead practise the use of your hand and arm movements.

* horizontal and vertical lines

* diagonal lines

* squares and rectangles

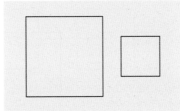

* circles

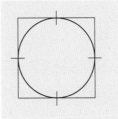

* ovals

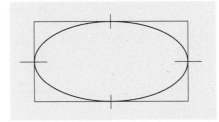

Section 2 – 3-D Shapes and Box Combination

1. Practise the following shapes and forms using the same techniques as above.
2. Concentrate on the proportion, so that a cube is a cube and not a cuboid etc.
3. Ghost the figures first before darkening in.

Section 3 – Rendering and Shadows on Shapes

1. Sketch the following shapes and render using the choices below.
2. Use ghosting techniques to build up the picture.
3. Use the **3-2-1 rule** to add effect to the shapes – 3 heavy strokes on any line

touching the ground, 2 strokes for vertical lines and 1 stroke for lines at top.

4. Apply different materials to different shapes for practice.

When finished practising rendering, try out some shadows from different directions

3-2-1 Technique

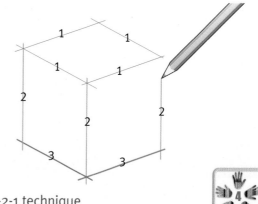

✸ 3-2-1 technique

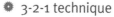

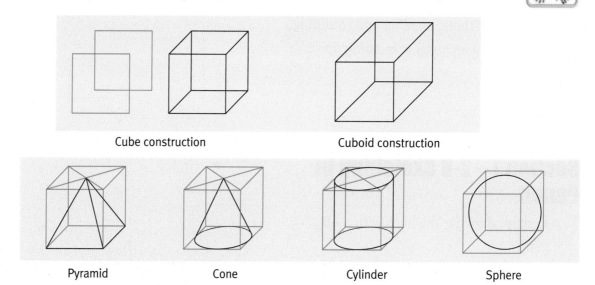

Cube construction   Cuboid construction

Pyramid   Cone   Cylinder   Sphere

✸ 3-D construction

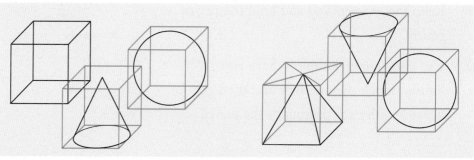

Combinations

Standard Rendering of Three Shapes Step-by-Step

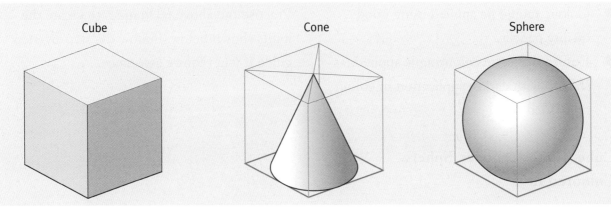

Cube   Cone   Sphere

✸ Rendering 3-D shapes

Application of Materials to Cubes – Wood, Steel, Glass, Fabric, Plastic

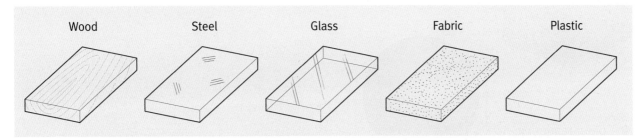

Wood   Steel   Glass   Fabric   Plastic

✸ Material rendering

Realism – Shadows Cast by Cube, Cuboid, Cylinder, Cone and Sphere

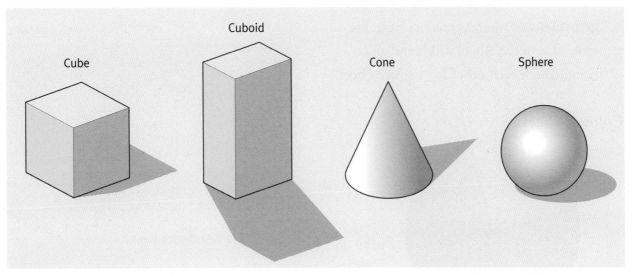

Cuboid

Cube   Cone   Sphere

✸ Shade projection

Section 4 – Using Colour

* Colour should be applied using good quality pencils.

* Ensure that solid colouring is applied (as shown) with darker application of colour on shaded sides.

Cube, Cone, Cylinder, Sphere Coloured In

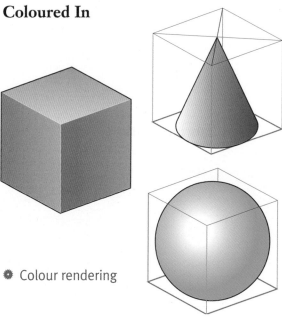

* Colour rendering

* Choice of colour can be decided using the colour wheel. Opposite colours will give great contrast whereas colours from the same side of the wheel will blend and complement each other for a softer effect.

Colour Wheel

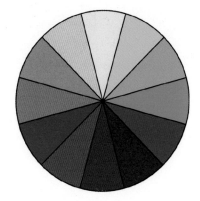

* Colour wheel

Section 5 – Sketching Joints

Practise the above techniques to create the joints shown below. Follow the step-by-step guide if you require assistance.

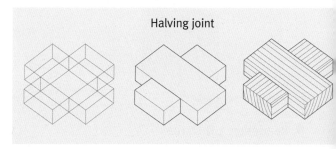

Halving joint

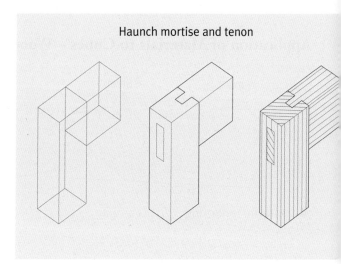

Haunch mortise and tenon

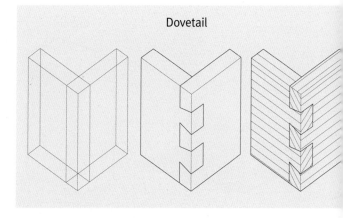

Dovetail

* Sketching woodwork joints

Section 6 – Sketch Storming Projects

Sketch storming is a means of developing ideas for your designs and can lead you on to the solutions required to approach the final design solution. Only one storm per design is shown below, but to fully explore ideas and solutions 3–4 may be required. An idea is sketched in the centre of the page and small details generated using different sketching techniques, as above.

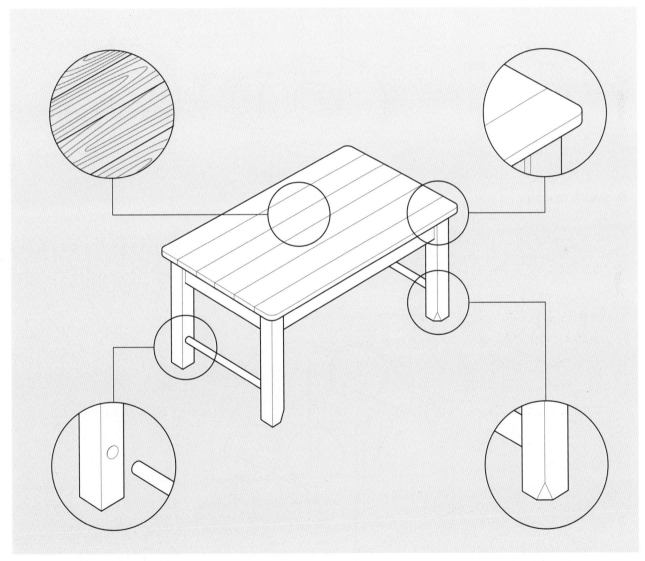

✸ Sketch storming –a table

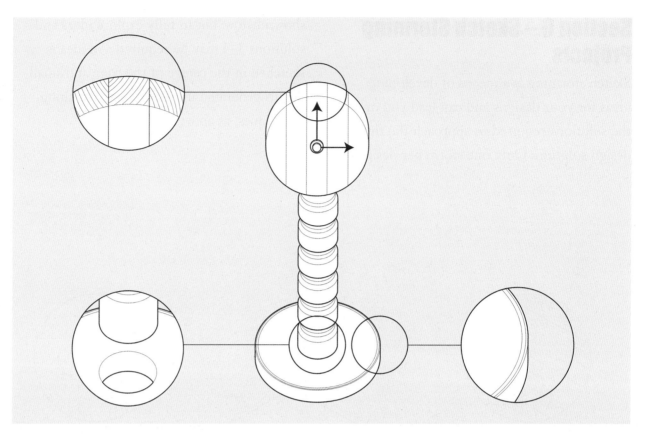

● Sketch storming – clock

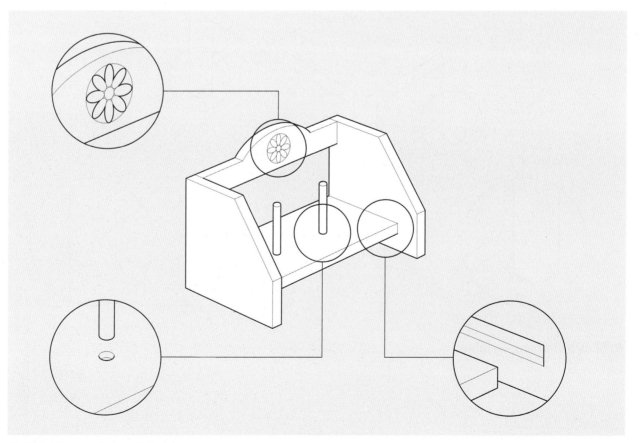

● Sketch storming –CD holder

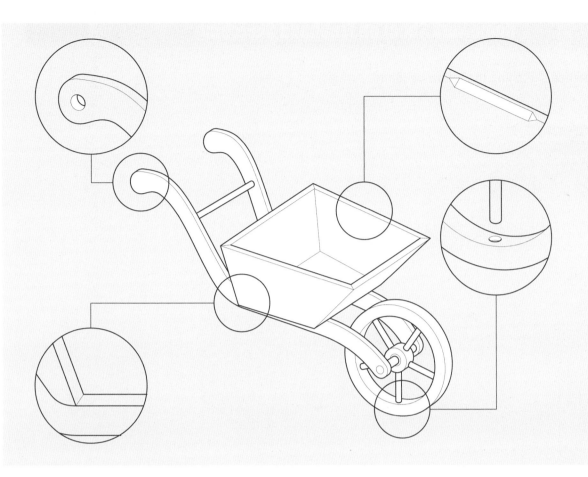

● Sketch storming – wheelbarrow

Hands-on Tasks

1 Obtain the required drawing materials for this chapter from the local art shop.

2 Practise drawing 2-D lines on A4 paper, 2–3 evenings per week.

3 Practise drawing 3-D solid shapes on A4 paper, 2-3 evenings per week.

4 Make a poster for the MTW room showing the 3-2-1 technique.

5 Make a large colour wheel poster for the MTW room.

6 Select any woodwork project you made then sketch the joints and the assembled complete project.

Homework Sheet on Freehand Sketching

1 Practise sketching the following joints.

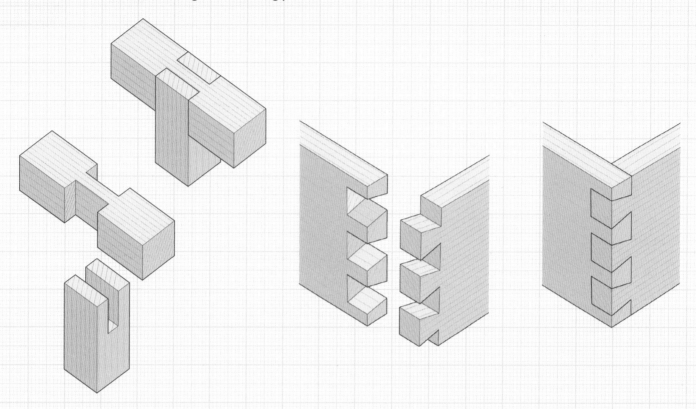

2 Practise sketching and rendering the following woodwork projects.

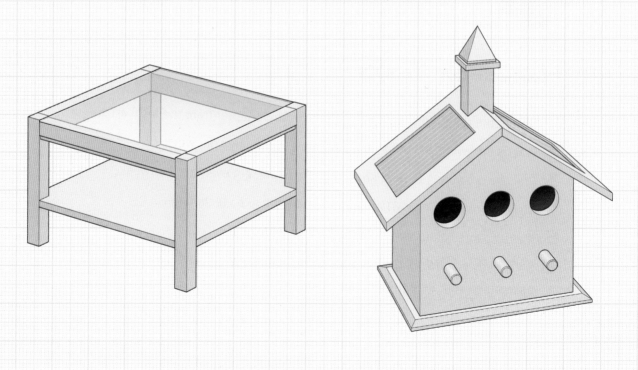

INTERNET LINKS AND TASKS

Visit the following (or similar) websites for more facts in relation to freehand sketching.

Sketching trees

> http://drawsketch.about.com/library/weekly/aao2o2o3a.htm

Pencil drawing tips

> http://www.artgraphica.net/free-art-lessons/free-art-tutorials/pencil-art-tips.htm

SEARCH

Sample Exam Question on Freehand Sketching

Higher Level	2010

The diagram shows an incomplete exploded isometric sketch of a **Stopped Housing Joint**.

Complete the sketch of the joint.

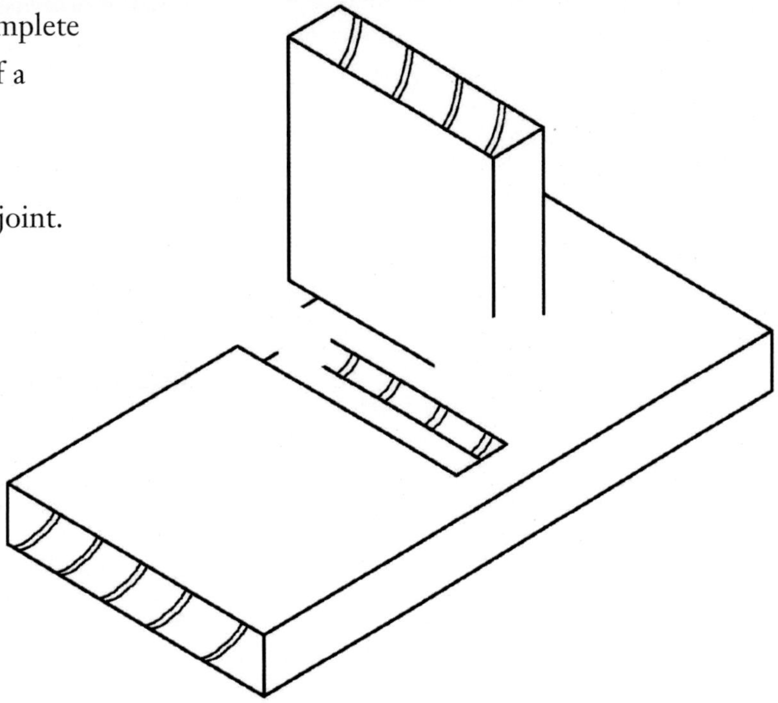

CHAPTER 30

Orthographic Projection for MTW

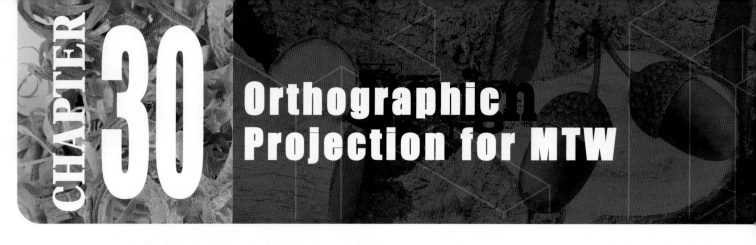

Introduction to Orthographic Projection for MTW

You may wish to present your design drawings in an architectural format so that others can make the design you have created. The simplest format to achieve this is to use 2-D drawings called **orthographic projection**. Learning to create these drawings will allow you to be more precise in the making of your designs – the added bonus is that there are marks awarded for these drawings in your project folio and as full questions in the final examinations.

Many students find it easy to see their design in 3-D before they make their project. Creating front, top and end views adds a new element to the design process and allows for the insertion of measurements known as **dimensions**. This will allow you see if the design will be in proportion in all sizes.

Practise using the drawing equipment for your folio. It will make the exam section easier as it involves drawing a design in 2-D from a 3-D picture. Those taking Technical Graphics will have a good knowledge of this area. Others may need special assistance from the class teacher to achieve the finished drawing – known as a **working drawing**.

Key Elements to Understand for Junior Certificate Course

* Representing designs in a 2-D format.
* The ability to apply dimensions to drawings.
* Converting 3-D drawings to orthographic format.

ELEVATION, PLAN AND END VIEW OF FINAL DESIGN

* Orthographic projection of a Junior Certificate Project

Equipment Required

* tee square
* drawing board
* rule
* 2H and HB pencils
* set squares
* compass
* protractor

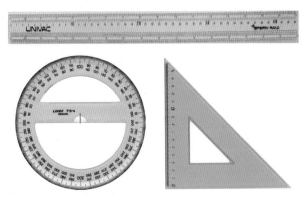

☀ Graphics equipment for orthographic projection

Laying Out a Sheet

1. Place a **tee square** to the left, at the bottom of the board, and place an A3 sheet on the top, level with the top edge of the tee square. Tape down the corners carefully.

Check that the paper is level again with the tee square.

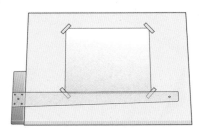

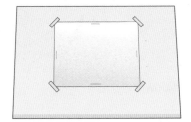

2. Mark a one centimetre mark at the four edges.

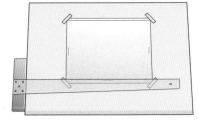

3. Use a tee square to draw the top and bottom of the border.

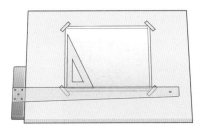

4. Use a set square on top of tee square to draw all the vertical lines including the border.

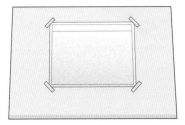

5. Draw a title box to the sizes shown. Fill in **name**, **sheet title**, **date** and **scale**, as shown.

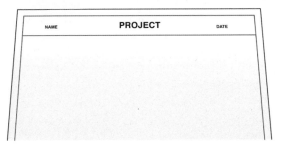

6. The sheet is now ready for use.

333

3-D to 2-D using Sketches

Using sketching techniques from Chapter 29, try to imagine and draw the three views of the box, as shown. The goal here is to get three views of the same object – **front**, **top** and **end** views. From the front we can see only the vertical surfaces of the step. From the top we can see the horizontal surfaces of the box. From the end we can see the step pattern of the box. It is a good idea to write in the overall outside dimensions of the three views at this stage.

Scale

We can see the sizes of the step in the 3-D drawing above. The sizes are too big to be drawn on the final sheet. Therefore we must make the drawing smaller so it can fit. For small items that you design, it may be possible to draw the object full size, but normally the projects are a little bigger than the sheet.

* We can half the size of the design = Scale of 1:2.
* We can quarter the size of the design = Scale of 1:4, and so on.

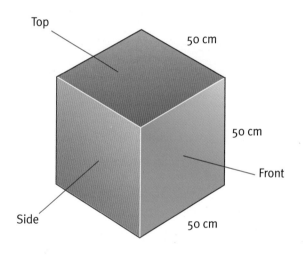

● 3-D view of cube

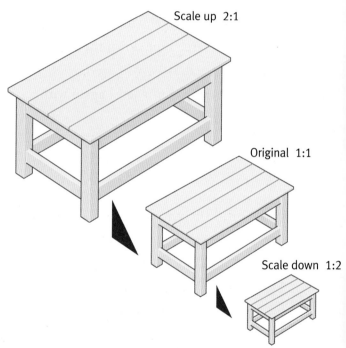

● Scaling up and down

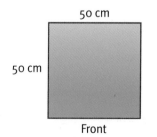  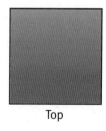

Front   Side   Top

● Front, top and side views of a box with dimensions

For our design a scale of 1:4 should suffice, so we divide all the measurements by four to find the sizes we need to draw the **orthographic views**, as shown.

Orthographic View of a Box

Now it is time to convert our sketches into usable drawings on the lined-up sheet.

Divide the page into four with **dark lines** to create the XY-axis and YY-axis, as shown.

* Set up a forty-five degree light line (as shown) to help draw the **end view**.
* Create three light boxes, these will accommodate the three **views** to come.

Ensure that the **top view** and **front view** boxes line up (as shown) and that the height of the **front** and **end views** are the same.

Use equipment to draw in **front**, **top** and **end views** making reference to the 2-D sketches done earlier. Ensure that the sizes are accurate.

Insertion of Dimensions and Scale

Inserting all the relevant measurements to the **drawing** above, will allow others to make your design accurately. Include the major dimensions first and then any extra measurements required to make the design.

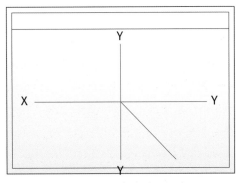
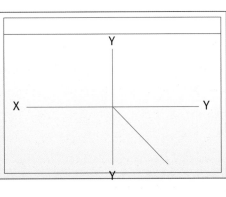

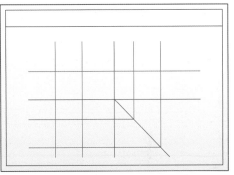

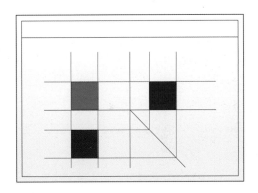

✴ Drawing the orthographic views

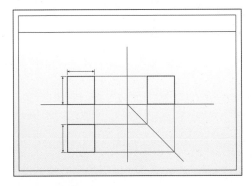

✴ Dimensioning drawing

Dimensions are indicated using arrows (as shown) along with the measurement in 3 mm

text. Radii for **curves** worked and **angles** can also be shown as in the diagram.

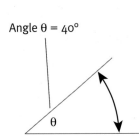

Angle θ = 40°

θ

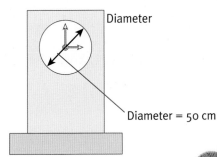

Diameter

Diameter = 50 cm

✴ Other dimensioning symbols

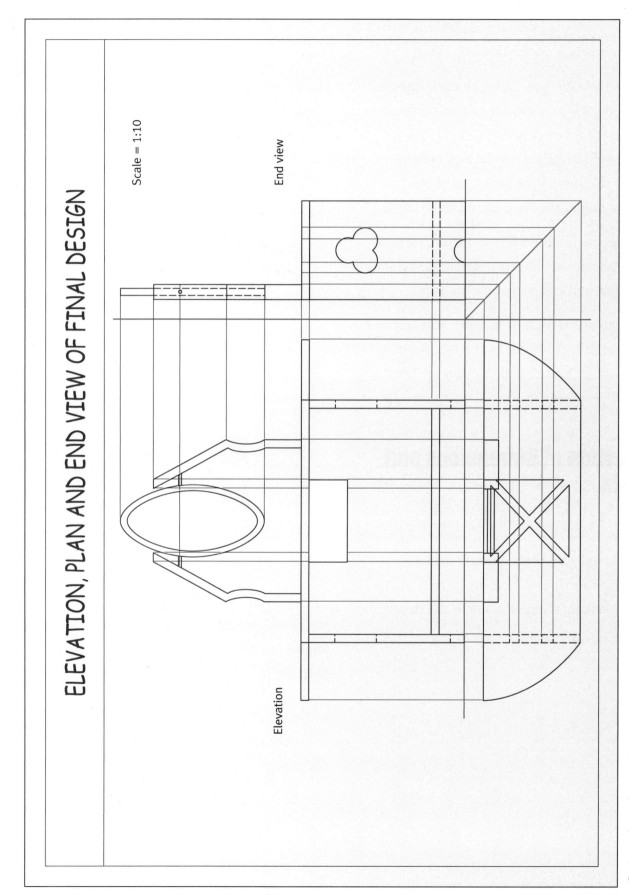

ELEVATION, PLAN AND END VIEW OF FINAL DESIGN

Scale = 1:10

End view

Elevation

✳ Sample orthographic problem

Hands-on Tasks

1. Take a look at a classmate's folders from the Technical Graphics course to see examples of **orthographic** drawing.

2. Obtain equipment from the list to use and practise drawing at home.

3. Line up ten sheets and keep them in a folder for easy use in the future.

4. Make a wooden ruler and insert scales of 1:2 and 1:4 on either side.

5. Search through a Technical Graphics textbook to find other drawing symbols used in dimensioning working drawings.

Homework Sheet on Orthographic Projection for MTW

1. Practise sketching **front, top** and **end views** of the following designs.

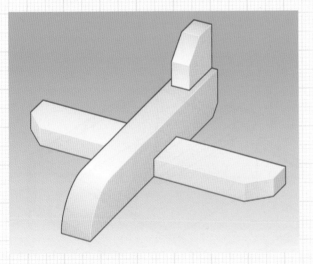

❋ Samples to work on

2. Draw the **orthographic views** of the projects at an appropriate scale.

3. Dimension the three views in each drawing.

Sample Exam Questions on Orthographic Projection for MTW

Ordinary Level — 2010

The diagram shows a pictorial drawing of a desk storage unit.
All material is **16 mm** thick.

(i) Draw, full size, a **Front Elevation** looking in the direction of arrow **A**.

(ii) Project an **End View** from the elevation.

Show the position of the dowel centre.

(iii) Include **four** main dimensions on the drawing.

Show clearly, the dimension lines, arrowheads, etc.

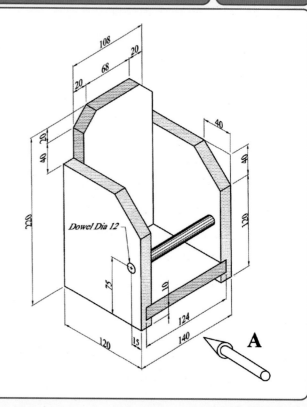

Ordinary Level — 2009

The diagram shows a pictorial drawing of a tray for carrying cleaning equipment (dusters, polish, etc.). The tray is made from **10 mm** M.D.F.

(i) Draw, full size, a **Front Elevation** looking in the direction of arrow **A**.

(ii) Project an **End Elevation** from this view.

(iii) Include **four** main dimensions on the drawing.
Show clearly all the dimension lines and arrowheads.

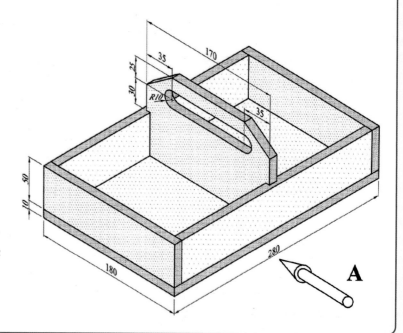

The diagram shows a dimensioned isometric drawing of a model of a wooden chair for a child.

Frame Material: 40 mm x 18 mm

Seat, Back and Table thickness: 18 mm

(i)   To a scale of 1:2, draw a **front elevation** of the chair looking in the direction of arrow **A** and an **end elevation** looking in the direction of arrow **B**. Include **FOUR** main dimensions on your drawing.

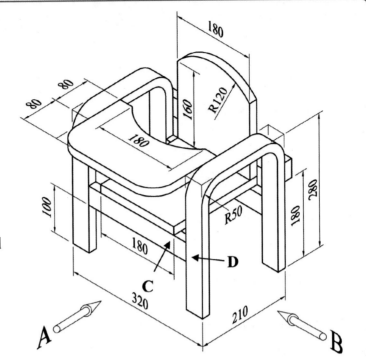

(ii) With the aid of notes and **_neat freehand sketches_**, describe a suitable method of jointing the members **C** and **D**.

The diagram shows a dimensioned isometric drawing of a frame for a fire-screen.

Material dimensions
50 mm × 20 mm

(i)   To a scale of 1:2, draw a **front elevation** of the wooden frame looking in the direction of arrow **A** and an **end elevation** looking in the direction of arrow **B**. Include **FOUR** main dimensions on your drawing.

(ii) With the aid of notes and **_neat freehand sketches_**, describe a suitable method of inserting a wooden panel into the frame.

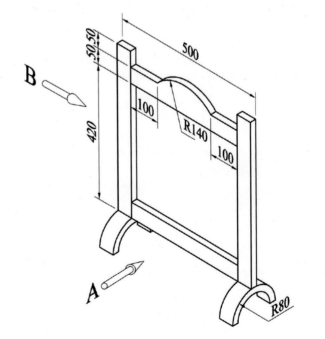

339

CHAPTER 31

Computer-aided Design (CAD)

Introduction to Computer-aided Design (CAD)

CAD is fast replacing all formal hand drawing (**technical graphics**) as the means of communicating technical information about project designs. Freehand sketches are still a vital part of the design process, but now we can draw in 3-D, any design in wood and other materials and obtain from these high-quality **orthographic drawings**.

Like any new skill, we must start with the basics of a CAD program and build up to drawing complicated drawings as we become better skilled and more familiar with the program.

CAD has many advantages: it is fast, easy to change mistakes, easy to create working drawings, easy to send drawings to a **computer numerically controlled** router (CNC) and easy to make multiple prints of the final designs.

With practice you will be able to take the basics laid out here and work toward more advanced drawings, which you can use in your Junior Certificate Project Folio. We will look at a program called SolidWorks™, which should be available in your **technical graphics** room in the school.

Key Elements to Understand for Junior Certificate Course

* creating a new part
* drawing simple 3-D shapes
* adding woodwork modifications such as chamfers and fillets
* rendering the parts in various material shades
* creating orthographic views
* dimensioning

✷ CAD computer

1. Creating a New Part

This is the first step in the creation of a CAD woodwork drawing. Click on the SolidWorks™ icon on the desktop display.

❋ SolidWorks™ logo

Next, click on the icon of the white blank page to start a drawing.

❋ New Drawing icon

Click on the icon for Part to make a drawing.

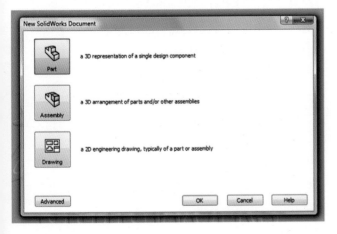

❋ New Part icon

The drawing page (screen) will then appear. Look around it to view all the icons you can use.

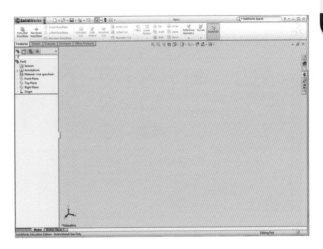

❋ Drawing screen

Save the drawing by clicking on File and Save As.

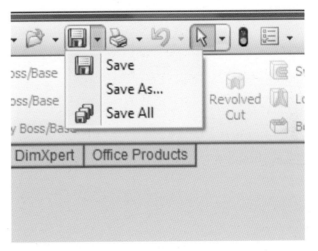

❋ File and Save As

Give the drawing a name to save it with.

❋ Name the drawing

2. Drawing Simple 3-D Shapes

Click on the Sketch icon to begin drawing.

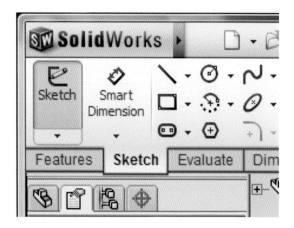

⏣ Sketch icon

Three planes appear asking you to choose whether you wish to draw in Top view, Side view or Front view.

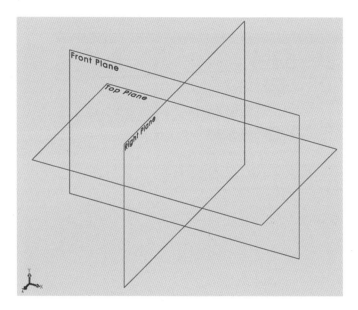

⏣ Drawing planes

At this stage practise using the three buttons on your mouse.

1. The left button is used to select icons and is held down to select large areas or to draw shapes.
2. The centre roller button is rolled to zoom in and out. Hold down the centre roll

button and move the mouse – this causes the drawing to rotate in 3-D.
3. The right button allows you to change zoom views.

⏣ Mouse for CAD

Click on the Rectangle icon to draw a rectangle.

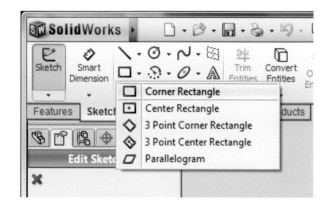

⏣ Rectangle icon

Click on the Red Origin Point and hold down the mouse left button. Drag to create a rectangle of any size.

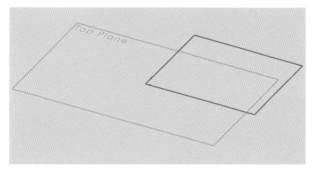

⏣ Drag mouse to create rectangle

To change the size of the rectangle to the required size, click on the line on the side of the rectangle.

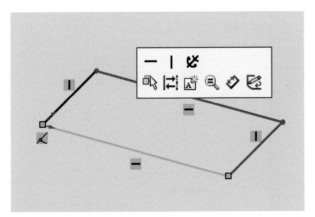

● Smart Dimension icon

Change the size of the line in the box on the left.

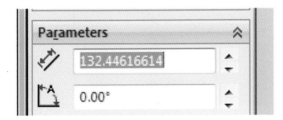

● Changing the length of a line

Click on the other side of the box and change its size.

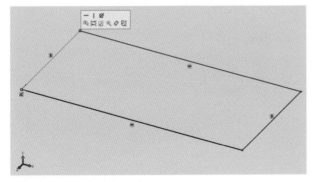

● Changing the length of sides

Click the green Correct icon to confirm sizes. Press F on your keyboard to centre the drawing on the screen.

● Click green dot to finish rectangle

To complete the box, click on the Features icon and then on the Extrude Boss icon.

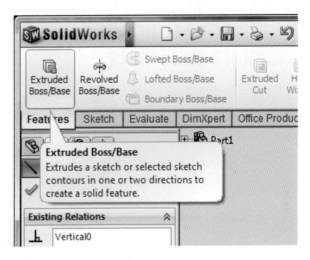

● Extrude Boss icon

You can then type in the height of the box or use the transparent ruler on the image as shown. Click the green button to confirm.

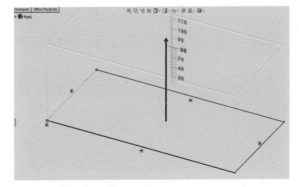

● Stating height of box

Then the 3-D box is complete. Press the Save icon.

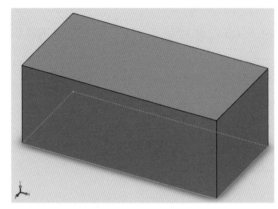

* Complete box

3. Adding Woodwork Modifications such as Chamfers and Fillets

To make the block look like a well-designed project we can use features that we use in woodwork to embellish the design. Chamfers and fillets are easy to create in CAD.

To make a chamfer, select the Chamfer icon from the Features toolbar.

* Chamfer icon

Change the size of the chamfer to suit e.g. 4 mm

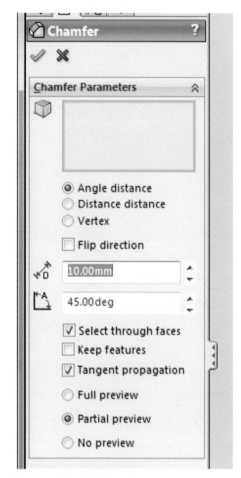

* Change size of chamfer

Select the edges to receive the chamfer.

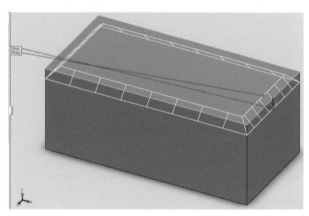

* Selecting edges to chamfer

The chamfers are complete when you click the green Correct button.

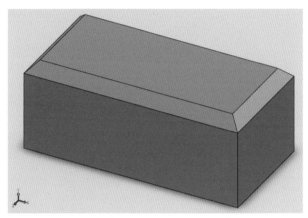

❋ Confirm chamfers

To create round fillets select the Fillet icon from the features toolbar and select the edges to be filleted, continue as per completing chamfers above.

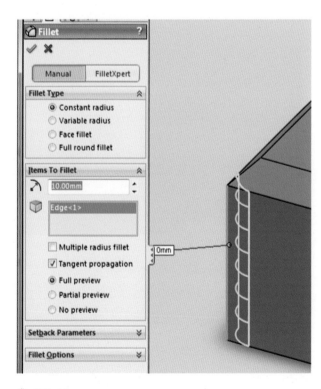

❋ Fillet icon

To return to the Normal view, right click the screen or press the spacebar on the keyboard to select Trimetric view.

❋ Returning to Normal 3-D view

This gives the original view of the altered design.

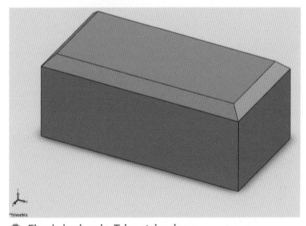

❋ Final design in Trimetric view

Next, we need to make some recesses to hold pencils and an eraser. Select the surface to draw on by left clicking over it. It should turn green.

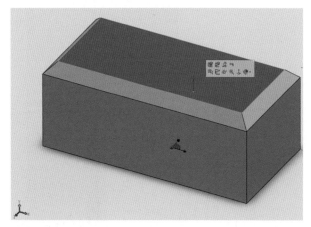

❀ Selecting surface to draw on

Select the line command from Sketch Toolbar, and draw a line from halfway on one edge to the other. Halfway will show up as a red dot automatically.

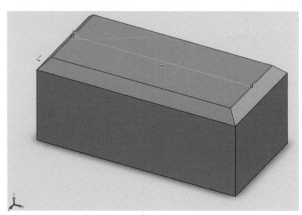

❀ Drawing midway lines

Repeat the line command to draw two half lines on top of the full line, as shown.

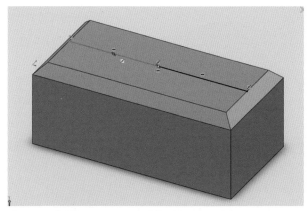

❀ Drawing extra control lines

Select the Circle command and draw a circle on the midway point of the line.

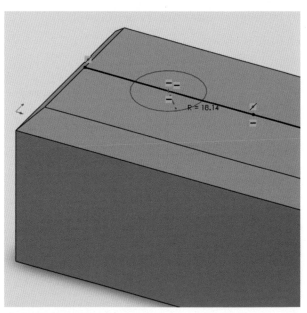

❀ Drawing a circle

Change the radius using the left toolbar, which pops up.

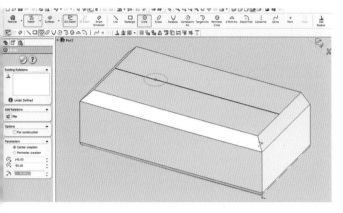

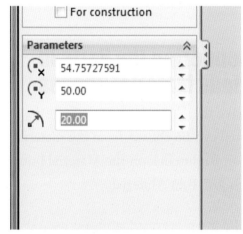

❋ Setting radius of circle

Draw a second circle and size it the same as the first.

❋ Second circle for pencil holder

Click on Extrude Cut from the Features bar and select both circles. Set depth to 30 mm in the left toolbar and click the green icon to complete.

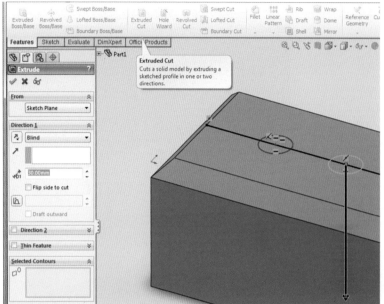

❋ Cutting out pencil holders

Rotate the solid with the mouse wheel to view the design.

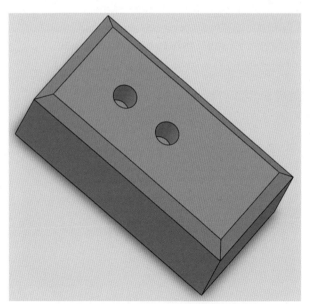

❋ Rotated view using mouse wheel in held down position

Repeat this procedure to make a recess for the eraser.

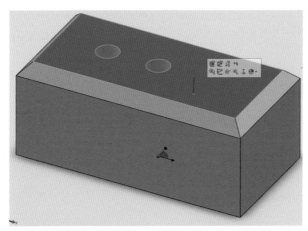

❋ Step 1 – Eraser recess – select top

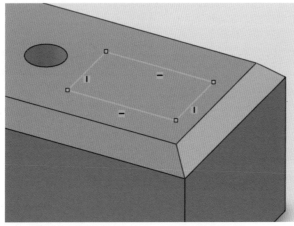

❋ Step 2 – Eraser recess – draw rectangle

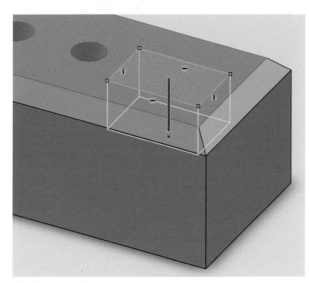

❋ Step 3 – Eraser recess – extrude cut

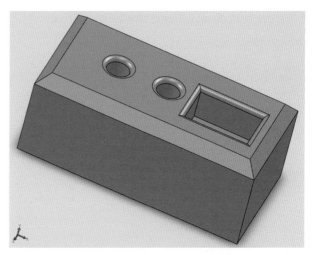

❋ Step 4 – Eraser recess – fillet edges

4. Rendering the Parts in Various Material Shades

To make the object look more realistic, a material can be chosen from the materials toolbar. Right click on the Material button and choose Edit Material.

❋ Materials toolbar

Select your desired material – wood – and then the type of wood by clicking on it.

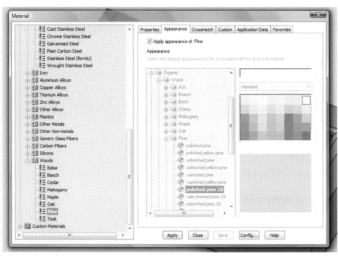

● Selecting material

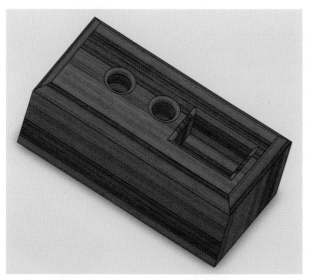

● Selecting specific wood type

Save your work as shown.

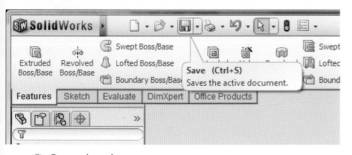

● Save drawing

5. Creating Orthographic Views

Top, Side and End Views can be created by clicking the Orthographic Symbol on the top toolbar under New Drawing. It is the icon which looks like a sheet of paper with drawings on it.

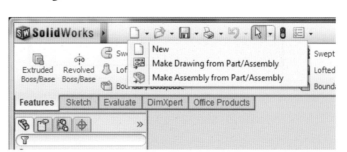

● Orthographic projection icon

Select sheet size for printing purposes – A3 in this case.

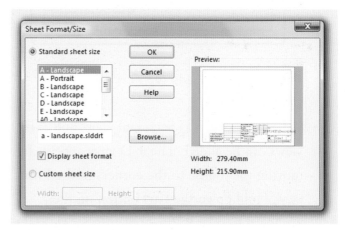

● Selecting sheet size

Moving the mouse around you will see outline views of Front, Side and Top views and you may place them neatly on the screen by left-clicking to position.

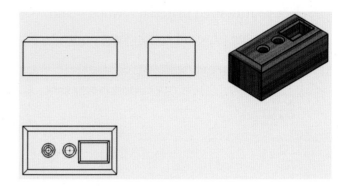

● 3-D in working drawing

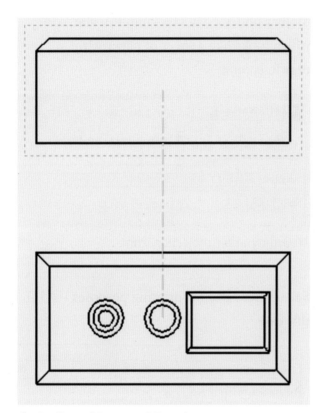

● Outline of Front and Top view

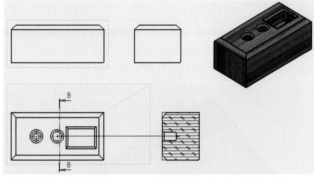

● Sectional view

Other views such as Sectional views and 3-D views can be added. The 3-D view appears by moving the mouse to the corners of the Front view. Hold down the Ctrl button on the keyboard to select a final position for the 3-D view. The Section view is obtained by clicking on the Section view icon and then drawing a line through wherever it is required. Detail views in circular format can also be chosen from the Detail view icon.

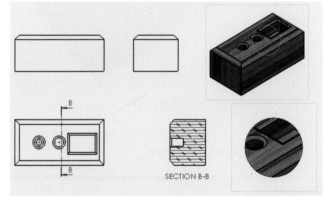

● Detail view

6. Dimensioning

The Dimension function allows the views to have measurements included. Select Annotations icon and then the Smart Dimension Icon.

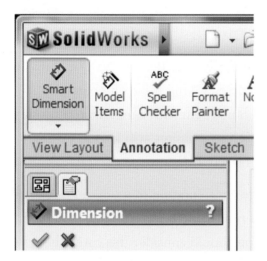

● Smart dimensioning

Left click and drag any line on the drawing to insert dimension.

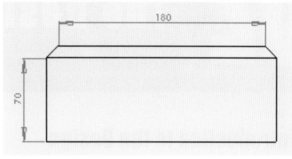

● Dimensioning lines

Dimension enough lines and circles to allow you to make the project from a printout.

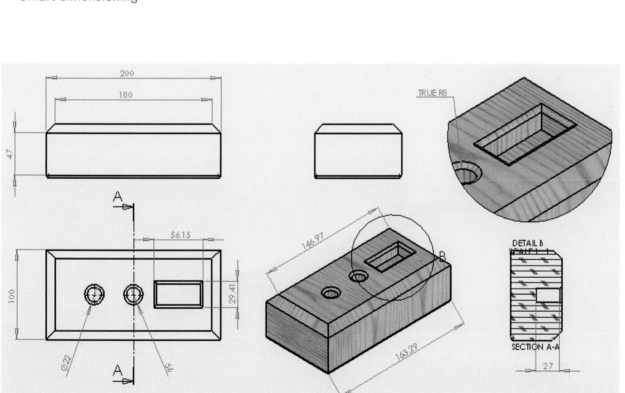

● Complete working drawing

The Design Process

Introduction to the Design Process

The ability to design is a very important skill to develop. By following a simple design process, you will be able to create your own variation of any artefact you wish. In MTW, this means that you will be able to create your own distinct designs from various materials.

There are many elements of good design, which are directly related to projects made

from the materials that you will be using in this course. Taking these on board and combining them with a logical step-by-step approach to a design, will lead to excellent results in your designs.

A large consideration in modern design is the use of renewable materials in the final artefact and you should consider this carefully in your designs.

❋ Concorde – ultimate design

● Dyson vacuum cleaner – elegance in design

Key Elements to Understand for Junior Certificate Course

* Create designs that are individual and creative.
* Design as a means to an end product.
* Application of critical appraisal to final designs.
* The use of assorted materials in the final design.
* Appreciation of the design process.

Factors Affecting Good MTW Design

The following list of important factors will help you identify whether the final design is of a good standard. If these factors are taken into account during the design process and the construction stages, this will lead to good results in the final evaluation of the artefact.

Fitness for Purpose

The final artefact must reflect the brief set out at the beginning of the project. It must also demonstrate excellent performance of the task for which it was designed. In MTW, an example would be of a small trophy or award. It would have to be light enough for the recipient to hold and yet large enough for it to be viewed on a mantlepiece.

● Computer table – fit for purpose

Shape

The **shape** of the design refers to the main geometry of the design. This may mean that the shape is based on a square or a triangle etc. It describes the general outline of a design such as a Pringles carton which has a circular shape when viewed from one end and a rectangular shape when viewed from the side.

● Chairs of various shapes

Most MTW designs would have linear box shapes as their main outline – but this does not always have to be the case.

Form

The form of a design relates to the three-dimensional design aspect. Form almost immediately breaks away from the linear

● Egg chair

shapes described above and allows the designer to be more creative in the final design. The form will also help explain what the function of the design is, such as an award for a footballer in the shape of a boot.

Finish Quality

The quality of the finish in any design is of utmost importance. It not only gives a pleasing look to the eye, but is also crucial in the function of the piece, e.g. non-toxic paint on a child's toy or French polish on a handmade piece of furniture. A badly applied finish can ruin even the best designs, so great care should be taken in the selection and application of the final finish.

● Colour – child's toy

Appropriate Materials

With the cost of materials rising all the time, designs should be made from the most suitable material with the least cost. The material should also have the ability to be recycled easily by the user of the design. The material choice should also be serviceable, so that if any element of the design gets damaged it should be easily fixed by the final user or someone they know. This is known as

🌑 Aircraft in aluminium

appropriate technology. Finally, the material should suit the design in terms of appearance and weight. A desk tidy made from a heavy material such as Oak may not be a suitable material for a portable bookstand due to the weight.

🌑 Skateboard in plywood

Cost

When designing goods for sale, material choice is a huge factor in the end price. More expensive woods and other materials require more labour in construction. Thus, the end price can be high compared to lighter and cheaper woods.

Safety

Safety in design is of great importance. It is obvious that the end product must not damage anyone who uses it. Critical areas of attention here for the MTW designer are no sharp edges, safe non-toxic finishes, stability, weight, security of moving parts and surface smoothness.

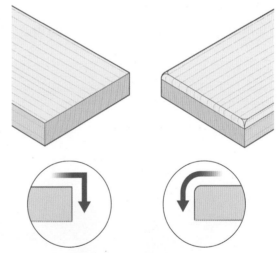

🌑 Sharp vs. round edge for safety

Carbon Footprint/Renewability

All the parts of the design should be renewable. Woods and metals are easily renewed but make sure to select plastics from Chapter 12, Non-wood Materials: Plastics, which can be recycled at least once. Information should be given to the end user regarding which elements of the design are renewable. A renewable symbol could be placed on each of the elements of the design.

🌸 Recycling centre

Ergonomics/Anthropometrics

Ergonomics in design relates to suiting the size of the design to the end user. Designers will follow sizes which can be found for in everyday items such as books and on websites as that for British Standards. Averages are taken for the sizes of people's heights and reach etc. These are used to determine the best average sizes for everyday items such as tables and chairs. These sizes are selected so that the user of the artefact will not experience any discomfort in using the item.

Anthropometrics falls more on the designer's shoulders, because it is in this discipline that the layout of the various parts of a design (such as a dashboard of a car) are decided. The location of switches and knobs etc. must be such that their use is almost instinctive and they are within easy reach of the operator. Anthropometrics works in harmony with ergonomics.

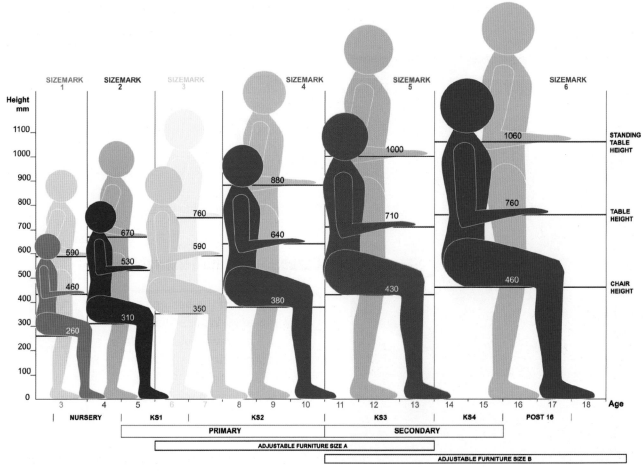

🌸 British Standards for a chair

● Ergonomic layout of car dashboard – Ford Focus RS

A Design Process for MTW

Bearing all of the above in mind, it is now time to study the step-by-step procedure which has been found to be suitable to the needs of the MTW stud ent projects. We will follow this process for the design of a simple bedside lamp table.

Start ➲ Design Brief ➲ Brief Analysis ➲ Research ➲ Design Ideas ➲ Design Solutions ➲ Working Drawing ➲ Manufacture ➲ Evaluation ➲ Finish

Design Brief

This is the description of the project that needs to be designed and built. It will always list the functions and requirements of the **final** design. It will often start with a general statement and then give some of the specific details that the design must include.

> **Example:** A small table is useful beside any bed. Design and make a table on which to place a bedside lamp. The design should be modern in appearance, of lightweight construction and have the facility to hold a cup.

Brief Analysis

Here we take the wording of the brief and disassemble it into smaller parts so we can look at each requirement that the design must have. This can be done by underlining each word.

> A <u>small</u> table is useful beside any <u>bed</u>. Design and make a <u>table</u> on which to <u>place a bedside lamp</u>. The design should be modern in appearance, <u>of lightweight construction</u> and have the <u>facility to hold a cup</u>.

We then analyse each word, firstly looking up the meaning online or in a dictionary and then relating the meaning of the word to our design. For our table we can look at the word **lightweight**.

<u>Lightweight</u> = Not heavy, meaning easy to lift and manoeuvre around the bedroom.

Research

Research is divided into primary and secondary formats. Primary means hands-on research where you go and photograph, measure and evaluate actual artefacts with a relationship (function, appearance, materials) to the brief you have at hand. You can make notes or draw diagrams to note any features that might be useful for designing your table. This could be a sketch of a small table in a local furniture shop with a list of the features of the design that you would consider good design in relation to the criteria discussed earlier in this chapter.

You are looking for ideas to develop for your design. This can be aided by secondary research where you go on the Internet, read magazines or get other readily available material related to your design. Sketches and diagrams (or cut outs) must have an accompanying note to explain the relevance of the pictures to your design. For our table this could be some images online, cut and pasted from the Google site (Images search section) along with an accompanying note, as shown.

The research section can be used for you to evaluate different woods and finishes used in your MTW room (and other places), to identify possible materials and finishes for your design. The advantages and disadvantages of each material and finish can be laid out in chart form, as shown.

Lamp

Diameter 60

Width 50

Length 2 metres

Diameter 300

● Primary research

● Secondary research

For: Stable, nice handles, easy to build.
Against: Old fashioned, Wood damages easily, uses a lot of material.

FOR: Modern, useful, portable.
AGAINST: Weak top, square look.

FOR: Modern, nice material.
AGAINST: Handles poor, cost of wood, too tall.

1.   2.   3.

⚙ Secondary research sketches

Comparing Materials for the Final Project

MATERIAL COMPARISON		
PROJECT: Bedside Table		
MATERIAL	**FOR**	**AGAINST**
PINE	– light – cheap – renewable	– easily dented – may warp
OAK	– looks good – finishes well – native	– heavy – expensive
TEAK	– fine finish – joints easy to make – reusable	– imported – carbon footprint – heavy
STEEL	– modern – clean	– heavy – expensive – hard to work in the MTW room
ACRYLIC	– modern – light	– expensive – environmental damage – weak under pressure

Design Ideas

Now it is time to be creative and start drawing (based on your research) to solve the brief. The goal here is to create multiple ideas and then refine them down to just two or three ideas. These two or three ideas can then be combined to create the best idea.

Take an A3 sheet of paper and, using the drawing and sketching techniques shown to you earlier, draw any ideas that come to mind. Add in details from your research or other ideas that you have. This sheet can be laid out randomly (as shown) – we can make neater sketches later. Exploded views and close-up views can be utilised to highlight specific areas. Note that some of the ideas are expanded from those in the research section. This gives a sense of flow and direction in the design process.

Design Solutions

Now we must focus on finding a final solution. Make two or three 3-D neat sketches, as shown.

These ideas contain the best of the design ideas identified on the A3 pages. An explanation of jointing, materials, safety and finishes can be useful here to evaluate the designs. A model of each on SolidWorks™ will also help decision-making. Each design

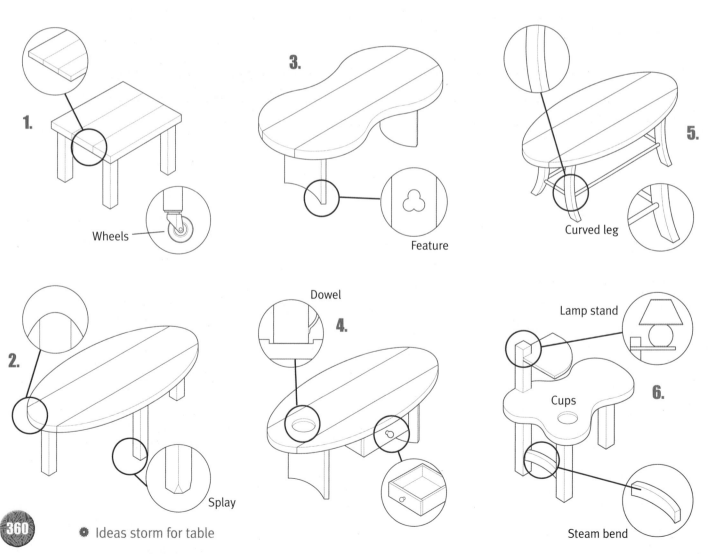

360

⁎ Ideas storm for table

FOR: Easy to make, cheap to make, functions well, good storage.
AGAINST: Old fashioned, soft wood damages easily, doesn't fit with room.

FOR: Stylish, modern, attractive wood, purposeful.
AGAINST: Laminate legs difficult to work, too wide due to ellipse, no storage.

FOR: Modern, good functions, looks well, good storage space.
AGAINST: Expensive to make, complicated to build, too wide and tall.

A.
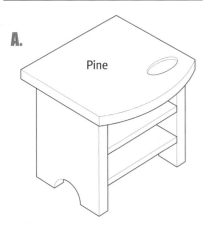
Pine

B.
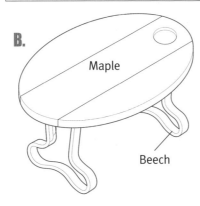
Maple

Beech

C.
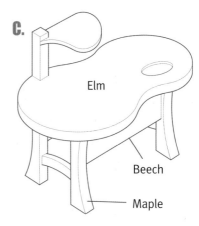
Elm

Beech

Maple

❋ Three ideas for table design – design sketches

must contain the elements underlined in the design brief analysis stage for the design idea to be valid. A simple checklist (as shown) will be of great help here.

Finally, repeat the process to combine the best of the initial ideas to form the **final solution**. Again, as shown, this will take the format of a

3-D sketch with an explanation of the shapes, form and stability etc. and the reasons for their selection in solving the problem in the brief.

Either a model made from card or a quick drawing in CAD, will help you to visualise the solution.

FOR:
Fit for purpose
Modern
Safe
Removable lamp shelf
Use as chair
Stylish
AGAINST:
Wood expensive
Much work needed

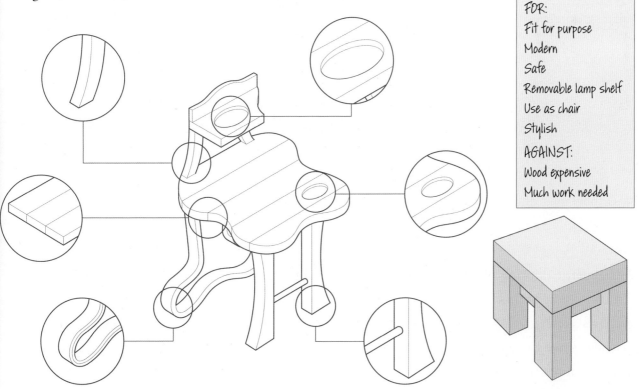

❋ Final idea and appraisal

❋ Model table from scrap wood

Working Drawing

In order to make the design, some drawings will have to be prepared so that accurate cuts can be made with the materials.

The basic drawing required is the **orthographic projection**. This will show the front, top and side view of the design. Include as many measurements as required to make the design. The drawing can be drawn to a scale which suits the paper you are using. Usually 1:4 should suffice for a table. This drawing may be completed in your Technical Graphics class if time is an issue.

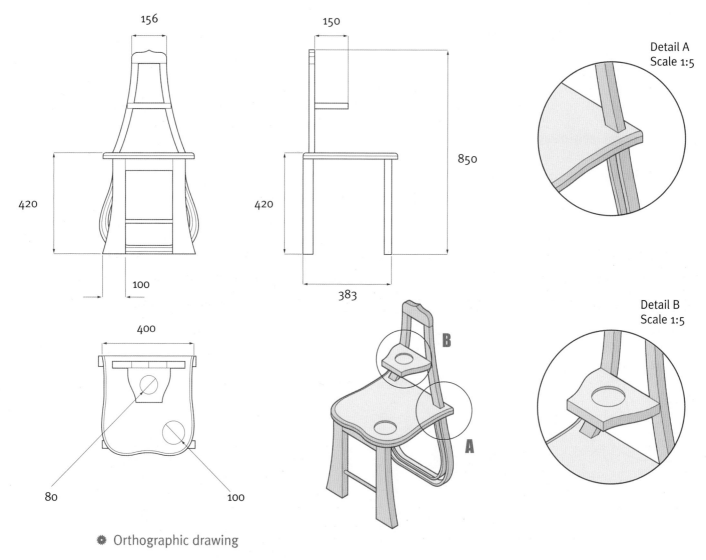

Detail A
Scale 1:5

Detail B
Scale 1:5

✸ Orthographic drawing

An isometric drawing of the design can be difficult if you are not studying technical graphics. A neat, 3-D drawing using a ruler may also serve the same purpose. This drawing shows (from a technical viewpoint) how the table looks upon completion. More able students may also try an exploded view. Of course, if you are using SolidWorks™ to create the drawing it will generate all the views required, see Chapter 31, Computer-aided Design (CAD).

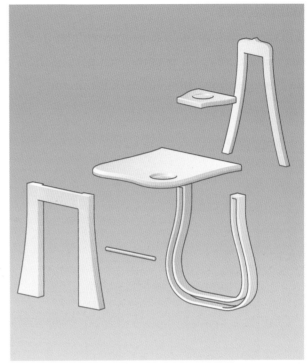

A <u>cutting list</u> will be required by your teacher in order to cut materials for you. It lists the materials and sizes you require to make the design. It is the link between your entire folio of design and the making of the project – it is therefore vital. A sample is shown above.

Name:			
Project Name:			
Part	**Material**	**Size**	**Quantity**
Leg Laminate	Ash	$1200 \times 50 \times 3$	10
Front Leg	Ash	$400 \times 100 \times 30$	2
Front Rail	Ash	$350 \times 100 \times 30$	1
Seat	Pine	$400 \times 400 \times 30$	1
Lamp Holder	Pine	$200 \times 150 \times 30$	1
Top Rail	Ash	$120 \times 70 \times 30$	1
Rear Supports	Ash	$400 \times 200 \times 30$	2

Manufacture

This section lays out a step-by-step plan for the design creation. It takes each part of the design and shows how to mark it out and process it. A sample from the table leg is shown here. Finally, it shows how to assemble the parts and the application method of the chosen applied finish.

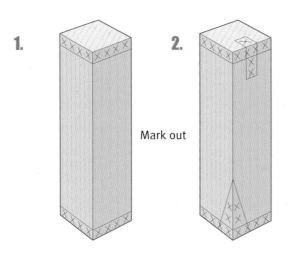

1.
2.

Mark out

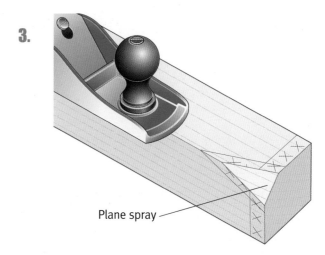

3.

Plane spray

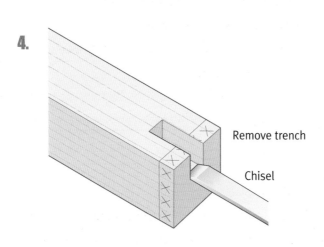

4.

Remove trench

Chisel

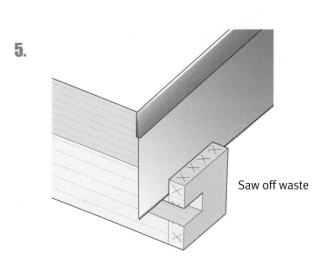

5.

Saw off waste

✹ Manufacture of table leg

Evaluation

The final section is crucial to the process of becoming a great designer. Good evaluation will lead to better designs in the future – in any area of life. You must look at your design with an open mind. You are not criticising yourself here but just evaluating the strengths and weaknesses of the design so that future models can be improved. Analyse the design under the following (or other) headings of your choice. A short note or diagram will suffice for each one – you are effectively evaluating under the criteria for good design as laid out earlier.

Does the design fulfil the requirements of the brief?

It has the useful features of a small table and a facility to hold a lamp securely. The frame structure lightens the weight and there is a small recess to hold a cup securely.

Do the shape and form complement each other?

The square shapes in plan and elevation complement the curves as they are based around the same sizing.

Is the design stable?

The solid front legs and the wide laminate legs at the rear give good stability along with the fact that the design is not too high.

Are there any safety issues with the design?

As the lamp is placed high on the design it may break if it falls over – the recess for the lamp should stop this problem. The edges of the top had to be rounded for safe use.

What quality of finish was applied and how does it look?

The high-gloss varnish looks good and will protect the wood from spillages.

What parts of the design are renewable and where can they be recycled?

All the wood can be used again in other designs for tables or as scrap for practising with – then for firewood.

Is the design comfortable to use and at the right height?

The height of the top allows me to place the cup on the table easily from the bed. The lamp is high to light up more area of the table position.

What aspects of the design would you change if you had to make the design again?

I would use some other materials such as stainless steel for supports to add to the modern look of the table.

I would make the lamp area smaller to avoid knocking the lamp off when using the table area.

What manufacturing problems did you come across in the construction?

Getting the curves right on the legs was difficult on the belt sander.

The laminates for the top of the table warped a little after the clamp was removed.

Any other comments in the design and making of the project?

I really enjoyed making the project and have improved my skills throughout the process. The designing of the project was most enjoyable and the finished project turned out as I had hoped.

Tasks

Second Year Students – Complete small folios for the following briefs and make the project if the teacher gives permission. Alternatively, vote on the most suitable design and make this.

1 A pencil holder is a useful artefact to have on your desk at home.

Design and make a desk tidy unit for your home study. The design should include a facility to hold ten pens, three pocket size books and a calculator. The design should match the colouring and materials of your desk.

2 A coat hanger can help tidy up a cluttered hallway.

Design and make a coat stand for use in your hallway. The design should include a storage facility for umbrellas and three hats.

3 A small toy can give hours of fun.

Design and make a small, colourful toy suitable for a child. The toy should make sounds as it moves and have a money box included in the design.

Third Year Students – Complete full folios for one of the following briefs and make the project if the teacher gives permission. Alternatively, vote on the most suitable design and make this.

4 A mobile phone docking station can help keep phone accessories in one place.

Design and make a mobile phone docking station which has a facility to charge the phone. The design should include storage for accessories and should be based on a sporting or cultural theme.

5 Local heroes in the community are a rarity and should be celebrated when possible.

Design and make a decorative artefact to celebrate the achievements of someone from your locality. The design should reflect the greatness of their achievements and should also convey the discipline in which they excelled. Native materials to the area should also be used to convey the sense of local pride.

4 A child's toy can help develop their imagination.

Design and make a toy which will challenge a child's mind. The design should reflect the colours of the rainbow and include a mechanism to propel the toy in any direction.

Homework Sheet on the Design Process

1 List five key factors of good design.

2 Differentiate between shape and form in design.

3 What is meant by the expression **fit for purpose**?

4 Explain what is meant by the term **appropriate technology**?

5 Suggest five different materials found in the MTW room which could be recycled.

6 Look at the two designs below:

One is an electronic water pump system and the other a mechanical example.

❋ Electronic water pump

❋ Manual water pump

Which is the most suitable design for use in a developing country location, and why?

7 Create a cutting list for the project below from the drawing supplied.

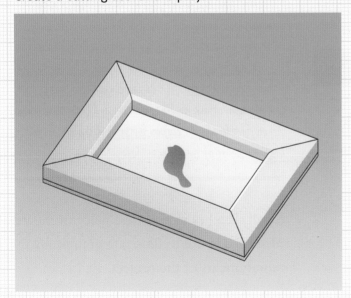

❋ Sample project to create cutting list

Introduction to the Design Portfolio

A design folder or folio is required for the completion of Junior Certificate Materials Technology (Wood). This folio should show how the final design for the **practical** element was created, and contain drawings so that anyone reading your folio can make your design correctly and completely.

While there are many standard elements in the folio (compared to Chapter 32, The Design Process) there is no limit to what a student can include as long as it is relevant to the final design. In fact, the following sample folio is simply a guide for the student to help in the start, progression and conclusion of the folio and not an exact template. Most folios are presented in A4 format.

Key Elements to Understand for Junior Certificate Course

- It is important to remember that a correctly designed project, following a design process, will lead to greater marks and a much more suitable artefact to meet the design briefs chosen by the Exams Commission.

Sample Brief

> A bird table is a desirable part of any modern garden layout.
> Design and make a decorative bird table to enhance your back garden. The design should include a facility to hold bird food and water. The design should also protect the birds from attack by other animals and birds. Show how you considered your **carbon footprint** in the design and manufacture of the project.

Analysis

The next phase of your folio relates to analysing the brief as given. There are a number of ways to do this. The key words of the brief can be underlined and their meaning explained individually.

> A <u>bird table</u> is a desirable part of any <u>modern garden</u> layout.
> Design and make a <u>decorative</u> bird <u>table</u> to enhance your back garden. The design should include a <u>facility to hold</u> bird <u>food and water</u>. The design should also <u>protect the birds</u> from attack by other <u>animals and birds</u>. Show how you considered your <u>carbon footprint</u> in the design and manufacture of the project.

Small sketches may also be made of the items identified above to illustrate graphically the requirements of the project.

Bird Table – stand, shelter, roof, sturdy, wooden, weatherproof.

Modern Garden – grass, paths, ponds, trees, water

Table – legs, flat top, wooden, metal, rectangular or round

Facility to Hold – cups, trays, netting, plastic feeders

Food and Water – seeds, fruit, nuts

Protect the Birds – roof, isolation from cats, non-toxic applied finish

Animals and Birds – hawks, cats, dogs, owls

Manual tools, recycled materials, local supplies, water-based varnish.

At this stage, analysis, you may consider ways to reduce your carbon footprint.

A <u>spider diagram</u> (brainstorm) may be used as an alternative to tease out the key requirements of the brief. As each layer progresses, ideas will also expand and assist you to explore all the aspects of the design.

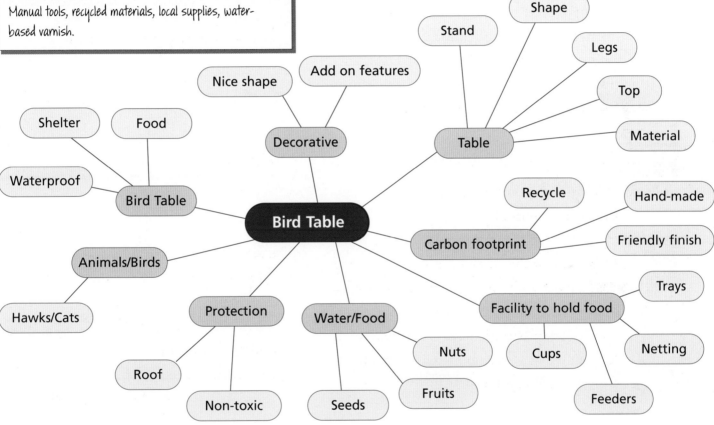

❋ Spider Diagram for Analysis

Research and Investigation

The next stage is to gather as much information about other bird table designs (and other relevant information) so that you can start to design a project to meet the brief requirements.

There are two main types of research which can help you in the process and both should be used to cover the multitude of other designs that will be on the market already.

Research may also include interviews with craftspeople that have made bird tables before. Ask them about ten (up to a maximum of fifteen) questions in relation to the design and manufacture of their designs.

Primary Research

This is based around the student obtaining real examples of other relevant artefacts and examining them graphically, noting the features as well as advantages and disadvantages of the design. This may also involve the student photographing the item and using these photos to analyse the artefact.

Secondary Research

Here the student can search magazines and the Internet to obtain images of other designs similar to the brief. The images can be copied, taking care to credit the original author. The advantages and disadvantages of the designs can be discussed or graphically compared.

Bird box in neighbour's garden

100 mm

150 mm

Diameter 8o mm

100 mm

200 mm

250 mm

Bird stand heights (DIY shop)

2000 mm

Bird hole sizes (Local garden centre)

60 mm

80 mm

100 mm

Food holder size (Pet shop)

Ø 40 mm

200 mm

50 mm

50 mm

150 mm

FOR: Easy to make, safe for birds, no food can get wet.
AGAINST: Looks poor, no water facility.

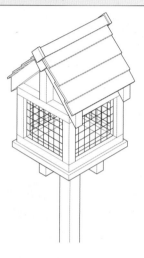

FOR: Safe from cats, easy to make, material re-usable.
AGAINST: Old fashioned, unstable leg.

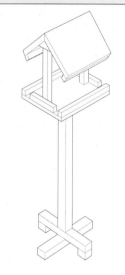

FOR: Stylish, stable legs (tripod), easy to build.
AGAINST: Cats may climb it, food not safe for birds.

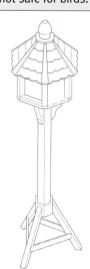

FOR: Stylish, feeds the birds, hangs from table.
AGAINST: Food gets wet, small size.

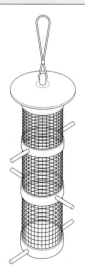

❀ Primary research

❀ Secondary research – existing designs from Internet and Gardening magazines

The key finding of the research may be summarised on one page – identifying the key parts of other designs that could assist you with your sample designs later.

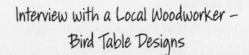

Key Findings from Research

1. Size of the bird table = 250 mm × 200 mm × 300 mm
2. Height = 2 m
3. Hole size = 40 mm × 60 mm × 100 mm
   Auger = 66 mm approx.
4. Large food holder = 240 mm long
5. Tripod stand is more stable.
6. Use water-based outdoor varnish, if available.
7. Mesh around table to protect birds.
8. Styled in an octagon shape.
9. Must include plastic water tray.

Interview with a Local Woodworker – Bird Table Designs

Name of Woodworker:

_____

Date of Interview: _____

1. Have you built a bird table before?
2. What wood do you recommend using?
3. What finish should I apply to it?
4. How tall should I make it?
5. Is it better to use screws or joints for outdoor work?
6. How can I hang a bird feeder from it?
7. Should the roof have an angled or a flat surface?
8. How would I design it to stop cats attacking the birds?
9. How can I recycle the bird table when it is finished with?
10. How can I make the design very stable?

The final areas for consideration at this stage are the materials, applied finishes and possible jointing methods for a bird table. One or two pages detailing joints and fasteners, suitable outdoor applied finishes and sturdy materials (from the theory part of the subject) will suffice. Reference should be made to how selected items are relevant to a bird table design.

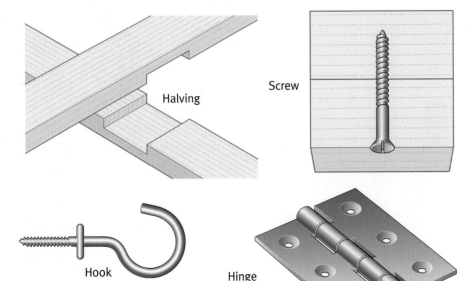

Halving

Screw

Hook

Hinge for door

MATERIALS:
PINE – cheap, re-usable, light, portable.
ASH – heavy, stable, hardwearing, looks good.

FINISH:
YACHT VARNISH – hardwearing, waterproof, easy to apply.

❋ Relevant research

Design Ideas

The next stage of the process is to sketch initial ideas which are largely based on the earlier research – but may include new concepts from the student. Three ideas will suffice, however, better design may be achieved by sketch brainstorming using graphic techniques practised earlier in the course. The three main initial ideas should be described in terms of advantages and disadvantages along with a description of materials, finishes and relevance to the design brief.

FOR: Secure for birds, looks well, sturdy design.
AGAINST: Only one bird will nest, no water store, not a table.

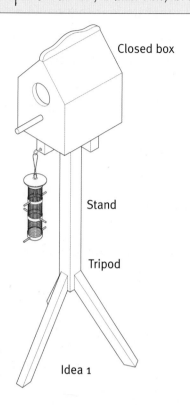

Closed box

Stand

Tripod

Idea 1

FOR: Water and food storage, elegant feet, roof protection.
AGAINST: Open to wind, may be unstable.

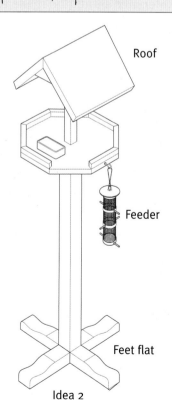

Roof

Feeder

Feet flat

Idea 2

FOR: Modern design, water and food stores, perch for resting.
AGAINST: Complicated design, open to hawks, cats might climb legs.

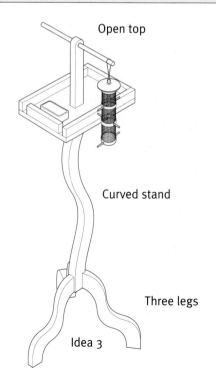

Open top

Curved stand

Three legs

Idea 3

✷ Initial ideas

A

Pole   Tenon saw

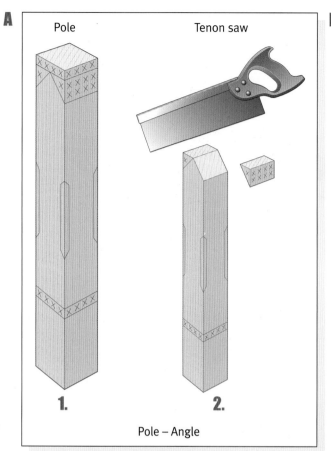

1.   **2.**

Pole – Angle

B

Chisel

3.

4.

Pole – Chamfer

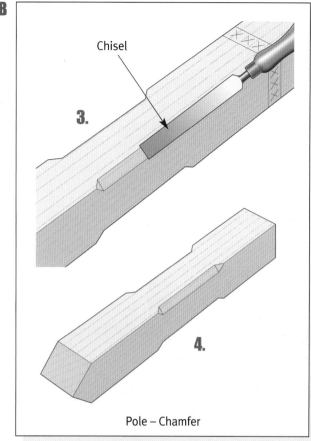

C

5.

Table

6.   Saw

Table – Base

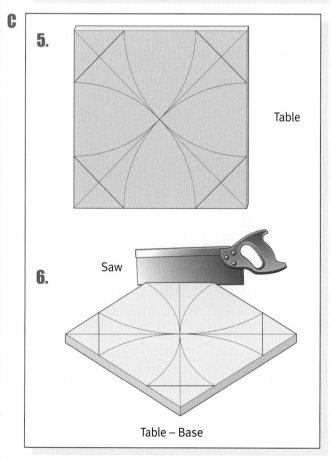

D

8.   **7.**

× 8

9.

Table – Sides

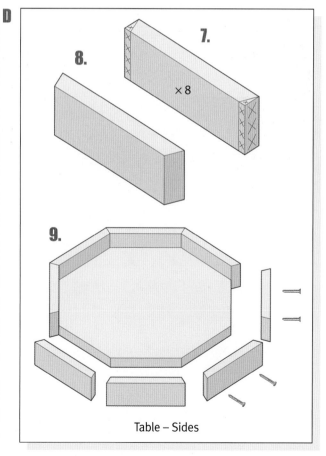

❊ Manufacturing Steps (a, (b), (c) and (d)

E

10.

Feet ×2

11. Bandsaw

Bobbin sander

12.

13.

Feet

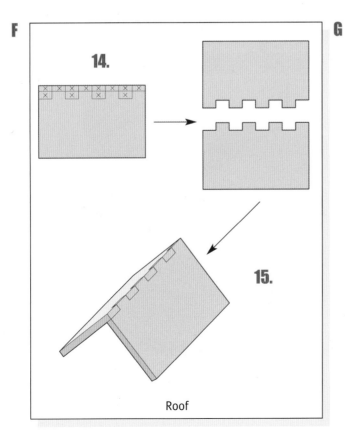

F

14.

15.

Roof

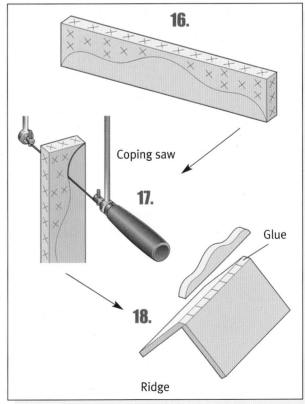

G

16. Coping saw

17.

Glue

18.

Ridge

❋ Manufacturing Steps (e), (f) and (g)

Conclusion/Evaluation

This is a crucial stage of the design project and allows the student to reflect and learn from the experience. The crucial thing to emphasise here is to show how your design meets the design brief set out earlier. A short essay discussing your design (under the headings shown below) should cover all you need to learn from the experience.

* Does the design meet the brief?
* How safe is the design?
* How close is the design to the final idea and drawings?
* What changes were made along the way to finish the project?
* What parts of the design are recyclable?
* How did the manufacture and the time plan work in reality?
* How does the project appear overall, e.g. shape, stability, colour and finish?
* How well does the project function?
* What changes would you make if you were to start over again?

The student may also wish to thank those who helped along the way.

Evaluation and Conclusion

1. **Does the design meet the brief?**

   Yes, the design meets the brief as it performs all the functions laid out in my analysis of the brief. It is decorative, holds food and water with add-on containers, and protects the birds from animals and birds of prey. The processes used in the construction were environmentally friendly.

2. **How safe is the design?**

   The table is very sturdy due to the large feet fitted to the pole and all edges have been rounded or chamfered.

3. **How close is the design to the final idea and drawings?**

   Very close, except I did not use a perch for the birds because space was limited under the roof. The feet turned out a little larger than I had planned but actually added to the stability of the project.

4. **What changes were made along the way in order to finish the project?**

   I had to make the table a little larger to keep it in proportion with the feet of the table. I had to omit the perch to allow more space and also I had difficulty obtaining some dowel.

5. **What parts of the design are recyclable and how did you reduce your carbon footprint?**

   All the wood can be reused to make smaller outdoor projects, or as firewood. I hand-built the project, except for some use of the cordless drill, and I used old screws from a project I had at home.

6. **How did the manufacture and timeplan work in reality?**

   I finished on time in the end even though I lost some time deciding on a final design in the folio segment. The manufacture of the project went as planned.

7. **How does the project appear overall with regard to shape?**

   The shape is elegant and the octagon gives it a modern appearance. The table is very stable due to the wide feet and tripod feet design. The colour is a little dark as I used a stain on Oak wood that was already dark. The finish is very smooth with no varnish drips evident.

8. **How well does the project function?**

   It will have to be put out in the garden to see the true results but it should perform well as it meets the brief.

9. **What changes would you make if you were to start over again?**
   * narrower post
   * larger table
   * more decorative
   * use more screw joints (quicker)

Introduction to Design Projects

Each year, three projects are put out to students to work on as part of the coursework. These design problems require the student to follow the design process as outlined in previous chapters.

Projects are set at two separate levels: <u>Ordinary</u> Level and <u>Higher</u> Level. The amount of work required to solve each level is considerably different so choose the project level to suit your ability.

Project briefs come in two parts – firstly a general description of the problem at hand,

and secondly the specifics on requirements and limitations. New requirements in the brief include a consideration of the <u>carbon footprint</u> of the design solution. It is important to understand that this refers to where you source your materials, your choice of materials, choice of applied finish, amount of power tool involvement, amount of recyclable parts and fittings, and other factors which are deemed to have an adverse effect on the environment.

The samples below, and the past exam briefs, should allow you to practise problem-solving skills when combined with the design process in Chapter 32.

● Designer at work

* Solving problems in order to reflect individuality and creativity.
* A critical appraisal of solutions.
* The constraints and limitation on design.
* The reduction of student carbon footprint in the design and manufacturing solution.

Sample Design Briefs for Student Practice

Ordinary Level Samples

A bedside locker is useful for holding small personal items at night.
Design and make a bedside locker with the facility to hold in place a lamp and three small personal items. The design should include a facility to charge a mobile phone.

Children derive many hours of enjoyment from wooden toys.
Design and make a small wooden toy which incorporates a noise-making mechanism. The design should be finished in attractive and non-toxic colours.

Mobile phones come with many accessories for use with the phone.
Design and make a mobile phone holder for a desktop. The design should include storage for two phone accessories and a phone charger.

Higher Level Samples

Hallways can become cluttered with many personal items used by the entire family.
Design and make a hall table to facilitate the storage of bags, umbrellas and letters in the hallway. The design should include a facility to hold personal grooming products and a mirror.

School teams include members from many cultural backgrounds.
Design and make an award for the player of the year which would reflect the different nationalities represented on the team. The design should make reference to the team activity involved.

Garden ornaments add greatly to the aesthetics of a modern garden.
Design and make a wooden garden ornament which is modern in appearance and has a moving part. The design should reflect the natural beauty of the garden and the flora and fauna of the locality.

Ordinary Level Exam Briefs

Design and make a decorative artefact to display one small bathroom towel and which will neatly store three other towels.

The artefact should be elegant in appearance and should reflect an aquatic theme.

Design and make a decorative mirror which incorporates a theme to reflect your favourite pastime.

The mirror should be elegant and attractive in appearance and should include an open-storage facility to hold small personal items.

Design and make a small decorative garden ornament to indicate wind direction.

The artefact should be of robust construction and incorporate a theme based on Irish wildlife.

Design and make a decorative mobile to suggest the theme of space exploration.

Design and make a decorative moneybox that is capable of being reused.

Design and make a desk tidy suitable for placing on a desktop.

It should give easy access to pens and pencils. It should also incorporate storage for other stationery items.

Design and make a decorative unit to hold and display up to ten DVDs and a selection of your favourite compact discs (CDs).

The unit should be attractive and stylish in appearance and fit in with the furniture in the room.

Design and make a small folding picnic table suitable for use by two people.

The table should be lightweight, sturdy in construction and designed for use both indoors and outdoors.

Design and make a coat stand suitable for use by a child.

The coat stand should be well-finished, pleasing to look at and should include a feature that a child would find attractive.

Design and make a small mirror unit suitable for use in a bathroom.

The design should suggest a marine theme and the unit should include a facility for holding a small number of personal grooming items.

Design and make a desktop artefact that will hold pens, pencils and a calculator.

The artefact should be attractive and stylish in appearance and the design should suggest the theme of changeover to the Euro currency.

Design and make a lamp suitable for use in a young person's bedroom.

The design should suggest a theme that is of particular interest to you. All electrical connections and fittings should comply with current safety standards.

Design and make a small toy which would be suitable for a young child.

The toy should be safe when in use and should incorporate an interesting form of motion that would attract the attention of a child.

Design and make a small artefact that would hold a selection of basic hand tools.

The artefact should be portable, attractive and be designed to contain a selection of tools suitable for minor repairs in the home.

Design and make an artefact that would allow for the easy feeding and observation of small birds.

The artefact should be stylish in appearance and designed to protect the small birds during winter

Design and make a small toy, which would be suitable for a young child.

The toy should be safe when in use and should incorporate a circus theme that would make the toy visually attractive to the child.

Design and make a table lamp suitable for a young person's bedroom.

The lamp should be attractive in appearance and should incorporate a facility to display a small photograph. All electrical connections and fittings should comply with current safety standards.

Design and make an attractive key rack to hold a number of keys.

The key rack should incorporate a facility to store a small torch and spare batteries. The artefact should be attractive and stylish in appearance.

Design and make a footstool suitable for use in a living room.

The stool should be elegant in appearance and should harmonise with the other furniture in the room.

Design and make a small unit for the safe storage of charging devices for use with battery-powered items.

The artefact should be compact, attractive in appearance and should store a minimum of three such charging devices.

Design and make an attractive CD holder suitable for use on a desk.

The CD holder should accommodate ten of your favourite CDs and display the CDs in an attractive manner. The artefact should also incorporate a music theme.

Design and make a decorative artefact to display one small bathroom towel and which will neatly store three other towels.

The artefact should be elegant in appearance and should reflect an aquatic theme.

Design and make a decorative mirror which incorporates a theme to reflect your favourite pastime.

The mirror should be elegant and attractive in appearance and should include an open storage facility to hold small personal items.

Design and make a small decorative garden ornament to indicate wind direction.

The artefact should be of robust construction and incorporate a theme based on Irish wildlife.

Higher Level Exam Briefs

A stool as an item of furniture has many uses.

Design and make a sturdy and elegant stool for use in the home. The stool should be designed to include a secondary function specific to the area in which it is to be used. You should demonstrate how you considered your carbon footprint in the design, selection of materials and in the processes used in the manufacture of the stool.

Many people partake in artistic or craft activities as a form of relaxation and as a means of expressing their creative talents.

Design and make a decorative artefact to reflect a particular artistic or craft activity. The design idea should be inspired by the intrinsic beauty of the wood and the artefact should be elegant to behold in a setting of your choice.

Many young people like to sketch and paint.

Design and make a small portable artefact for use when sketching and painting in an outdoor setting. The artefact should accommodate storage for sketching and painting materials and should be designed to incorporate an ergonomically suitable work surface.

A stool as an item of furniture has many uses.

Design and make a sturdy and elegant stool for use in the home. The stool should be designed to include a secondary function specific to the area in which it is to be used. You should demonstrate how you considered your carbon footprint in the design, selection of materials and in the processes used in the manufacture of the stool.

Many people partake in artistic or craft activities as a form of relaxation and as a means of expressing their creative talents.

Design and make a decorative artefact to reflect a particular artistic or craft activity. The design idea should be inspired by the intrinsic beauty of the wood and the artefact should be elegant to behold in a setting of your choice.

Many young people like to sketch and paint.

Design and make a small portable artefact for use when sketching and painting in an outdoor setting. The artefact should accommodate storage for sketching and painting materials and should be designed to incorporate an ergonomically suitable work surface.

The safe storage of medicine is a concern in many homes.
Design and make a slim storage facility for medicine. It should be capable of being secured so that a child would find it difficult to obtain the medicine.

In 1998, the Tour de France started in Ireland for the first time.
Design and make a decorative artefact reflecting the significance of this sporting occasion, which could be presented to the winner of an Irish stage of this race.

It is difficult to read information from a sheet lying on a horizontal surface when using a computer.
Design and make an artefact to support an A4-size sheet of paper. The artefact should be adjustable for the angle of reading and it should also be portable.

Remote control units for televisions, video and audio players can be easily mislaid.
Design and make a decorative artefact that would store a remote control unit when not in use. The artefact should be sturdy, lightweight and include a facility for supporting a cup or a glass for drinks. It should also incorporate a device that would indicate when a control unit has not been replaced.

The year 2000 marked the end of the last millennium and the dawn of a new one.
Many people look to a new millennium with renewed hope for a better future. Design and make a decorative artefact to commemorate the beginning of a new millennium. This artefact should suggest light as a symbol, representing the theme of renewed hope.

Plastic shopping bags are detrimental to the environment and their proper storage is often difficult in the home.
Design and make a neat, well-proportioned artefact that will store and dispense plastic shopping bags for recycling. Include a visually attractive consumer information leaflet that might help to market this artefact.

Many young people are interested in music and may have a small music system.
Design and make an elegant stand to hold such a system. The stand should incorporate a storage facility for a remote control unit and ten of your favourite CDs or cassette tapes. These items should be easily accessible.

Young people are particularly aware of the importance of caring for the environment. This is often expressed through involvement in projects to improve their local surroundings.

Design and make a decorative artefact that could be presented as an award to an individual or group to celebrate involvement in a local environmental project.

A portable sketching unit is often used by people who sketch.

Design and make a portable sketching unit that will store a selection of sketching equipment. The unit should be compact and lightweight and should accommodate an A4-size sketching pad when in use.

A table for use by the side of an armchair is often convenient when relaxing.

Design and make a small table suitable for use by a person when seated. The table should be sturdy, elegant in appearance and should incorporate storage for a small number of items useful to a person when seated.

Many young people are inspired by scientific discoveries and innovations which make an invaluable contribution to human advancement.

Design and make a decorative artefact which could be presented as a youth achievement award to an individual or group. The artefact should be inspired by a scientific discovery or innovation and should reflect the nobility of human endeavour.

An organised bedroom is the delight of every teenager and parent.

Design and make an artefact suitable for the storage of footwear in a bedroom. The artefact should hold a minimum of four pairs of shoes and should incorporate a facility for the storage of materials and equipment for the care of shoes. The artefact should be freestanding, elegant in appearance and should complement the furniture in the room.

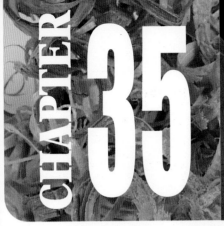

CHAPTER 35

Woodwork Projects: Levels 1, 2 and 3

Introduction to Woodwork Projects, Levels 1, 2 and 3

Outlined below is a selection of typical Junior Certificate practical projects. The projects are divided into Year 1, Year 2 and Year 3.

While each project is designed for a particular year of study, each can be modified by you or the teacher to reflect your ability level – you may add on or subtract some parts to suit.

While some jointing methods are displayed, you may choose your own joints and fixings based on your level of knowledge of the course.

You may also use timber of your choice as well as modifying the dimensions and sizes to suit your own needs.

Plane

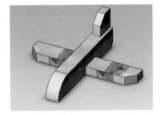

☀ 3-D view

Boat

☀ 3-D view

Train

☀ 3-D view

Table

☀ 3-D view

Bird House

☀ 3-D view

Desk Tidy

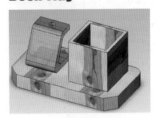

☀ 3-D view

Lamp

☀ 3-D view

Marquetry Picture

☀ 3-D view

Carved Boat

☀ 3-D view

Level 1, Year 1
Plane

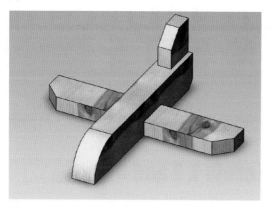

◉ 3-D view

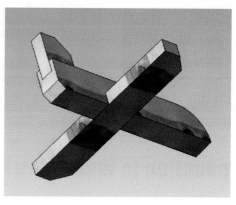

◉ Exploded view

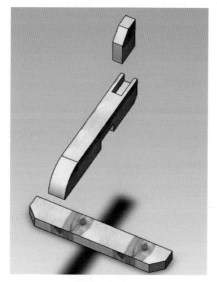

◉ Additional 3-D view

Cutting List		
Plane		
Fuselage	270 × 44 × 30	pine
Tail	60 × 44 × 18	pine
Wing	270 × 44 × 18	pine

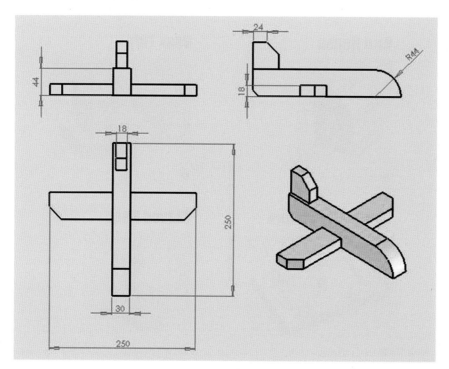

◉ Working drawing

Boat

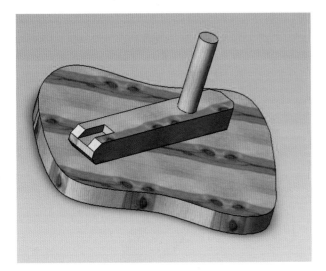

● 3-D view

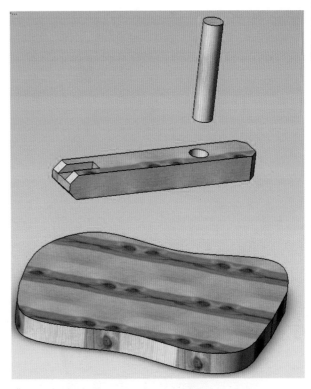

● Exploded view

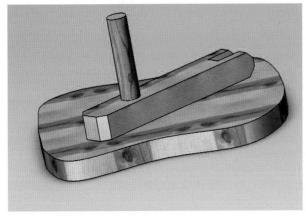

● Additional 3-D view

Cutting List		
Boat		
Base	300 × 300 × 20	pine
Hull	250 × 44 × 30	pine
Mast	R12 × 100	pine

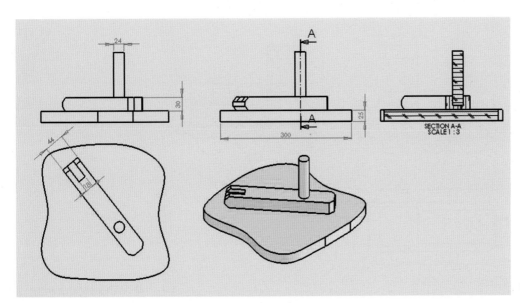

● Working drawing

Train

🌸 3-D view

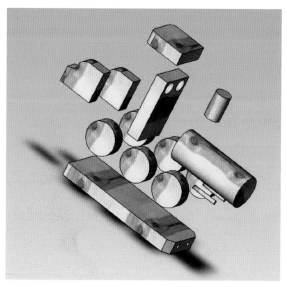

🌸 Exploded view

🌸 Additional 3-D view

Cutting List		
Train		
Wheel × 6	R25 × 20	pine
Base	460 × 75 × 20	pine
Engine	R25 × 120	pine
Front Cab	100 × 60 × 20	pine
Side Cab × 2	55 × 50 × 20	pine
Top Cab	70 × 60 × 20	pine
Buffer × 2	R3 × 40	pine
Chimney	R12 × 40	pine

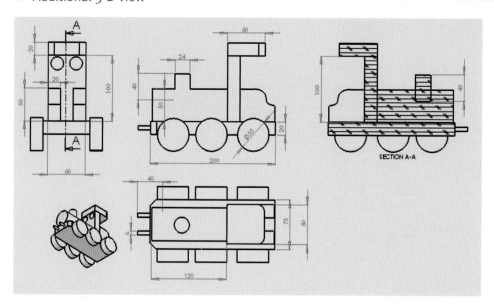

🌸 Working drawing

Level 2, Year 2
Table

● 3-D view

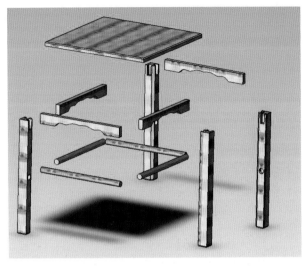

● Exploded view

● Additional 3-D view

Cutting List		
Table		
Top	492 × 492 × 20	pine
Leg × 4	495 × 44 × 44	pine
Rail × 4	400 × 44 × 20	pine
Supports × 4	R10 × 400	pine

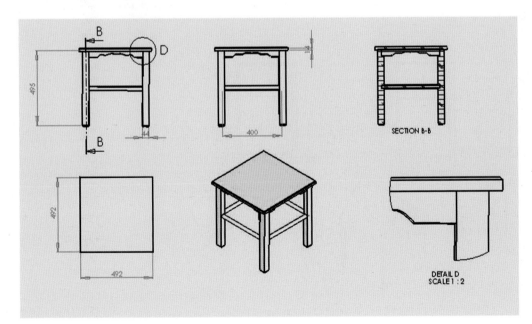

SECTION B-B

DETAIL D
SCALE 1 : 2

● Working drawing

Bird House

● 3-D view

● Exploded view

Cutting List		
Bird House		
Front	$300 \times 200 \times 10$	plywood
Back	$300 \times 200 \times 18$	plywood
Base	$172 \times 164 \times 18$	plywood
Side $\times$ 2	$172 \times 200 \times 18$	plywood
Roof $\times$ 2	$200 \times 160 \times 6$	plywood
Perch $\times$ 2	$R5 \times 60$	pine

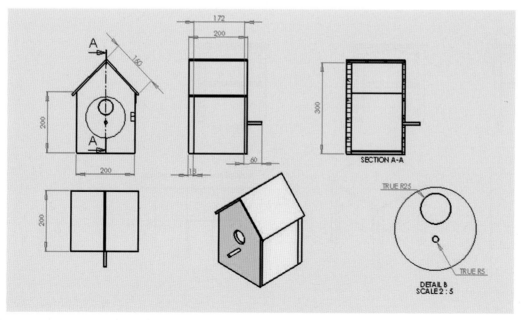

● Working drawing

Desk Tidy

● 3-D view

● Exploded view

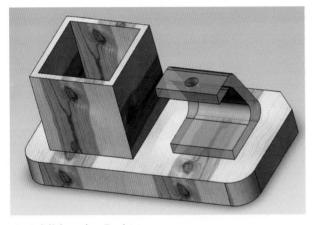

● Additional 3-D view

Cutting List		
Desk Tidy		
Base	240 × 120 × 25	Oak
Pencil Holder	150 × 60 × 4	perspex
Box Side × 4	80 × 80 × 10	pine

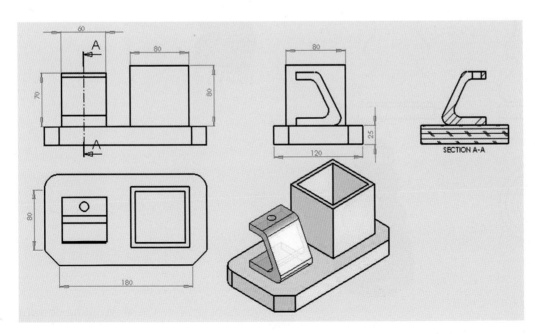

SECTION A-A

● Working drawing

Level 2, Year 3
Lamp

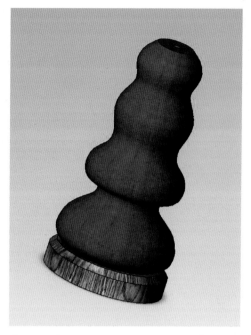

● 3-D view

● Exploded view

Cutting List		
Lamp		
Base	$200 \times 200 \times 30$	maple
Pedestal	$300 \times 200 \times 200$	ash

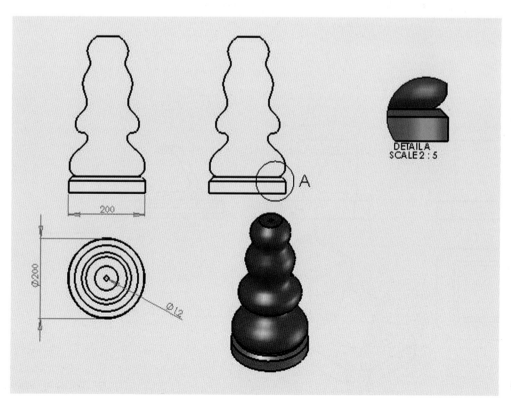

DETAIL A
SCALE 2 : 5

200

Ø200

Ø12

● Working drawing

Marquetry Picture

❋ 3-D view

❋ Exploded view

❋ Additional 3-D view

Cutting List		
Picture Frame		
Back	250 × 175 × 6	plywood
Large Frame Side × 2	250 × 40 × 20	pine
Small Frame Side × 2	175 × 40 × 20	pine
Veneer × 2	170 × 95 × 1	maple and cherry

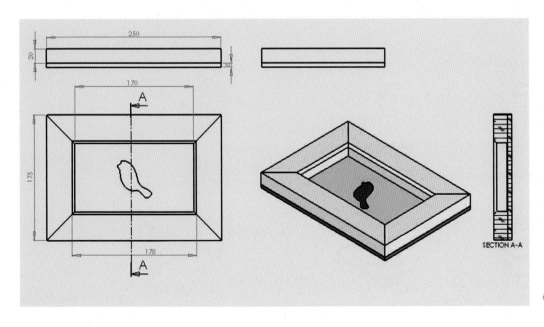
❋ Working drawing

SECTION A-A

Carved Boat

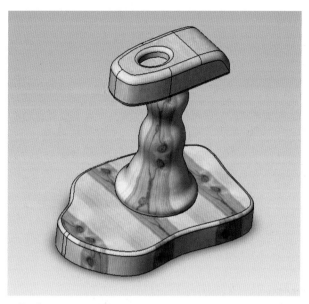

3-D view

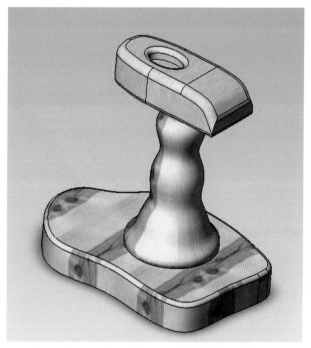

❋ Additional 3-D view

Cutting List		
Boat Carving		
Boat	180 × 100 × 50	lime
Stand	300 × 120 × 120	cherry
Base	300 × 200 × 40	maple

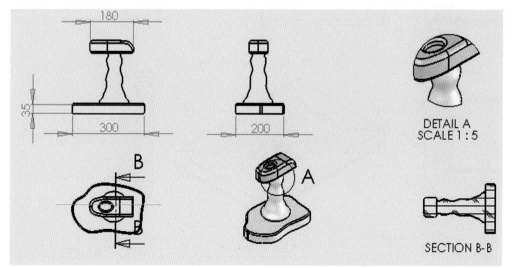

❋ Working drawing

Index